A Laboratory Manual

INTRODUCTION TO LANDFORMS

FOURTH EDITION

George Brook
Royle James Heyl
A.S. Hopkins

CONTEMPORARY PUBLISHING COMPANY OF RALEIGH, INC.

5849 Lease Lane, Raleigh, NC 27617 • (919) 851-8221
www.contemporarypublishing.com

Publisher: **Charles E. Grantham**
Production Editor: **Erika J. Kessler**
Marketing Director: **Sherri Powell**
Cover Design: **Piedmont Litho**
Printer: **Edwards Brothers Malloy**

ISBN: 0-89892-373-5

Printed in the United States of America.

10 9 8 7 6 5 4 3 2

Table of Contents

Preface to the Fourth Edition

Since the first edition of this manual technology and data availability have transformed the science of landform studies. We can now look in great detail at any area on Earth, and also areas on other planets, using high-resolution satellite imagery that is freely available using the **Google Earth™** mapping service on the Internet. This web-based program allows users to view a photo-realistic 3-D model of the Earth, to see the Earth from a variety of angles, and to even fly through areas as if in an airplane. It is essential that students studying landforms become familiar with what Google Earth™ has to offer. Therefore, the fourth edition incorporates the use of Google Earth™ satellite images into most of the exercises. In addition, the manual directs students to other important websites with information relating to landforms, such as the United States Geological Survey and NASA. This is an attempt to familiarize students with the wealth of information on landforms that is available to them on the internet. With this new emphasis in the manual, Exercise 1 is designed to familiarize students on the use of Google Earth™. The new edition also includes 3-D anaglyphs of each stereo pair of aerial photographs in the manual; these are located in Appendix D. Red-blue 3-D glasses are provided with the manual for easy 3-D viewing of these anaglyphs.

The use of recent Google Earth™ satellite images in the exercises also allows students to see for themselves how landscapes have changed over time, up to the present day, and how land used for human activities has expanded in most areas around the world. This is an important lesson for students to learn as destruction of natural resources, coupled with global warming, is putting significant stresses on both the natural and built environments of the earth.

To the Instructor

Field research in geomorphology is almost always preceded and supported by map and photographic evidence, remotely sensed data, and often by preexisting data sets. Students of geomorphology should, therefore, have a thorough working knowledge of these data sources and be able to recognize their value in the interpretation of landscapes. This manual introduces landform and landscape characteristics through a series of practical laboratory exercises which utilize maps, aerial photographs, and current technology. Some of the lab exercises will also incorporate actual fieldwork problems utilizing the local area as on option for the instructor.

The manual contains enough material for at least 14 two to three-hour laboratory sessions. It can be used independently of other texts and requires very little additional equipment, other than a computer with Internet access. Exercise introductions provide an essential minimum of information necessary for the completion of the questions. For more detail it is recommended that the references at the end of the manual be consulted, as well as the numerous web-based information sites available. Students will need access to a few items to include a lens stereoscope (a plastic, hand-held version is included with the manual), red-blue 3-D glasses (included with the manual), colored pencils, a ruler, and a protractor.

Student Name______________________________

Exercise 1

GOOGLE EARTH™ *MAPPING SERVICE EXERCISE*

MATERIALS

Computer with Google Earth™ downloaded software.

OBJECTIVES

1. Learn to navigate the globe using Google Earth™.
2. Locate places using the place name of the area and the latitude and longitude coordinates.
3. Properly utilize the various functions and features of the Google Earth™ mapping service.

INTRODUCTION

In this exercise you will become familiar with Google Earth™, which can be downloaded free from **http://earth.google.com**. This web-based program will allow you to view a photo-realistic 3-D model of the earth and to correlate these views with the topographic maps, and stereo pairs used in the exercises in this manual. The web site has tutorials on the various features of the program and how to use them. We suggest you work through several of the online tutorials before completing the exercises below.

SECTION 1: Search Methods

Once you have downloaded and started the program, make sure that the necessary toolbars, sidebars and other applications are engaged. To do this, click on **View** and select the options you wish to use. We suggest that you at least use: Toolbar, Sidebar, Compass, and Status Bar. You can try the other options to see which you would like to work with on a regular basis. There are several ways to locate a particular place. You can type the name of the location in the search box located on the upper left-hand side of the page and then click on the search icon. The program will automatically move the image to that area. Another option is to type in the latitude and longitude coordinates for the location instead of the name. You can also scroll to the location yourself by moving the computer mouse while holding down the left mouse button. You can also navigate around the globe by utilizing the on-screen arrows of the compass located in the upper right-hand corner of the screen or by using the arrow buttons on the computer keyboard. You zoom in and out by using the scroll wheel on the mouse or the zoom bar on the screen (upper right-hand corner, below the navigation arrows). Notice that as you scroll across the screen the latitude and longitude (lat/long) coordinates change automatically (lower left or lower center of image), the Elevation of the cursor location changes (lower middle of screen), and the Eye Altitude changes as you zoom in and out.

A. Search using a location name.

Type the following location names in the search box, click on the search icon and list the latitude and longitude coordinates shown on the resulting image (at the bottom of the scene).

Washington, DC ______________________________

South Pole ______________________________

Eiffel Tower ______________________________

Mt. Kilimanjaro______________________________

Pick one of your own______________________________

B. Search using latitude and longitude.

You can search by latitude and longitude using the directional abbreviations N, S, E, and W or by using minus signs (-) to define South and West. The North and East directions do not require a symbol. Be sure to type the coordinates with the correct spacing as shown below. Latitude coordinates are entered first followed by the longitude coordinates. It is not necessary to include commas, or the degree, minute, and second symbols.

Type the following coordinates in the search box, click on search, and describe the area that appears.

38° 37′ 37.09″N, 90° 12′ 08.90″W ______________________________

38 37 37.09, 90 12 08.90______________________________

-33 25 31.27, -70 33 59.29 ______________________________

25 20 37.93S, 131 02 09.57E ______________________________

Pick one of your own______________________________

SECTION 2: Layers

You can add layers of information to the image on your screen or if they are not useful you can remove them. A listing of the various layers is available under **Layers** on the left side of the screen. If the only layer listed is Primary Database, then click on this box to open the layers file. Go back to the Eiffel Tower, Paris, image and experiment with the various layers to see which are useful and which not, and what is added and/or removed? In the spaces below list which of the layers you think is the most useful and which the least useful? To activate or turn off a layer, locate it on the side toolbar (left-hand side of the screen) and click on the box to the left of the layer name. If there is a check mark in the box, then the layer is active; if it is blank, then the layer is turned-off.

Most useful ____

Least useful ____

Click on 2 or 3 of the lettered place marks (i.e. A, B, C, etc.) in the Eiffel Tower image and see what happens. The site you click on should disappear from the screen. Click it again and it should reappear.

Now click on the box next to the term Panoramio under the Layers section and notice that several blue boxes will appear (or disappear). If you click on one of these blue boxes, a photograph appears in a separate window. The pictures have been uploaded by individuals and you can also do this if you wish. Clicking any icon on the image will reveal similar information, either a photograph or information on the site.

How might this be useful? ______________________________________

____

Activate the layer **Street View**. Several camera icons will appear. Click on some of these to look at photographs taken at street level. Click on **Show Full Screen** and see what happens. Exit the photo and then zoom out to get back to the larger image of Paris.

How might this be useful? ______________________________________

____

Experiment with other layers to see what they provide and how they can be useful.

SECTION 3: *Oblique Views and Image Rotation*

Next we will view the Grand Canyon from an oblique angle (side view). First, navigate to the Grand Canyon and then locate the navigation wheel or navigation bar in the upper right of the screen. Left click on the top arrow and hold the button down and you will see the image change from a vertical to an oblique view. The bottom arrow on this wheel will bring the image back to a vertical perspective. The right and left arrows rotate the image to the east (right arrow) or west (left arrow). Now move the mouse while holding down the right and then the left buttons to see how the image changes perspective. What happens with each movement of the mouse?

____

____

SECTION 4: *Navigating to Your Hometown*

Now use what you have learned in Sections 1-3 to examine your home town. Type the name of your home town in the search box. If the name of your town is not unique, then a list of towns will appear in the space below the search box. Select the correct location and click on the search icon. If you type in the city name and the state abbreviation, then the image should go directly to that location.

Name of home town ______________________________________

Latitude & Longitude ______________________________________

What is the name and latitude and longitude of your present location? ______________

____

Also become familiar with the icons on the top toolbar and the other options available with the Google Earth™ mapping service. We suggest you try the online tutorials by clicking **Help** and selecting **Tutorials**, or **User Guide**. You may also wish to view **Keyboard Shortcuts**.

SECTION 5: *Practice*

1. The following locations are in which of the **world's oceans**?

   03° 35′ N 64° 04′ E (Eye alt 4000 miles) ______________________________

   41° 11′ N 170° 53′ W (Eye alt 4000 miles) ______________________________

2. Locate Mount Fuji (Japan) and give its **lat/long coordinates**.

   ____

3. Locate Monte Vesuvio (Mount Vesuvius, Italy) and give its **lat/long coordinates**.

____

4. What are the **latitude and longitude coordinates** of the following locations?

   Six Flags over Georgia, west of Atlanta, Georgia ____________________

   Mt. Rainier National Park, WA ____________________

5. What feature do you see at the following locations?

   33° 51′ 24.95″ S 151° 12′ 54.89″ E **(anthropogenic)** ____________________

   43° 04′ 48.37″ N 79° 04′ 16.41″ W **(natural)** ____________________

6. What is the **state and county** at the following coordinates?

   43° 02′ 24.68″ N, 115° 13′ 14.03″ W ____________________

   43° 49′ 29.05″ N 88° 17′ 51.72″ W ____________________

7. Find the following locations using Google Earth™ and determine which **river delta** you are looking at in each case.

   0° 16′ 19.47″ S 50° 28′ 26.07″ W ____________________

   29° 11′ 43.07″ N 89° 15′ 07.83″ W ____________________

8. Which **mountain ranges** are visible at the following locations on Google Earth™ images?

   46° 02′ 02.50″ N 07° 36′ 41.95″ E ____________________

   10° 52′ 15″ S 75° 46′ 36″ W ____________________

9. Which **island or island group** can be seen in the Google Earth™ image at the following coordinates?

   19° 02′ 44″ N 71° 05′ 25″ W ____________________

   0° 114° 30′ 15″ E ____________________

10. What are the **latitude and longitude coordinates** for each of the following locations?

Mount Everest ____________________

Grand Canyon National Park ____________________

Madagascar ____________________

Iceland ____________________

Great Salt Lake, UT ____________________

Simpson Desert, Australia ____________________

Death Valley, CA ____________________

11. Which **ocean water body** can be seen in the Google Earth™ satellite image centered on the following coordinates?

43° 23′ 44″ N 34° 36′ 25″ E ____________________

59° 20′ 25″ N 175° 30′ 15″ W ____________________

12. For this question you will need to use the **Ruler** located under **Tools** on the Menu bar. Click on Tools and then Ruler on the drop-down menu. Select miles for the length measurement, then measure the distance between the following locations. You can also see what the distance is in kilometers.

Washington, D.C. to London, England ____________________

Sydney, Australia to Beijing, China ____________________

Student Name________________________________

Exercise 2

TOPOGRAPHIC MAPS

MATERIALS

Ruler with 1/16 inch and millimeter gradations, computer with Google Earth™ software.

OBJECTIVES

1. Recognize the various types of map used to study landforms.
2. Read and manipulate map scales.
3. Properly utilize information around the margins of maps.
4. Calculate slope (gradient) from topographic maps.
5. Construct a simple hypsometric (contour) map.
6. Construct profiles from topographic maps.

INTRODUCTION

Planimetric maps depict spatial information such as house locations, political boundaries and forests. A state highway map, or a map of your local city, is an example of a planimetric map. ***Hypsometric maps*** also include additional information about landscape form. Height is displayed by the use of ***contours,*** which are lines joining points of equal height above sea level (a.s.l.). Hypsometric maps are more commonly referred to as topographic maps. Colors and symbols are used to depict the natural and human-made characteristics of the landscape (see the Topographic Map Symbols pamphlet in the back pocket of the manual).

SECTION I: Map Scale

Most maps are smaller than the ground area they represent. The relationship between map distance and actual ground distance defines the ***map scale,*** which may be expressed as a ratio, such as 1:500 or 1:2,000,000. Such ratios are known as ***representative fractions*** (RF). A representative fraction of 1:500 simply means that one inch on the map represents a distance of 500 inches on the Earth's surface, or that one centimeter on the map represents 500 centimeters on the ground. ***Verbal scales*** such as "one inch to one mile" or "one centimeter to five kilometers" are often used for convenience when measuring distances on maps. A verbal scale of one inch to one mile is equivalent to a ratio scale of 1:63,360. Most maps also include ***bar scales***, which are visual representations of the verbal scale. Examples of bar scales can be seen in Appendix A.

The scale of a map determines how much detail can reasonably be included on it. A map with a scale of 1:125,000 is twice as large as a map with a scale of 1:250,000, but will cover or show an area of the Earth's surface that is only one quarter the size if drawn with the same dimensions. Think of it this way, when both maps are drawn on the same size sheet of paper, the map with a scale of 1:250,000 will cover or show 4 times the area shown on the map with the 1:125,000 scale. It will show twice the distance in the horizontal direction (E to W) and twice the distance in the vertical direction (N to S), thus overall 4 times the area. Similarly, a 1:50,000-scale map will cover 100 times the area covered by a 1:5,000-scale map (10 times in the E to W direction and 10 times in the N to S direction). Generally maps are classified into large, medium, and small scale although there is no standard practice as to the scale boundaries between each class. In this manual we will define ***large-scale maps*** as those with a scale between 1:1 and 1:60,000, ***medium-scale maps*** those with a scale between 1:125,000 and 1:60,000, and ***small-scale maps*** those with a scale of 1:150,000 or smaller. The concept of small versus large in map scale refers to the number resulting from the operation of division of the RF. For example, 1:24,000 is 1 divided by 24,000 or 0.0000417 (a large-scale map), while 1:250,000 is 1 divided by 250,000 or 0.000004 (a small-scale map). It may be easier to remember the relationship in this way: ***a large-scale map shows a relatively small area of the Earth's surface, while a small-scale map shows a relatively large area of the Earth's surface***. A map of your campus would have a large scale, while a map of North America would have a small scale. Because parallels of latitude and meridians of longitude frequently form the boundaries of individual U.S. map sheets, these are often referred to as ***quadrangles***.

QUESTIONS

2.1 Choose examples of large-, medium-, and small-scale maps from the maps found in this manual and list the following information for each.

Large-scale map (Fig. number, map name and map scale) ______________________

Medium-scale map (Fig. number, map name and map scale) ____________________

Small-scale map (Fig. number, map name and map scale) ______________________

2.2 Two maps of similar size have scales of 1:5,000 and 1:20,000, respectively. Which map has the larger scale? How much bigger is the area covered by the smaller-scale map compared to that covered by the larger-scale map?

SECTION 2: *Map Information*

Individual maps may be referred to by the ***sheet name*** (e.g. Pittsburgh Quadrangle), or the ***sheet number*** (e.g. 101-NW). They may also be identified by the geographic coordinates of the lower right hand corner of the map and by the series name. For example, N4015-W7645/15 indicates that the map is one of the 15 minute series, and that the latitude and longitude coordinates of the southeast corner are North 40° 15′ and West 76° 45′ respectively.

Information in the margins of a topographic map constitutes the ***map legend***. Frequently included is a location diagram showing the map area in relation to a county, state or country, or an index diagram giving the names and numbers of adjoining sheets of the same map series. On some maps this information may be displayed around the edges of the mapped area. Most maps give details of when and how the map was initially constructed, subsequent revisions, and the map projection used. This information is extremely important to the user for there is no point in using a map last revised in 1952 to plot the distribution of forested land in 2010. This map would, however, be useful to analyze landscape and land use changes when compared to current satellite imagery, but only if the date of the map information is known.

The ***geographic grid,*** consisting of intersecting lines of latitude and longitude, is used on almost all topographic maps with ***true north,*** fixed by the North Pole, to the top of the map. The angular difference between true north and ***magnetic north,*** the ***magnetic declination,*** is also given so that maps can be correctly oriented in the field by using a compass. Points on a map can be located using latitude and longitude coordinates and generally it is sufficient to quote only in degrees and minutes (e.g. 40° 15′N and 76° 45′W). In this manual, a square grid has been superimposed on all maps and photographs so that points can be rapidly located or specified in terms of simple coordinates. For example, point X in Fig. 2.1 is located at B.5-2.4 and point Y is at D.5-1.5. In addition, all figure headings include a statement that gives directional information. The figure heading for Fig. 2.2 states that A.0-1.0 is in the southeast corner of the figure and indicates that north is to the right (as indicated by the north arrow **N↑**).

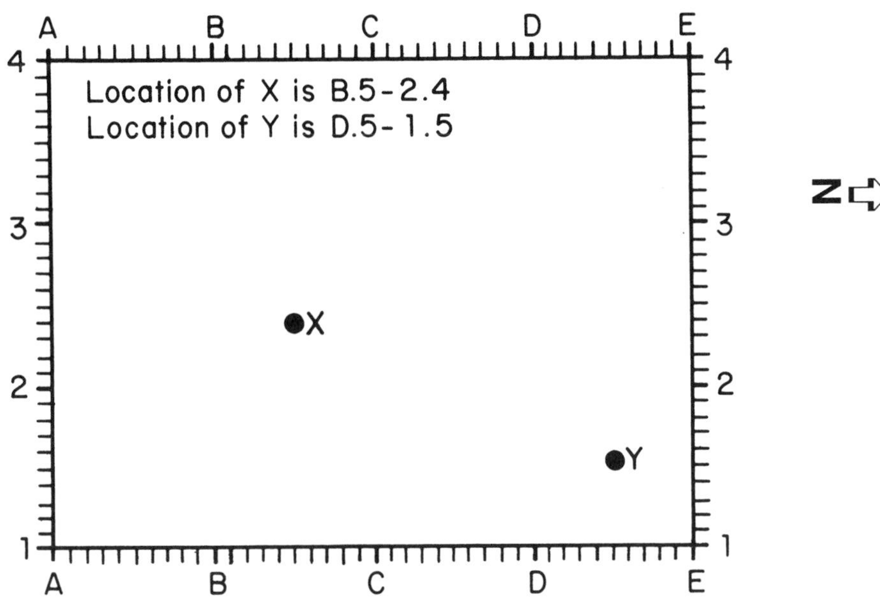

Fig. 2.1 Locating and referencing points with the grid used in this manual (A.0-1.0 is in the southeast corner of the figure).

QUESTIONS

2.3 This exercise requires you to work with the Kingston, RI and Philipp, MS maps (both published in 1957), and also satellite images of these areas acquired using Google Earth™. An image of the Kingston area can be obtained by typing either Kingston, RI in the Earth™ search box, or the following coordinates: 41° 28′ 19.76″ N, 71° 31′ 38.82″ W. Start viewing with se an Eye alt of 16,000 feet. An image of the Philipp, MS area can be obtained by typing Macel, MS, or the following coordinates in the search box: 33° 48′ 32.77″ N, 90° 07′ 36.11″ W. Start viewing with an Eye alt of 40,000 feet. Looking at the Google Earth™ images should prove useful throughout this exercise. Remember that the map information is much older than the image and thus a good deal may have changed.

Examine Figs 2.2, 2.3, and 2.4, the Kingston map and the Philipp map and legend, and add the relevant information to the following table.

Map Name	Philipp Quadrangle	Kingston Quadrangle
Map Series		
Mapping Agency		XX
Publishing Agency		XX
Geographical Grid/Series Identity		XX
Source of Topographic Information		XX
Map Projection		XX
Date Issued		1957
Magnetic Declination and Date		14 1/2°W, 1975
Revisions (if any)		1975
Representative Fraction		
Verbal Scale in in/mi		
Verbal scale in cm/km		
Name of Map to South		XX
Name of Map to Southwest		XX
Contour Interval		10 feet
Area Covered (sq. miles)		

Next Page: **Fig. 2.2 Kingston, Rhode Island (1:24,000, 7.5 Minute Series, A.0-1.0 in southwest corner).**

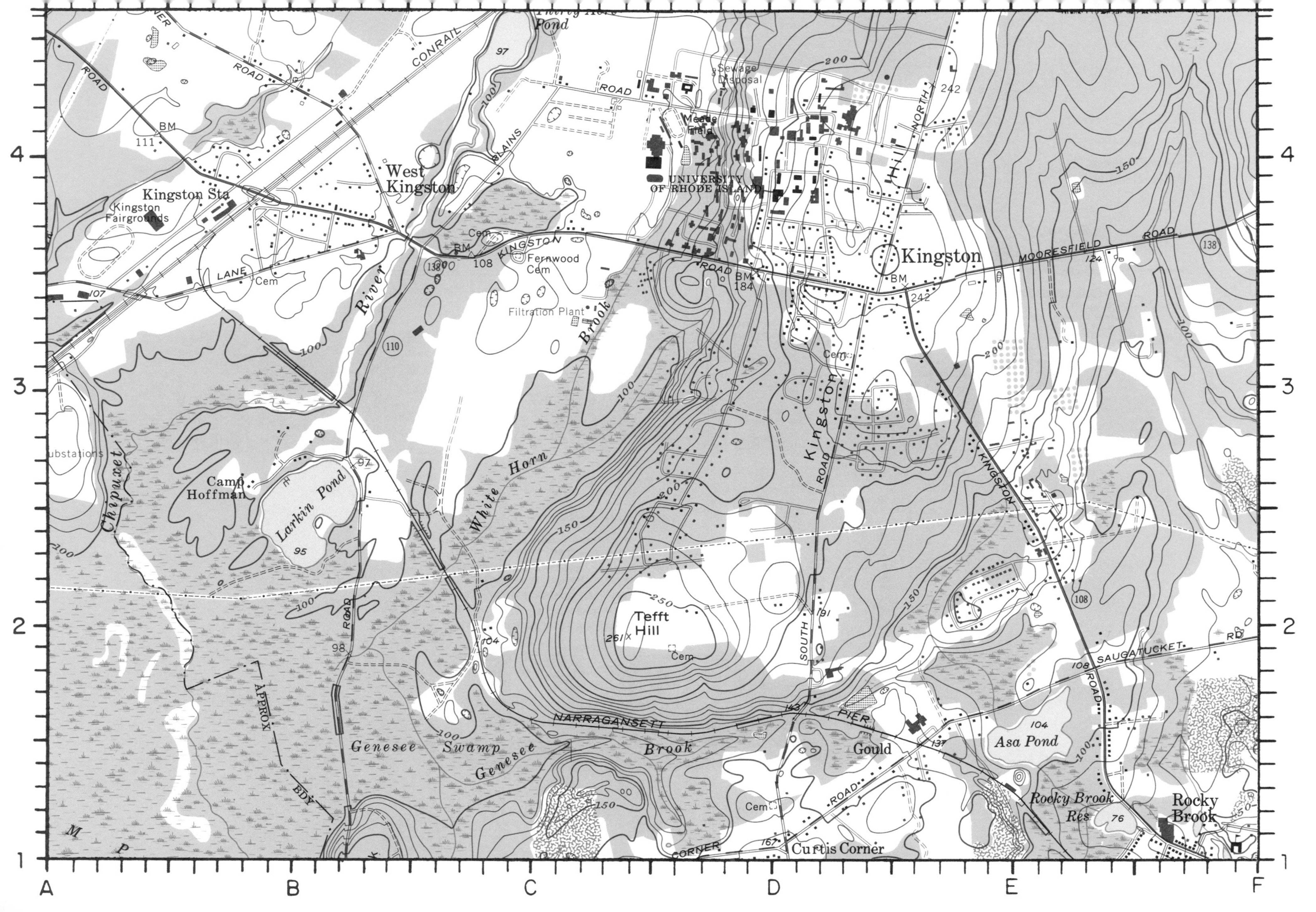

Kingston
West Kingston
Kingston Sta
Kingston Fairgrounds
UNIVERSITY OF RHODE ISLAND
Meade Field
Sewage Disposal
MOORESFIELD ROAD
KINGSTON ROAD
NORTH ROAD
SOUTH ROAD
PLAINS ROAD
LANE
CONRAIL
Fernwood Cem
Filtration Plant
Chipuxet River
White Horn Brook
Larkin Pond
Camp Hoffman
Tefft Hill
NARRAGANSETT PIER
SAUGATUCKET RD
Genesee Swamp
Genesee Brook
Gould
Asa Pond
Rocky Brook Res
Rocky Brook
Curtis Corner
CORNER ROAD
APPROX BDY
Cem
BM
Substations
A
B
C
D
E
F
1
2
3
4

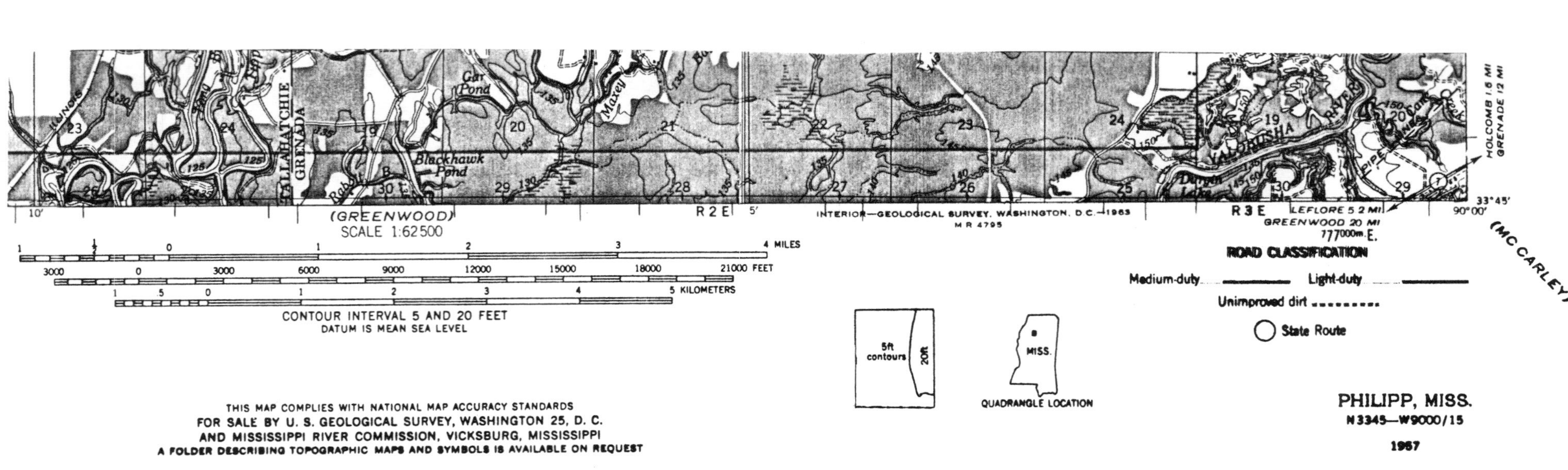

Fig. 2.3 The legend of the Philipp, Mississippi topographic map.

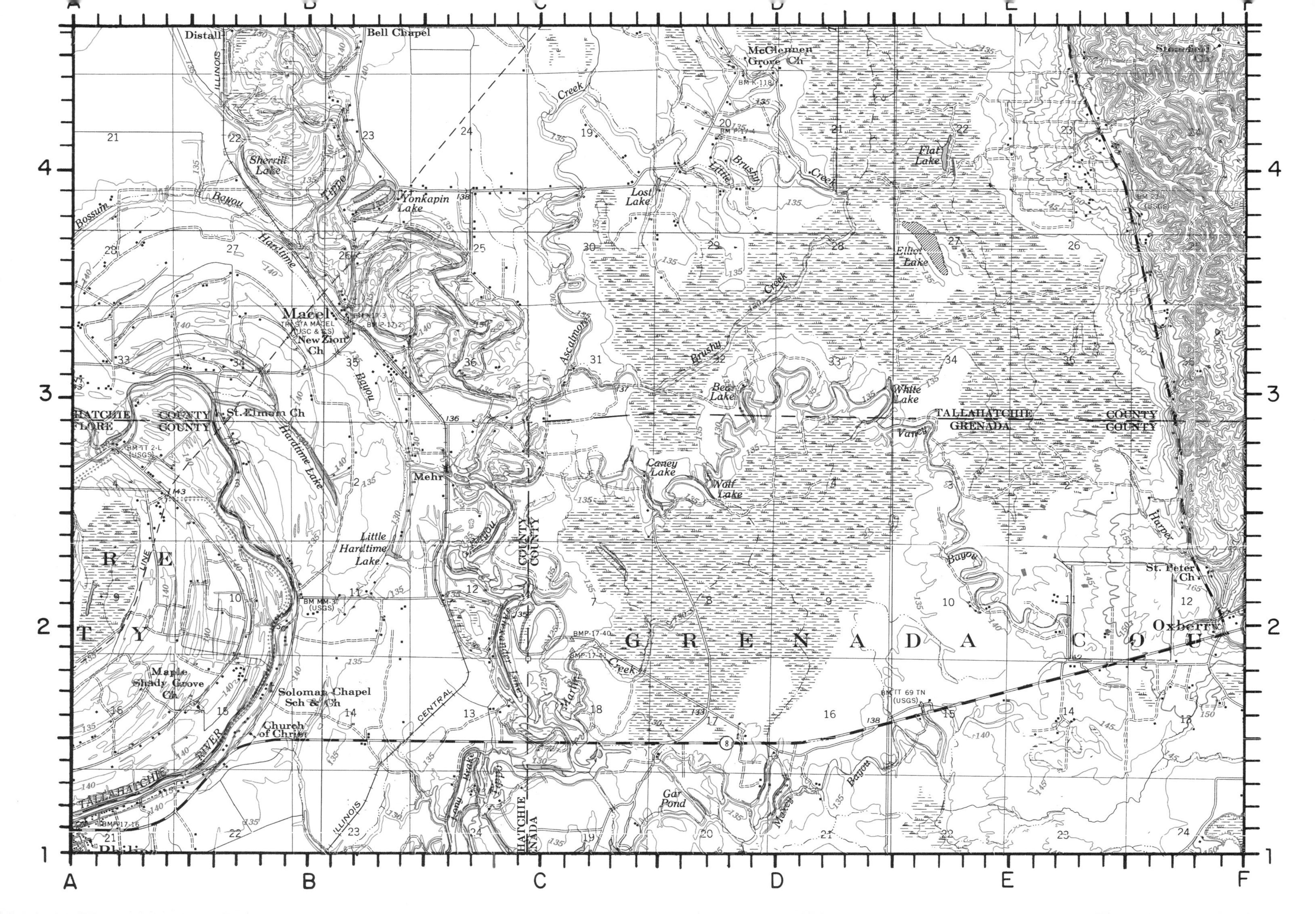

Distall
Bell Chapel
McGlennen Grove Ch
Stonefield Ch
Sherrill Lake
Yonkapin Lake
Lost Lake
Flat Lake
Elliot Lake
Macel
New Zion Ch
St. Elmum Ch
Hardtime Lake
Mehr
Little Hardtime Lake
Bear Lake
White Lake
Caney Lake
Wolf Lake
TALLAHATCHIE COUNTY
GRENADA COUNTY
St. Peter Ch
Oxberry
Maple Shady Grove Ch
Soloman Chapel Sch & Ch
Church of Christ
Gar Pond
G R E N A D A
TALLAHATCHIE
RIVER
ILLINOIS
CENTRAL
A
B
C
D
E
F
1
2
3
4

QUESTIONS

2.4 Examine Figs 2.2 and 2.4 and complete the following table.

Map	Location	Grid Coordinates
Kingston	Crest of Tefft Hill	
Kingston		E.1 – 1.5
Kingston	Bench Mark at Junction of Kingston and Mooresfield Roads	
Philipp	Bear Lake	
Philipp		D.5-3.0
Philipp	Macel	

SECTION 3: Contour Lines

Several methods are used to depict vertical relief on maps, including hachuring, contouring, layer shading and tinting, and hill shading. ***Spot heights*** (e.g. x1692) and ***bench marks*** (e.g. xB.M. 1622) are often used in conjunction with other methods to provide precise height information for accurately surveyed points. Brass plates pinpoint bench mark location in the field. The use of ***contours*** is the most common method of depicting relief. Modern photogrammetric methods and machines allow extremely accurate and rapid contouring to be carried out from air photographs with a minimum of ground control. ***Index*** or ***key contours*** are shown on maps in a heavy-weight, brown line, usually every fifth line. ***Intermediate contours*** are depicted in a lighter-weight, brown line, and ***supplementary contours*** are shown in a light-weight, brown dashed line. Where natural hollows or depressions exist in a landscape, contours are ticked in the direction of the depression.

QUESTIONS

2.5 The map of a small area surveyed using a theodolite and GPS includes lakes, rivers, roads, forested areas, buildings, and a number of accurately determined spot heights (Fig. 2.5). Complete this map by drawing contours at intervals of 50 feet starting with a 700 foot contour (i.e. 700 feet., 750 feet., etc.). (Note: contour lines do not cross each other and the area inside closed lines is higher unless the contour is ticked to indicate a depression.)

Previous Page Fig. 2.4 Philipp, Mississippi (1:62,500, 1.0-1.0 in southwest corner).

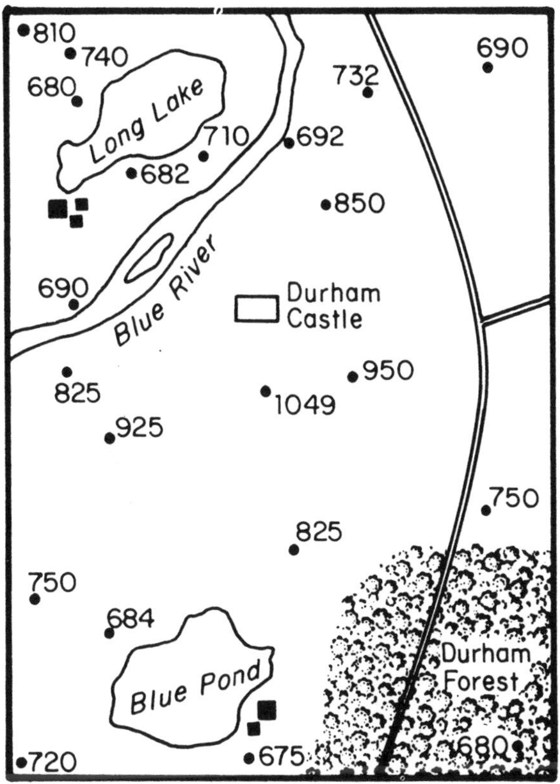

Fig. 2.5 Small area surveyed by theodolite and GPS.

SECTION 4: Vertical Exaggeration and Slopes

One of the advantages of contour (topographic) maps is that topographic profiles can be drawn from them. In the construction of profiles, the vertical scale is generally made larger than the horizontal scale to enhance relief. The relationship between the vertical and horizontal scales is known as the ***vertical exaggeration*** (V.E.). For example, if the horizontal scale is 1:63, 360 and the vertical scale is 1:12,000, then the vertical exaggeration is 5.28 times (63,360 ÷ 12,000).

Ground slope or gradient can also be obtained using topographic maps by measuring the horizontal distance or ***horizontal equivalent*** (HE) between two points and noting the difference in elevation or ***vertical interval*** (VI) between the two points. Gradient may be expressed verbally as the ratio VI/HE, with both expressed in the same units. For example, if VI is 150 feet and HE is 500 yards, the gradient will be 150/1500 (both in feet), or 1 in 10. In other words, if you were to traverse the distance between the two pints, for every 10 feet of horizontal movement your elevation would change 1 foot, on average. Gradient may also be measured or expressed as an angle, such as 1° or 10°. Alternatively, a slope can be expressed as a percentage, for example, a slope of 1 in 10 would be a slope of 10%.

QUESTIONS

2.6 A topographic profile has a horizontal scale of 1:25,000 and a vertical scale of 1 inch to 100 feet. What is the vertical exaggeration?

2.7 The horizontal distance between two points on a gravel road is 520 yards and they differ in elevation by 500 feet. The road slopes evenly from one location to the other. What is the average gradient (verbal) along the road?

2.8 Using bench mark and spot height elevations, calculate the average down gradient of Mooresfield Road out of Kingston, Rhode Island (Fig. 2.2). Express this verbally and in angular and percentage terms.

SECTION 5: Topographic Profiles

How to Construct Profiles (use Figure 2.6):

1. Looking along the *profile line* drawn between points A and B, determine the highest and lowest elevation on the line. This is done by first noting where the highest and lowest contour lines cross the profile. The highest contour line that crosses the profile line is the 500 feet contour and the lowest is the 350 feet contour. You can see that the profile goes to elevations above 500 feet but not to 550 feet otherwise the 550 feet contour would cross the profile. The lowest elevation on the profile is less than 350 feet but is more than 300 feet otherwise this contour line would cross the profile line.
2. Choose a vertical scale that will allow the vertical dimension of the graph paper to accommodate the elevation spread along the profile line. Here the elevation range is from 300 feet to 500 feet, which is a vertical difference of 200 feet. This translates to 1 inch of vertical distance on the graph paper being equivalent to 200 feet elevation on the ground giving a vertical scale of 1inch to 200 feet or 1:2400. Since the map scale is 1:24,000 the VE is 10 times. (If you wish to use more of the graph paper, you could use a vertical scale of 1 inch to 100 feet.)
3. Now mark units of elevation on the vertical axis of the graph paper, starting with 300 feet for the bottom line of your graph/profile and 500 feet for the top line and indicate every 50 feet interval between these two.

4. Place a blank sheet of paper along the profile line on the map and mark points A and B and also the locations where contours and significant features such as streams intersect the profile. You should note the elevation of each contour that you mark. Then transfer these positions and elevations to the graph paper by marking the contour elevations on the vertical scale as crosses or dots.
5. Connect the crosses or dots on the graph to reconstruct the topography along the profile line.

QUESTIONS

2.9 Construct a topographic profile from Larkin Pond on the Kingston map (Fig. 2.2) through Tefft Hill to Asa Pond. Use a horizontal scale of 1:24,000 and a vertical scale of 1 inch to 100 feet. Calculate the vertical exaggeration.

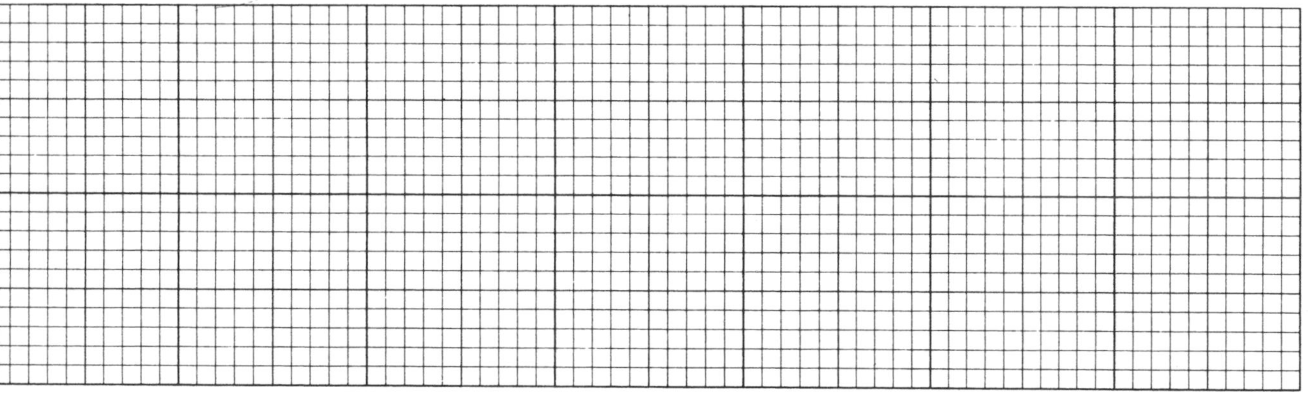

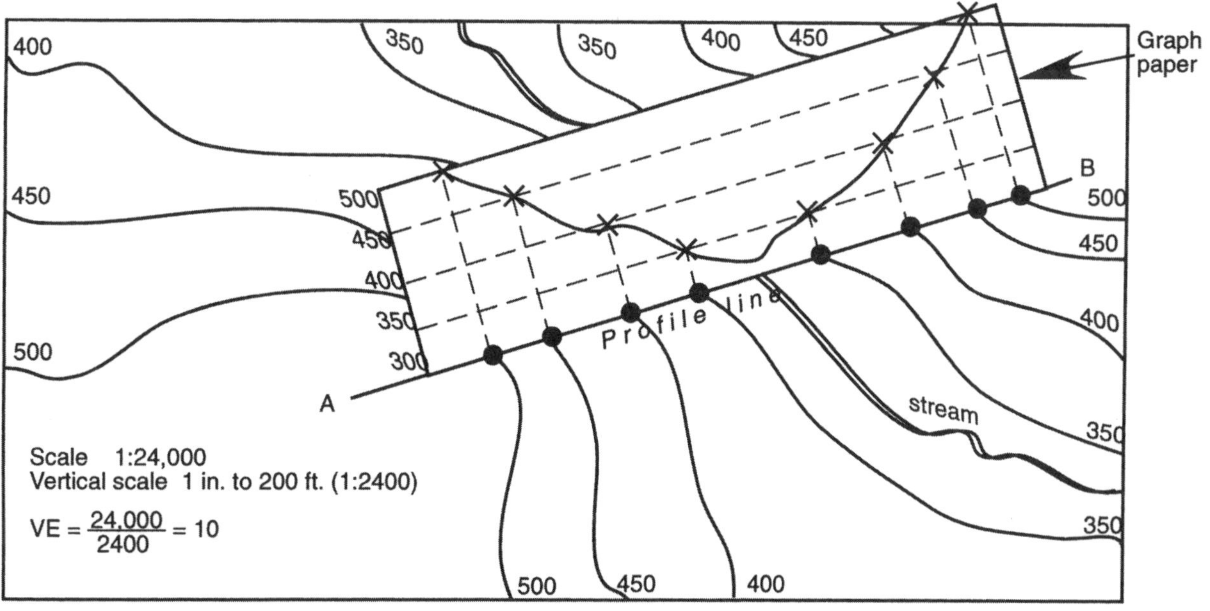

Fig. 2.6 Constructing profiles from a topographic map.

Student Name________________________________

Exercise 3

AERIAL PHOTOGRAPHS

MATERIALS

Lens stereoscope (plastic), red/blue 3-D glasses, ruler, computer with Google Earth™ software.

OBJECTIVES

1. Calculate the scale and ground coverage of air photos given information about the camera and aircraft elevation.
2. Calculate the scale of air photos using topographic maps of the same area.
3. Understand the advantages and disadvantages of air photos and topographic maps in landform analysis.
4. Calculate the height of objects visible on air photos.

INTRODUCTION

Most areas of the Earth's surface have been photographed from aircraft or satellites. These photographs have been widely used in topographic and geological mapping, land use survey, mineral exploration, and military reconnaissance. Many areas have been flown several times so that some sets of photographs show changes in the landscape over the last 50-60 years. Many such changes are related to earthquake, volcanic, flood, hurricane and human action. Throughout this manual you will be comparing past landscapes shown on older aerial photographs, 3-D anaglyphs made from them, and topographic maps, with recent conditions shown on Google Earth™ images, as well as images from NASA, USGS and other Internet-based sources. Be sure to refer to the 3-D anaglyphs to help you view aerial photographs in 3-dimensions. You can see the landscapes in 3-D by using the red/blue 3-D glasses with the blue lens on the right eye and the red lens on the left eye.

SECTION I: Types of Aerial Photograph

Two types of aerial photograph are generally used in landscape interpretation. ***Vertical photographs*** are taken with the axis of the camera as nearly vertical as possible and are by far the most widely used form for mapping purposes. ***Oblique photographs*** are taken with the axis of the camera lens intentionally directed between the horizontal and the vertical. A ***high oblique photograph*** is one whose field of view includes a portion of the horizon, while a ***low oblique photograph*** does not.

One of the great advantages of using low- and high-altitude aerial photography is that the Earth's surface can be viewed in three dimensions, that is, stereoscopically. Aerial photographs are generally taken so that they ***overlap*** by 60% in the direction the aircraft is moving, that is along the ***flight line***. Complete coverage of an area is achieved by overlapping at right angles to the flight lines by 20%. This is called ***sidelap*** (Fig. 3.1). For **stereoscopic vision**, two overlapping photographs are adjusted so that the same feature on each photograph is separated by a distance equal to that between the observer's eyes (approximately 2.5 inches). If the photographs are then viewed through a ***lens stereoscope***, the terrain will appear in three dimensions but with the relief and slope of the landscape exaggerated. This is because the observer is effectively looking at the ground as if one eye were more than a mile from the other. In this manual, pairs and triplets of photographs have already been arranged for stereoscopic study. If a lens stereoscope is correctly placed over adjacent photographs so that the left eye sees the same feature on the left photo as the right eye sees on the right photo, a 3-D image will come into view.

QUESTIONS

3.1 Indicate which type of photograph each of the following figures represents.

Fig. 5.3 ________________________ Fig. 7.7 ________________________

Fig. 11.5 ________________________ Fig. 12.7 ________________________

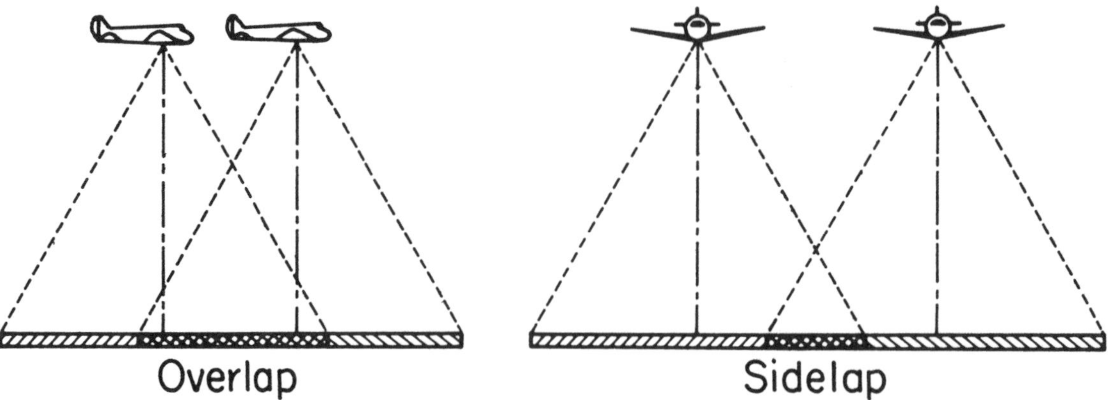

Fig. 3.1 Overlap and sidelap in aerial photographs.

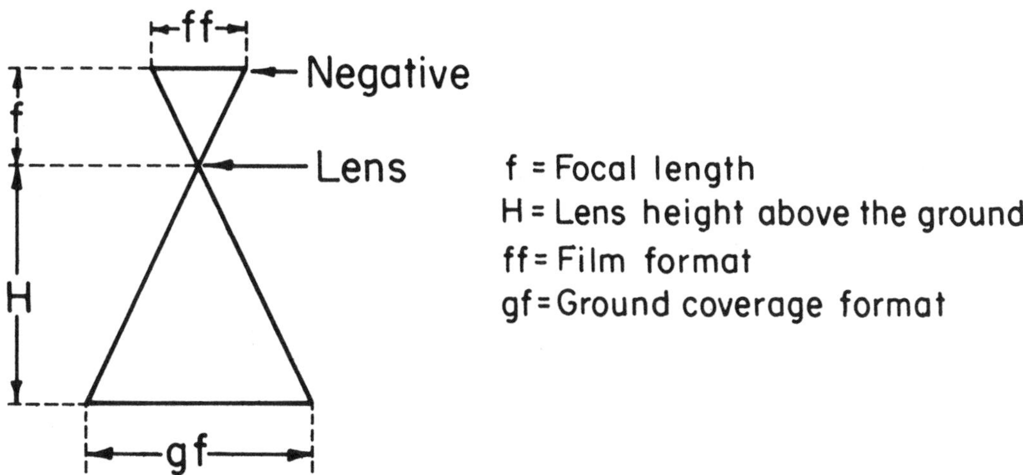

Fig. 3.2 Scale and ground coverage of aerial photography.

SECTION 2: Scale of Aerial Photographs

The ***scale*** of an aerial photograph depends upon the elevation of the photographic platform, the aircraft or satellite, above the ground surface (H), and the focal length of the camera lens (f) (Fig. 3.2). If these two values are known, the scale of the photograph can be calculated using the formula:

f/H = 1/scale factor (Sf) = RF (1:Sf)

where f and H are in the same units. When these values are not known, the photographic scale can be determined by comparison with a map of the same area and of known scale. If the length of an object (such as a road) is measured both on the map and photograph, the photographic scale factor is given by:

$$\text{Sf of photograph} = \frac{\text{dimensions of object on map x Sf of map}}{\text{dimensions of object on photograph}}$$

where dimensions are in the same units. Scale can also be calculated if the actual size of the object visible in the image is known. For example, if a road is known to be 83 feet 4 inches wide on the ground and is 0.05 inches on the photograph, then the photographic scale 1:20,000 is given by:

$$\text{Sf of photograph} = \frac{\text{dimensions of object on ground}}{\text{dimensions of object on photograph}}$$

where dimensions are in the same units. If the scale of the photograph is known as well as the initial film negative format size (Fig. 3.2), the ground coverage can be calculated from the relationship:

ground format (gf) = film format (ff) x photographic Sf.

QUESTIONS

3.2 The U-2 reconnaissance aircraft flies at 70,000 feet altitude above sea level. If a U-2 is used to photograph the ground surface and the film format is kept constant at 9 inches square, the scale of the photography obtained and the area of the ground covered will depend on the focal length of the camera lens. The greater the focal length the larger the photographic scale but the smaller the area covered. Demonstrate this by completing Table 3.1.

Table 3.1 Effect of camera focal length on area covered and photographic scale

Aircraft Altitude Above Ground (feet)	Focal Length of Camera (inches)	Photographic Scale Factor	Ground Coverage Format with 9″ x 9″ Film
70,000	6		
70,000	8.25		
70,000	18		
70,000	36		

3.3 Cameras used in aerial photography commonly have focal lengths of 6.0 or 8.25 inches. If a camera of 6 inch focal length and a constant film negative format of 9 inches square is used to photograph an area, the photographic scale and the area covered will depend upon the altitude of the platform above the ground. Demonstrate this by completing Table 3.2.

Table 3.2 Effect of flying height above the ground on photographic coverage and scale

Aircraft Altitude Above Ground (feet)	Focal Length of Camera (inches)	Photographic Scale Factor	Ground Coverage Format with 9″ x 9″ Film
60,000	6		
30,000	6		
10,000	6		
5,000	6		

3.4 An area of varied terrain is photographed from an aircraft flying at 20,000 feet above sea level. The focal length of the camera lens is 6 inches and the film negative format is 9 inches square. The area covered is broadly divisible into three regions: (i) a broad lowland of average elevation 1,000 feet, (ii) a high plateau with an elevation of 4,000 feet, and (iii) a mountainous area at 10,000 feet. How will the scale and coverage of the photography vary from one region to the next? What problem does this pose if a map is to be prepared from the photographs?

3.5 Use the topographic map in Fig. 9.2 to calculate the scale of the photograph in Fig. 9.3. The 3-D anaglyph of Fig. 9.3 is number 15 in Appendix D. Distances can be obtained directly by using the Ruler option in Google Earth™. To obtain an image, type the following coordinates in the search box: 37° 05′ 31.11″ N, 86° 04′ 00.25″ W. Start viewing with an Eye alt of 20,000 feet.

3.6 An automobile is clearly visible on the aerial photograph of an urban area. On the photo, the automobile is 0.05 inches long but its true length is known to be 14 feet. What is the scale of the photograph and, assuming it was taken with a 6 inch focal length lens, what was the aircraft flying height?

3.7 Skylab, the first American space station, was launched in 1972 and returned to Earth in 1979. While in orbit Skylab astronauts took thousands of photographs of the Earth using the Earth Resources Experimental Package (EREP). Skylab orbited the Earth every 90 minutes at an altitude of 235 miles. The EREP included a camera assembly with six high precision multispectral cameras of 6 inch focal length which utilized a film format of 2.25 inches square. What is the size of the area covered by each photograph? The EREP also included an Earth terrain camera with a film format of 5 inches square. Fig. 14.6 and 14.7 are examples of photography taken with this camera. Assuming the area covered by each frame is 59 miles on a side, determine the scale of the photography and the focal length of the Earth terrain camera.

3.8 Several 70 mm color photographs of southern Arizona and northwestern Sonora were taken by Virgil Grissom and John Young during the first manned Gemini flight. It was found that most of the geological detail shown on a 1:375,000 map could be seen on a photo whose scale, as taken, was approximately 1:2,250,000. If the focal length of the camera was 80mm, what was the distance in kilometers between the astronauts and the Earth when the photographs were taken?

SECTION 3: Measuring Relief Displacement in Aerial Photographs

Photographs differ from maps in that scale is not constant across the photograph. Scale variations are caused by the ground being hilly or mountainous instead of flat. Features on the top of a mountain are imaged at a larger scale than features in a valley nearby because the mountain is closer to the camera. All features on a map are shown at the same scale regardless of their relative elevations. Away from the center of a photo, its ***principal point***, the top of an object, such as a tall building, will not occupy exactly the same position as its base. This relief displacement is more apparent at increasing distances from the principal point and is due to the camera viewing the terrain at an increasingly oblique angle toward the edges of the photograph. The amount of displacement, d_e, is given by:

$$d_e = \frac{h}{H} \times r$$

where h is the height of the object, H is the flying height of the platform, and r is the radial distance from the principal point to the top of the object (Fig. 3.3). H and h must be in the same units (e.g. feet), while d_e will be in the units of r (e.g. inches). If vertical photographs of downtown Los Angeles were taken from 5,000 feet elevation, and the Crocker-Citizen Plaza, which is 42 stories and 620 feet high, was located 6 inches from the center of one photograph, the relief displacement would be 0.74 inches. The top of the building would be 0.74 inches from its base so that its sides would be visible. If the flying height of the photograph is known and d_e and r can be measured on the photographs, the heights of objects can be calculated approximately:

$$h = \frac{d_e \times H}{r}$$

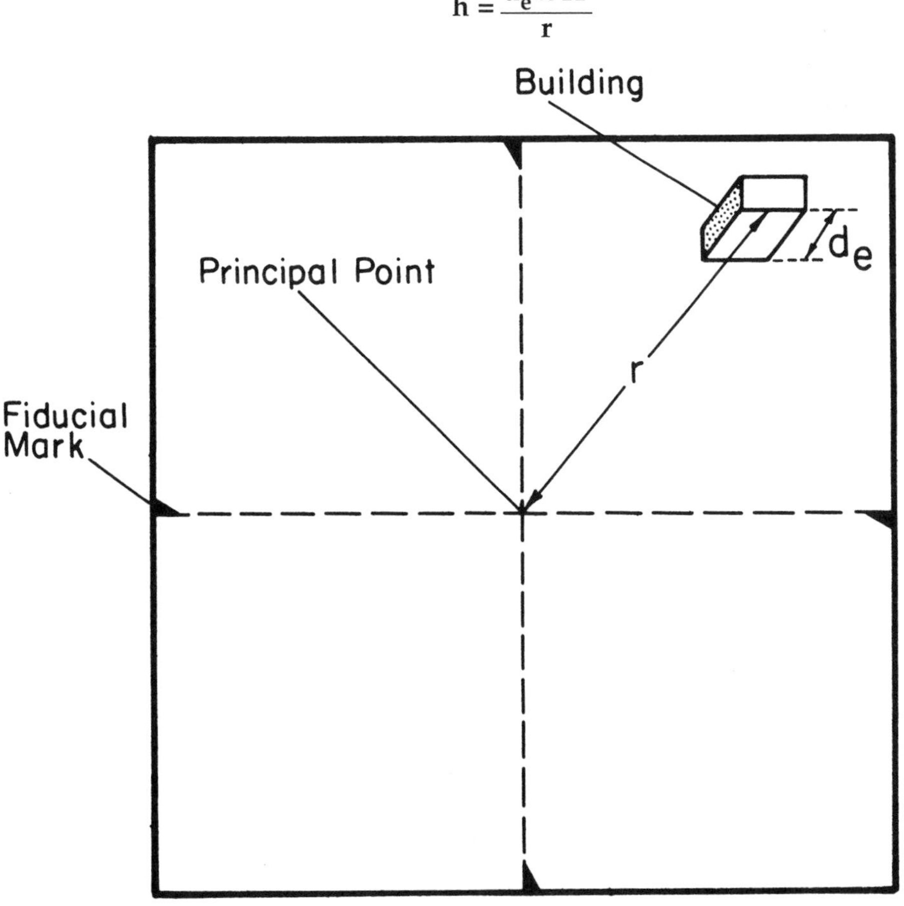

Fig. 3.3 Details of relief displacement in a single aerial photograph.

Photomosaics, when made from several aerial photographs, should be constructed from the central portions where relief displacements are at a minimum.

QUESTIONS

3.9 Measure d_e and r in Fig. 3.3. Given that the photograph was taken from an altitude of 5,000 feet, calculate the height of the building.

3.10 Now you will measure the basal length of the Great Pyramid at Giza, Egypt using Google Earth™ imagery and the Ruler tool. Locate the site on Google Earth™ at coordinates 29° 58′ 36.35″N, 31° 08′ 00.51″E. Measure the total length of the base of the largest pyramid (the pyramid to the top or north of the image) in feet or meters. What is this measurement? Are all the sides the same length or greatly different in length? Does the image appear to have been taken from directly overhead of the pyramid?

SECTION 4: Use of the Stereoscope

Commercial air photos are produced with precision equipment and specialized skill but the principle of stereoscopic vision is quite simple. To better appreciate how your brain and eyes work to give you 3-D vision, perform the following exercise:

1. Place both fists directly in front of your eyes.
2. Extend both forefingers horizontally and touch both sides of the bridge of your nose.
3. Looking "through" your forefingers and keeping them about one-half inch apart, move them slowly forward, away from your face.
4. At a distance of 2-3 inches from your eyes, a little "sausage image" should appear, unattached, floating between the tips of your extended forefingers. Your brain has created this "sausage image" from the two separate images of your forefingers that it has received.

When viewing two overlapping air photos, the brain likewise receives two images, slightly different, which it fuses into one 3-D image. The stereoscope simply helps in this process.

Now turn to Fig. 14.4 and orient it with the caption at the bottom. This is a "stereo pair", two identical photographs of the same area separated by the line down the center. Set your stereoscope on the stereo pair so that it is centered on the dividing line. The circular feature on the left photo should be under the left lens and the circular feature on the right photo under the right lens. Adjust the width to fit your eye separation and make small adjustments to the position of the stereoscope on the photos until you get a single, sharp image of the circular feature (a volcano). It should then appear three-dimensional. Once your eyes are "locked-on" in 3-D vision, you may move the stereoscope to other parts of the photo and view other relief features as long as you stay within the central band where the two photos overlap.

Now turn to Fig. 13.7 and repeat the above procedure. Note that the sand dunes shown in this figure appear to be very high with very steep slopes facing toward the southwest. The apparent excessive height and steepness produced by stereoscopic viewing is called ***vertical exaggeration***.

Another way to view images stereoscopically is by converting stereo pairs to ***3-D anaglyphs***. This has been done for every stereo pair in this manual and these can be found in Appendix D. If you have trouble viewing the stereo pairs with a lens stereoscope, then utilize the 3-D anaglyphs and the red-blue 3-D glasses in the manual. The best way to get a sense of how the stereoscope process works might be to refer to the stereo pair, the topographic map, and the 3-D anaglyph of the area. You might also try viewing the area on **Google Earth™**.

QUESTIONS

3.11 With reference to Figures 5.2, 5.3, 9.2, and 9.3, what are the advantages and disadvantages of aerial photographs, topographic maps, 3-D anaglyphs, and satellite images in the study of Earth's surfaces? You can obtain a Google Earth™ satellite image of the Menan Buttes, ID area (Figs 5.2 and 5.3) for comparison with the other images by typing the following coordinates in the search box: 43° 46′ 32.79″N, 111° 56′ 05.77″ W. Start viewing with an Eye alt of 35,000 feet.

Student Name________________________________

Exercise 4

PLATE TECTONICS AND EARTHQUAKES

MATERIALS

Lens stereoscope (plastic), red/blue 3-D glasses, ruler, compass (for drawing circles), computer with Google Earth™ software and Internet access.

OBJECTIVES

1. Describe and explain the pattern of continents, major landforms, and ocean basins.
2. Perform the basic technique involved in locating earthquake epicenters.
3. Describe how paleomagnetism relates to the history of the Earth's crust.
4. Describe and explain the recurring pattern of major earthquakes.
5. Speculate on the future map of the world.

INTRODUCTION

The theory of ***plate tectonics*** was developed in the 1970s to explain the dynamics of the Earth's lithosphere, its structural components and the mechanisms of formation. It incorporates early ideas on ***continental drift*** outlined by Alfred Wegener in his book *The Origin of the Continents and Oceans* (1915). It also incorporates theories and research on ***sea-flooring spreading*** and ***paleomagnetism***. The plate tectonics theory is supported by evidence from a variety of fields including paleontology, geology, oceanography, glaciology, and paleoclimatology. Plate tectonics theory argues that the Earth's crust is not one continuous slab of rock, but is instead made up of pieces or ***plates*** that can move with respect to one another. So far, some 20-25 plates have been identified, including 7 or 8 major plates. The lithospheric plates are thought to be moved by a combination of gravity and large, thermal, convection currents within the ***asthenosphere***. The movement of plates generates earthquakes, as well as volcanic activity. In this exercise we will investigate the theory and evidence for plate tectonics and its relationship to earthquake or seismic activity.

SECTION I: Plate Tectonics

The concept of ***continental drift*** is credited largely to Alfred Wegener, who wrote at length upon the subject in the early 1900s. His main thesis was that the continents were once joined in a single landmass he called ***Pangaea,*** which began to fragment approximately 200 million years ago. The northern portion of Pangaea, consisting of North America and Eurasia, is known as ***Laurasia***. The southern portion, including South America, Africa, India, Australia, and Antarctica, is known as ***Gondwanaland***. Although joined, these two "supercontinents" were indented by a huge stretch of ocean called the ***Tethys Sea***. Wegener's ideas were ridiculed for many years despite a considerable body of supporting geographical, geological, and paleontological evidence. Extensive research in the world's ocean basins led to the ideas of sea-floor spreading supported by the palaeomagnetic record, and together these have confirmed the theory of plate tectonics.

Ocean basins cover 71% of the Earth's surface, have a relative relief of more than 40,000 feet (compared to 30,000 feet on the continents), and can be subdivided into five major topographic zones. The submerged margins of the continents are characterized by a gently sloping platform, the ***continental shelf,*** which is generally less than 600 feet below sea level. Seaward of the continental shelf is the continental slope (average gradient 4.3°), which leads down to a deep ocean floor at an average depth of 12,500 feet. Research has revealed that the continents fit together almost perfectly if their edges are considered to be at a depth of 3,000 feet on the continental slopes. In some places continental slopes are deeply dissected by sinuous and often dendritic ***submarine canyon*** systems, a few of which appear to be continuations of major continental rivers. Where ***turbidity currents*** have funneled large volumes of sediment down these canyons, ***submarine fans*** or ***cones*** have been built on the ocean floor.

The deep ocean floor, once thought to be a featureless plain, is now known to be traversed by great submarine mountain ranges of volcanic origin, which extend down the axes of the major oceans and which often branch into less prominent ***plateaus*** or ***rises***. These mountain chains, which typically vary from 400 – 1,000 miles wide and from 5,000 – 10,000 feet high, form the ***mid-ocean ridge*** systems. Some of the higher peaks rise above sea level to form ***volcanic islands***, such as Iceland. ***Abyssal plains*** are best developed between continental slopes and mid-ocean ridges and are typically at depths from 10,000 – 20,000 feet. Although some plains are flat and featureless, most are dotted with submarine volcanoes that commonly occur in rows or clusters. These are known as ***seamounts***, or ***guyots*** if they have flat tops. ***Deep ocean trenches*** are long, narrow gashes in the ocean floor that are from 25,000 – 32,000 feet deep. Like mid-ocean ridges, trenches are narrow belts of intense earthquake and volcanic activity that define plate boundaries.

It is known that the Earth's lithosphere is composed of 20-25 ***lithospheric plates*** (Fig. 4.2), which can move over the underlying magma of the asthenosphere (Fig. 4.1). These plates are up to 45 miles (70 km) thick and are composed of continental or oceanic crustal material, or a combination of both. They are thicker in areas of continental material and may be as thin as 3–5 miles in areas of oceanic material. It is at ***plate boundaries*** that most seismic and volcanic activity occurs. There are three general types of plate boundaries, divergent, convergent and transform. ***Divergent plate boundaries*** are areas where two plates are pulling apart and new crustal material is being created as magma fills the expanding fissure. These occur at mid-oceanic ridges and in areas like the East African Rift Zone. ***Convergent plate boundaries*** are areas where two plates are coming together or colliding; mountain ranges and deep ocean trenches can form at such boundaries. Three separate types are recognized, oceanic-continental convergent plate boundaries, oceanic-oceanic convergent plate boundaries and continental-continental convergent plate boundaries. In the first two, one plate is subducted or forced under the other plate creating a ***zone of subduction*** and deep ocean trench. At ***transform plate boundaries***, the two plates slide laterally past one another. The San Andreas fault zone of California is such a boundary.

The ***theory of plate tectonics*** has revolutionized our understanding of the Earth's surface by explaining in a single concept the existence of major landforms and processes. These include mid-oceanic ridges, deep-sea trenches, major mountain belts, movement of the continents, and the extreme localization of tectonic activity. Scientists are now aware that most of the world's ocean basins are less than 200 million years old and, using ***paleomagnetic data***, can plot accurately the positions of the continents as they moved apart. As molten rocks cool, the Earth's magnetic field is locked into them. Because the inclination of the Earth's magnetic lines of force with respect to the horizontal varies (0° at the Equator, 63° at latitude 45° N & S, and 90° at the Poles), volcanic rocks also record their latitudinal position at the time they solidify. Paleomagnetic data from all over the world have not only added further support to the theory of plate tectonics, but have substantiated the essential correctness of Alfred Wegener's once-ridiculed theories of continental drift.

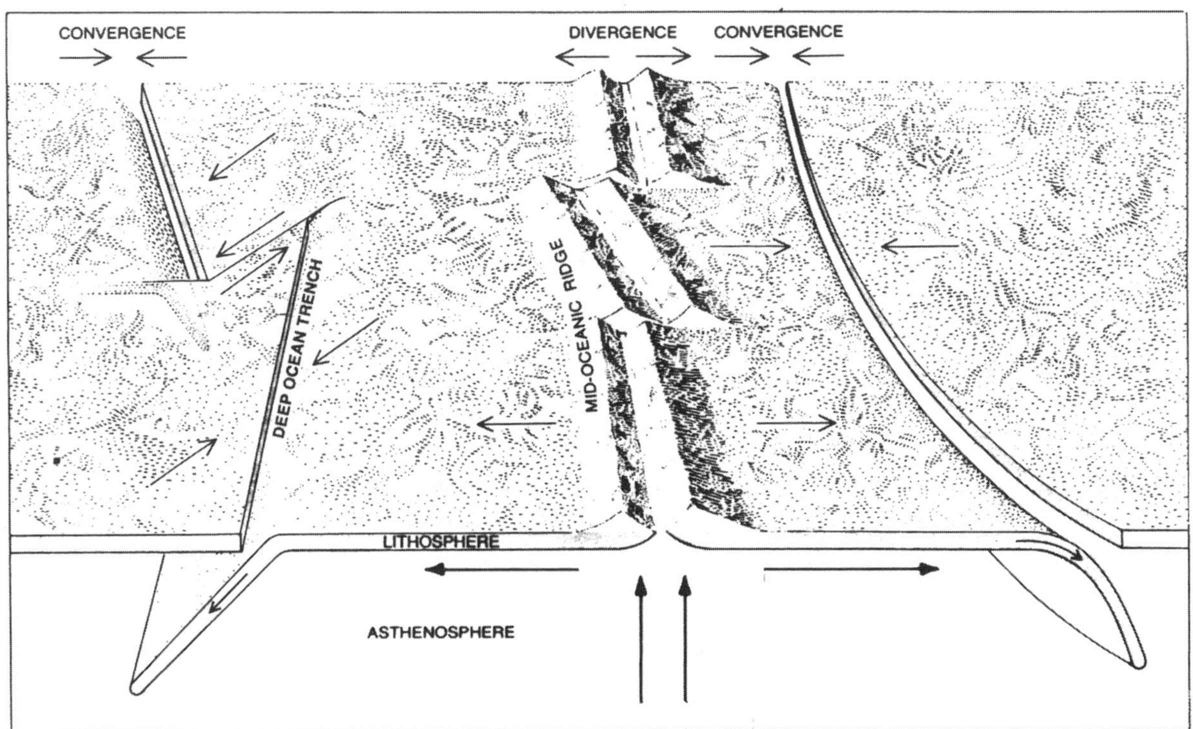

Fig. 4.1 Convergent and divergent plate boundaries.

QUESTIONS

4.1 Examine Fig. 4.3, the map entitled *Submarine Topography of the World's Oceans,* located in the pouch at the back of the manual.

(a) Identify on the map one example of each of the features listed below. Then, using the map and Google Earth™, list the latitude and longitude for each of the features you named.

Continental Shelf ____________________ Continental Rise ____________________

Abyssal Plain ____________________ Fracture Zone ____________________

Deep Ocean Trench ____________________ Guyot ____________________

Seamount (SMT) ____________________ Underwater Plateau ____________________

(b) In several areas, large cones are marked on the continental rise. Examples include the Mississippi Cone in the Gulf of Mexico, the Laurentian Cone off southeastern Canada, the Indus Cone off Pakistan, and the Ganges Cone off Bangladesh. What are these features and how have they formed?

(c) The island of Iceland in the North Atlantic has formed where the Mid Atlantic Ocean Ridge has built itself above sea level. From Iceland follow the ridge south into the Mid Indian Ocean Ridge and then into the East Pacific Ocean Ridge. Name three other islands or island groups that appear to have originated in the same way and give their latitude and longitude coordinates. What relationship, if any, is there between these islands and seamounts and guyots?

(d) Locate the Hawaiian Islands in the central Pacific and determine the approximate height of the islands, from base to island top. Give your answer in both meters and feet. (A metric-English conversion chart is provided in Appendix C)

(e) Estimate the relative, local relief (difference in elevation within an area) of the Mid Atlantic Ocean Ridge by comparing elevations along its crest with those in the abyssal plains on either side. Give your answer in both meters and feet.

4.2 Using Figs 4.2 and 4.3 and Google Earth™, answer the following questions.

(a) How has the Red Sea formed and which type of plate boundary is it? List its lat/long coordinates.

(b) What is happening to the Pacific Plate along its northern border with the North American Plate, and what features have been formed at this junction? What type of plate boundary is it?

(c) In Fig. 4.3, the Mid Atlantic Ocean Ridge seems to have a distinctive central rift. Why is this and what type of plate boundary is this?

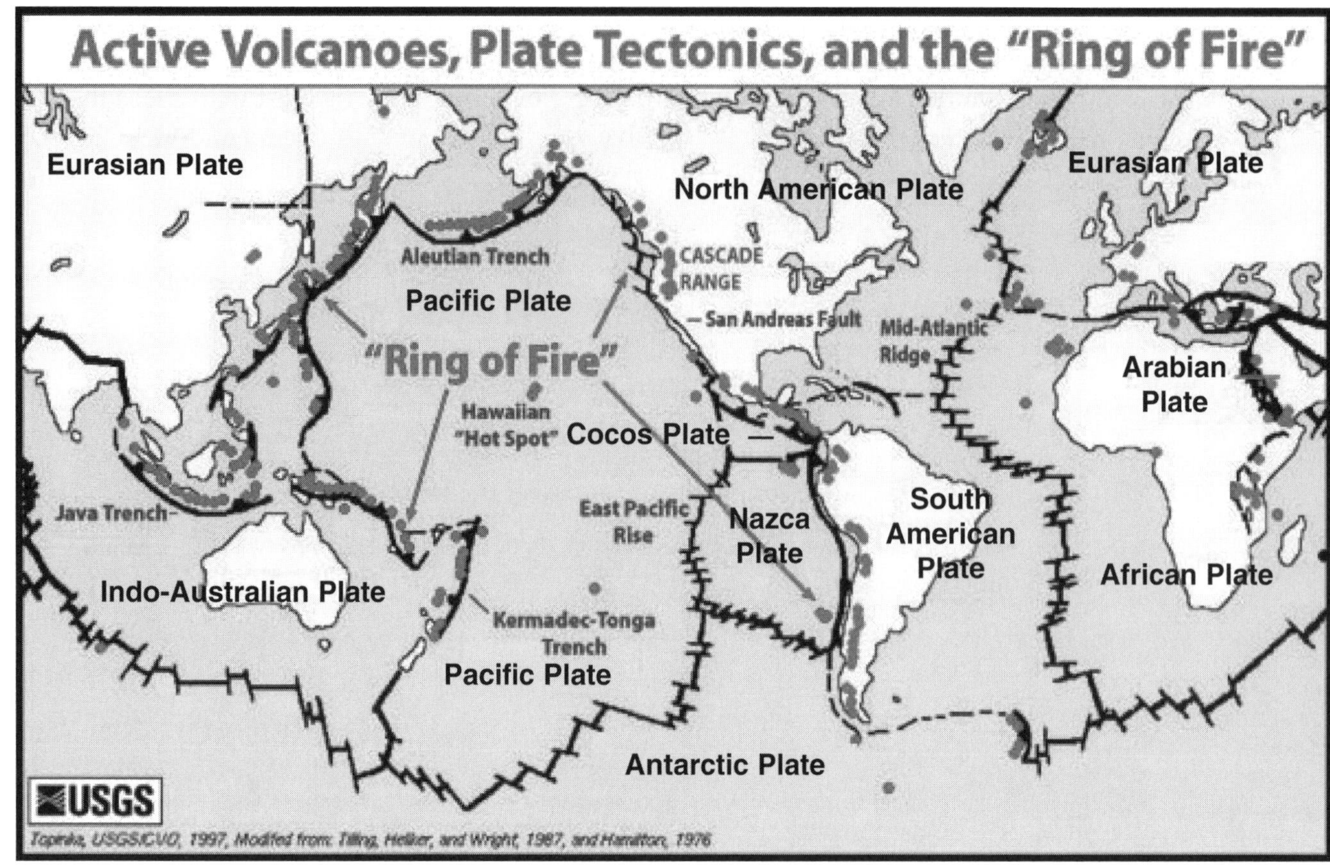

Fig. 4.2 Ten of the major lithospheric plates.

4.3 The relationship between the inclination of the Earth's magnetic lines of force (I) measured downward from the horizontal and latitude (L) is given by:

$$\text{Tan (I)} = 2 \times \text{Tan (L)}$$

where both I and L are in degrees (see Appendix B).

In one region, paleomagnetic evidence from a series of basalt flows shows that 100 million years ago the inclination of the Earth's magnetic lines of force was 5° to the north. Fifty million years ago it was 35° and 20 million years ago it was 45°. At present, the region is at latitude 32°N. Describe what has happened to this region during the last 100 million years in terms of its geographic position.

SECTION 2: Earthquakes

The average density of the Earth is 5.5 gm/cm^3 while surface rocks have an average density of 2.8 gm/cm^3, indicating that material within the Earth is denser than material at the surface. Most knowledge of the Earth's interior has been gained through the study of ***seismic waves*** released during ***earthquakes*** that occur when plates move or the crust ruptures along faults. The point where seismic waves originate is called the ***focus*** of the earthquake, and the point on the Earth's surface immediately above the focus is called the ***epicenter***. This is also the area that usually sustains the most damage. The point on the Earth diametrically opposite the epicenter is the ***anticenter***. Three types of seismic wave are recognized. Primary or ***P-waves***, are compressive, can pass through solids and liquids, and travel at 6.0 – 8.5 km/sec. Secondary or S-waves are shear waves, pass only through solids, and travel at 3.6-5.1 km/sec. Two other wave types, collectively known as Long or L-waves, travel in the surface rock layers of the Earth and are responsible for the majority of damage by earthquakes. By noting the time interval on a seismogram between the arrival of P- and S-waves, the distance from the seismograph station to the earthquake epicenter can be calculated. Records from three stations can therefore be used to determine the exact location of an earthquake. The location will be at the common intersection of the circumferences of three circles whose radii equal the distances of the earthquake epicenter from the respective seismograph stations.

An analysis of the behavior of seismic waves as they travel through the Earth has revealed that the planet is composed of distinctive internal layers. These layers vary in thickness, composition and consistency. The outer layer or ***lithosphere*** actually consists of two solid layers, the outer ***crust*** (oceanic and continental material) and the ***uppermost mantle*** and varies from 15-45 miles in thickness. A transition zone exists between these layers that is known as the ***Mohorovičić Discontinuity***. Below this is the plastic, deformable ***asthenosphere*** that reaches depths of about 155 miles. The next layer is the solid ***upper mantle*** composed primarily of olivine and silicate minerals, reaching depths of 410 miles below the surface. Below this is the ***lower mantle***, also solid, which extends to a depth of approximately 1800 miles. Another transition zone, the ***Gutenberg Discontinuity***, marks the break between the mantle and the core. The ***outer core*** consists primarily of molten iron and nickel to a depth of about 3200 miles. S-waves will not pass through the outer core because it is molten and thus a liquid. The outer core is also the layer that generates the Earth's magnetic field. In the center of the Earth, at a depth of about 3959 miles, is the ***inner core***. Like the outer core, this is comprised primarily of iron and nickel, but in a solid state.

The strength of an earthquake can be measured both ***qualitatively and quantitatively***. The ***Modified Mercalli Scale*** is a qualitative damage intensity scale and is useful in describing and classifying damage to human structures and reactions of human behavior. The ***moment magnitude scale*** is a quantitative scale that measures the magnitude of energy released by the earthquake. It is a modification of the ***Richter Scale*** first designed by Charles F. Richter in 1935. He defined the magnitude of an earthquake as the logarithm, to base 10, of the maximum seismic wave amplitude measured in thousandths of a millimeter as recorded on a seismograph at 62 miles from the earthquake epicenter. An earthquake registering 5.0 on the Richter Scale releases the same energy as 20,000 tons of TNT. An increase in magnitude of one unit increases the amount of energy released as seismic waves by 31.5 times. Thus an earthquake of 6.0 would release 31.5 times more energy than a 5.0 earthquake. The moment magnitude scale modifies Richter's original idea to include the amount of fault slippage, the size of the surface area that ruptured and the nature of the materials. One of the largest earthquakes recorded on the moment magnitude scale was M 9.6 for the 1960 Southern Chile quake. This killed an estimated 5,700 people. The 2004 earthquake off the northwest coast of Sumatra measured M 9.3. The 1989 Loma Prieta, California earthquake measured M 7.0, killed 66 people and caused an estimated $5.6 billion in property damage. It is estimated that an earthquake in San Francisco of M 8.0, lasting for one minute, would kill or injure 350,000 people.

With such great potential for damage, achieving some measure of protection from earthquakes assumes high priority. If the time and place of damaging earthquakes can be predicted, stiff zoning controls and building codes can minimize damage and evacuation can save lives. Some earthquakes have already been predicted to within a few hours by observing physical changes in the crust. The prevention of earthquakes includes the lubrication of active faults to prevent their lockup. The intent is to induce a series of small displacements along a fault, with the accompanying harmless ***microearthquakes*** preventing sudden major displacements that produce damaging earthquakes. Although this technique has been successful in laboratory experiments, its application to a stressed fault in a populated area carries obvious and perhaps unacceptable risks.

QUESTIONS

4.4 The first seismic waves from an earthquake that reach a seismograph are the P-waves. Lagging behind are the S-waves, which can be recognized on the seismograph by their greater amplitude. The difference in arrival time of the seismic waves at three widely-spaced seismograph stations can be used to calculate the distance of an earthquake epicenter from the seismograph station. S-waves travel at 2.7 miles/sec and P-waves at 4.8 miles/sec, making the P-waves 2.1 miles/sec faster. The time T_1 (in seconds) taken by S-waves to travel a distance D (in miles) from the epicenter to a seismograph station is:

$$\mathbf{T_1 = D/2.7.}$$

The time T_2 for P-waves to travel the same distance is:

$$\mathbf{T_2 = D/4.8.}$$

The difference in arrival time (ΔT) between the P- and S-waves is:

$$\mathbf{\Delta T = T_1 - T_2 = D/2.7 - D/4.8 \quad or \quad \Delta T = 2.1D/13.}$$

Therefore, the distance D from the earthquake epicenter to the seismograph station is given by:

$$\mathbf{D = 13\Delta T/2.1.}$$

Using this relationship, complete Table 4.1 and locate the epicenter of the earthquake using Fig. 4.3 and list its lat/long coordinates below. Use Google Earth™ to help you with the coordinates.

Table 4.1 Distance of epicenter of an earthquake from three seismograph stations.

Seismograph Station	Time Between Arrival of P- and S- Waves	Estimated Distance to Epicenter
Cape Town, South Africa	5 min. 31 sec.	
Rio de Janeiro, Brazil	7 min. 21 sec.	
Luanda, Angola	7 min. 45 sec.	

4.5 Table 4.2 is a selected list of severe earthquakes. Using Fig. 4.3 and Google Earth™ satellite imagery, determine their locations. What correspondence, if any, does there appear to be between earthquake activity and plate boundaries?

Table 4.2 Selected severe earthquakes

Date	Location	Moment Magnitude
Feb. 2010	Maule, Chile	8.8
Jan. 2010	Port-au-Prince, Haiti	7.0
Oct. 2005	Kashmir region, Pakistan	7.6
Dec. 2004	Northern Sumatra, Indonesia	9.3
Dec. 2003	Bam, Iran	6.9
Nov. 2002	Denali, National Park, Alaska	7.9
Sep. 1999	Oaxaca, Mexico	7.5
Aug. 1999	Izmit, Turkey	7.4
Feb, 1996	Indonesia	8.1
Jan. 1995	Kobe, Japan	6.9
Oct, 1989	Loma Prieta, California	7.0
Mar. 1964	Anchorage, Alaska	9.2
May 1960	Southern Chile	9.6
Sep. 1923	Kwanto, Japan	7.9

4.6 Using the United States Geological Survey (USGS) web site (http://www.usgs.gov/) answer the following questions.

When you have accessed the website, click on the icon for Recent Earthquakes, USA or World.

(a) List the date, location and magnitude of the three most recent earthquakes in the western US or Alaska.

(b) If you live outside the western US or Alaska, list the date, location and magnitude of the most recent earthquake in your area.

(c) Over the past 7 days, how many (if any) M 7.0 or higher earthquakes have occurred anywhere in the world and where were they? How many M 5.0 – M 7.0 earthquakes were there?

Student Name________________________________

Exercise 5

VOLCANIC LANDFORMS

MATERIALS

Lens stereoscope (plastic), red/blue 3-D glasses, computer with Google Earth™ software and Internet access.

OBJECTIVES

1. Distinguish between intrusive and extrusive volcanic features, in terms of process and appearance on block drawings.
2. Recognize several types of extrusive and intrusive volcanic features on air photos, satellite images, and topographic maps.
3. Analyze the sequence of volcanic events using evidence in aerial photos.

INTRODUCTION

A combination of molten rock (the melt), dissolved gases, suspended crystals, and solid rocks (xenoliths) associated with volcanic activity is known as ***magma*** when it is below the Earth's surface. When magma reaches the surface it is known as ***lava***. Various features are created as the magma or lava cools and solidifies depending on where it cools, within or on the Earth's crust. If magma cools within the crust it forms ***intrusive volcanic features***, while those features formed from the cooling of lava on the surface are ***extrusive volcanic features*** (Fig. 5.1). The temperature of molten rock lies between 900° and 1200° C, so the different cooling rates of the material (on or within the crust) will yield slightly different types of rock and features. ***Igneous*** rocks are formed by the ***crystallization*** of minerals from magma and lava and they cool. Granite, basalt, gabbro, andesite, rhyolite, and obsidian are some of the common types. In this exercise you will examine examples of volcanic features and the landscapes they create.

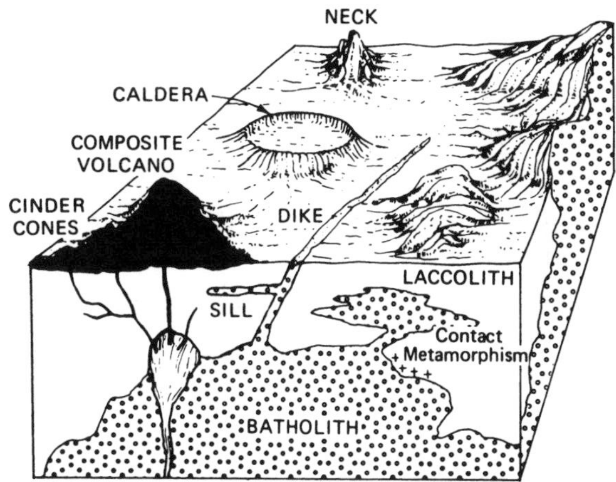

Fig. 5.1 Landforms associated with intrusive and extrusive volcanism.

SECTION I: Extrusive Volcanic Landforms

The most recognizable volcanic landform is the ***volcano or volcanic cone***. This is a ***vent***, or opening, in the Earth's crust through which magma erupts onto the surface. A ***crater*** or central depression forms at the crests of many volcanoes. Volcanic eruptions are either ***effusive*** or ***explosive***. The type of eruption depends on the ***viscosity*** of the magma as it reaches the surface. In general, magma viscosity (the property of a fluid to resist flowing) increases with an increase in the proportion of silica in the magma. Magma with a higher viscosity does not flow as easily and this allows gas pressure to build up in the magma and magma chamber, thus causing a more explosive eruption as the gas escapes. An eruption of this type typically creates a ***composite cone*** or ***stratovolcano***. These are steep-sided, conical volcanoes composed of alternating layers of lava and pyroclastic material or ***tephra***. Tephra consists of fragments of volcanic rock and lava that range in size from large ***bombs***, to ***cinders***, ***pumice*** and ***ash***. Many well-known volcanoes are of this type, including Mt. St. Helens, Mt. Fuji, Vesuvius, Pinatubo, and Kilimanjaro. Many stratovolcanoes, such as Mt. Etna on the island of Sicily, have numerous ***parasitic or flank cones*** on their sides as a result of ***flank eruptions***. Flank eruptions occur when magma migrates laterally under pressure along cracks in the sides of the central volcano. A ***cinder cone*** is also the result of an explosive eruption, but is comprised primarily of cinder-sized tephra and is usually less than 1000 feet in height. Perhaps the most devastating type of explosive eruption is the ***glowing avalanche*** or ***nuées ardentes*** that produces massive amounts of hot ash, pumice, rock fragments, and volcanic (often toxic) gases that flow down the flanks of the volcano because they are denser than the atmosphere. Almost everyone (30,000 people) in the town of St. Pierre, the capital of the Caribbean island Martinique, was killed by a glowing avalanche during the 1902 eruption of the Mount Pelée volcano. Explosive eruptions also tend to trigger ***volcanic mudflows*** or ***lahars***, which are a mixture of rock debris, volcanic ash and water that originates on the slopes of a volcano. Explosive eruptions and the volcanic features they create are most often associated with convergent plate boundaries.

Effusive eruptions occur where the magma has a much lower proportion of silica and is thus of lower viscosity. Not as much gas pressure builds up and the magma flows more easily so that the eruption is much less violent. Because of this, eruptions of this type from a central vent often produce a volcanic cone with broad, gentle slopes, composed of layer upon layer of fluid basalt lava. They are thought to resemble a warrior's shield and thus are called ***shield volcanoes***. The Hawaiian Islands are a chain of shield volcanoes created at a ***hot spot*** in the middle of the Pacific Ocean. If an effusive eruption issues from a series of long fissures it forms ***flood or plateau basalts***. The Columbia Plateau of the northwestern U.S. is one such flood basalt and the ocean floor is comprised almost entirely of basalt which has flowed from oceanic ridges. Some central-vent volcanoes have large depressions within the walls of their summits. These depressions are called ***calderas*** and have diameters that can be many times that of the initial vent or crater. Most calderas form by the collapse of the volcanic structure into an emptied, underlying magma chamber or cauldron during major eruptions (see 3-D anaglyphs 1 and 2 in Appendix D). This process is called ***cauldron subsidence***. ***Explosion calderas*** are formed by the violent removal of the upper part of the cone during an eruption. Three calderas up to 50 miles (80 km) long and 40 miles (65 km) wide make up much of the Yellowstone National Park area in Wyoming. The Yellowstone area, like Hawaii, is above a hot spot or mantle plume. Crater Lake in Oregon is another example of a caldera produced by cauldron subsidence after a major eruption. It is also linked to the mantle plume that currently underlies Yellowstone National Park.

QUESTIONS

5.1 Examine the map (Fig. 5.2), aerial photographs (Fig. 5.3), and 3-D anaglyphs (3 & 4 in Appendix D) of the Menan Butte area of Idaho. Also view a recent Google Earth™ satellite image of the area by typing the following coordinates in the search box: 43° 46′ 32.79″ N, 111° 56′ 05.77″ W. Start viewing from an Eye alt of 35,000 feet. The Menan Buttes are "tuff cones", or shallow, flat-floored craters comprised of tuff (a volcanic rock made up of a mixture of volcanic rock and mineral fragments in a volcanic ash matrix). These are often known as ash and cinder cones.

(a) Draw a southwest to northeast topographic profile through the volcanic cone shown in Fig. 5.2. Your profile should be 7 inches in length, starting at B.0-1.0 and passing through the spot mark in the crater (5227 feet). Use a vertical exaggeration of 1 inch to 400 feet. What is the relative height of the cone (its elevation above the surrounding plain) and the depth of the central crater? Explain why the cone and crater are asymmetrical and why so in this direction.

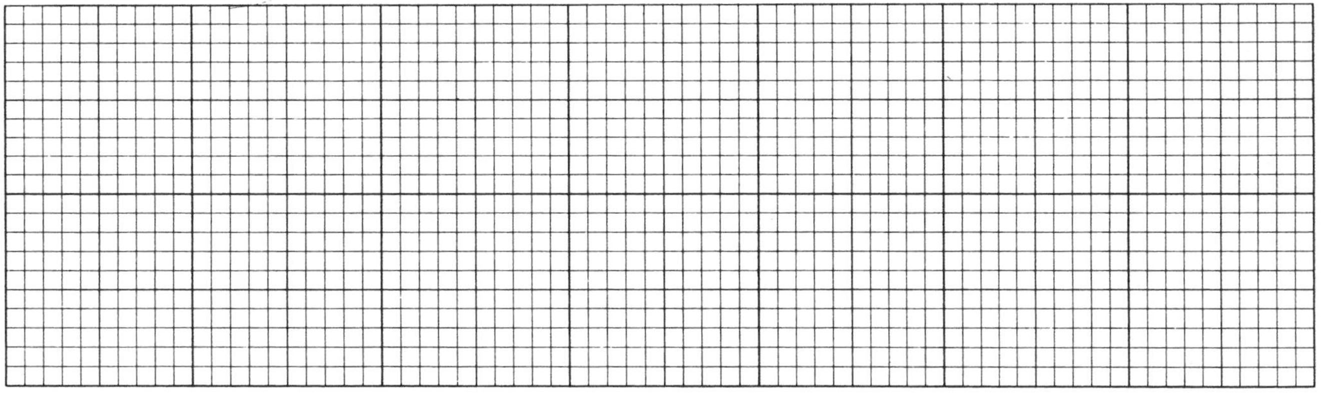

(b) What effect does the formation of the Menan Buttes appear to have had on the course of the Snake River, which runs on the southwest to south side of the buttes?

(c) Compare Fig. 5.2 (dating to 1951) and Fig. 5.3 (dating to 1950) and its 3-D anaglyph, with a recent Google Earth™ image of the area. What changes, both natural and due to human activities, have occurred in this area since the early 1950s?

Next Page **Fig. 5.2 Menan Buttes, Idaho (1:24,000, a.0-1.0 in southwest corner).**

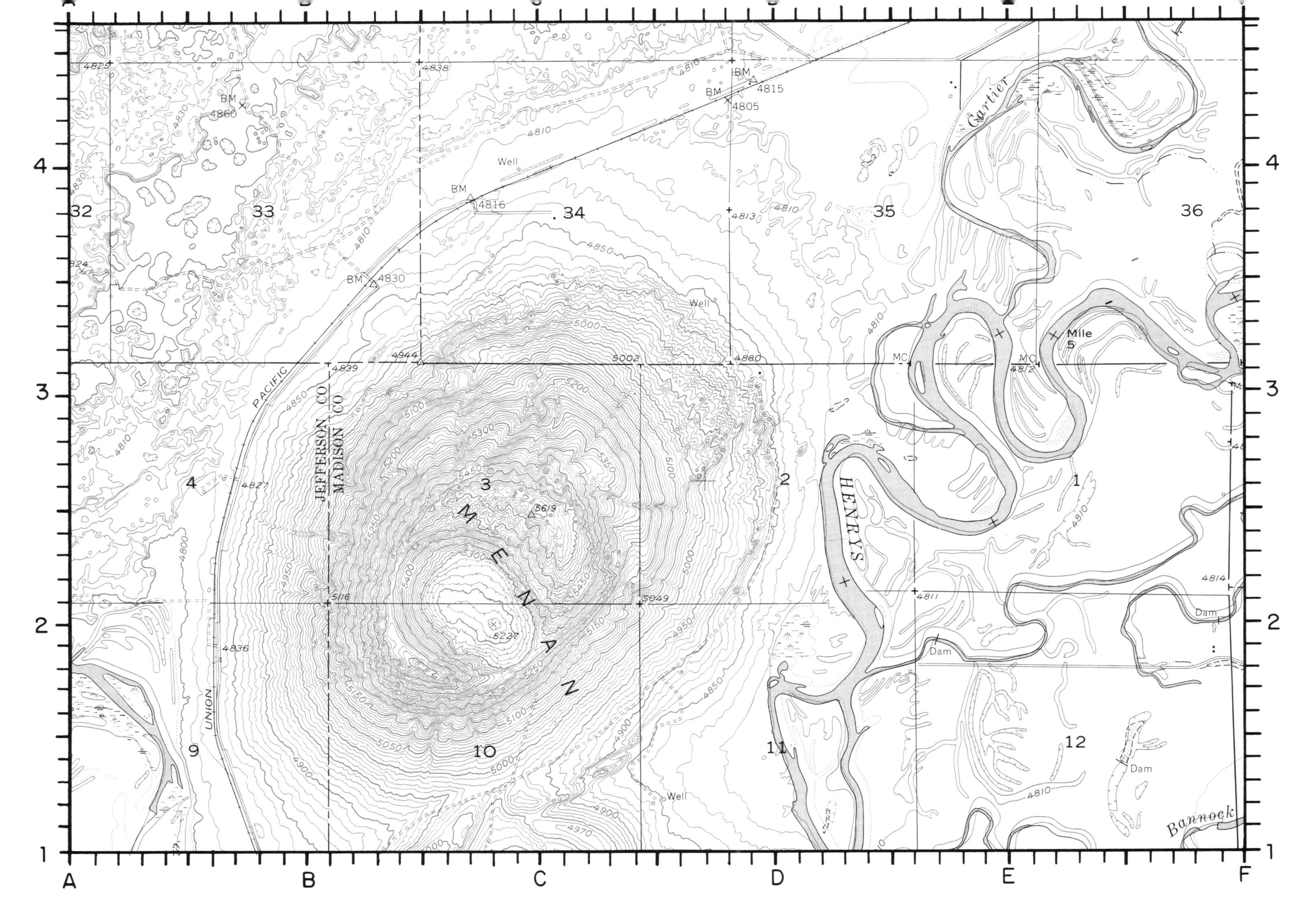

HENRYS
M E N A N
JEFFERSON CO
MADISON CO
UNION
PACIFIC
Bannock
Gartier
Mile 5
Well
Dam
BM
4815
4805
4816
4830
4860
5619
5227
36
35
34
33
32
1
2
3
4
9
10
11
12
A
B
C
D
E
F

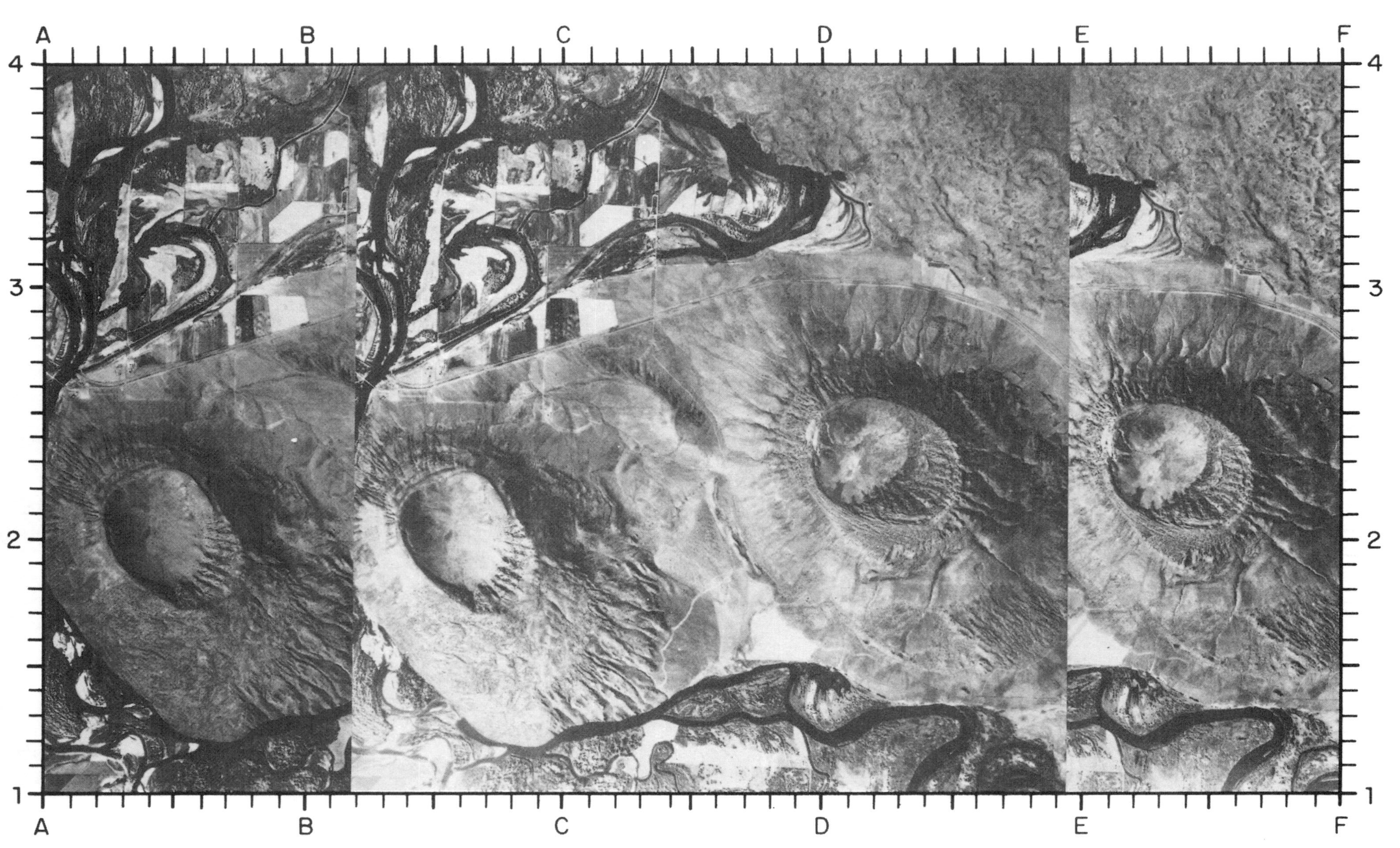

Fig. 5.3 Menan Buttes, Idaho (A.0-1.0 in southeast corner).

5.2 The aerial photographs in Fig. 5.4 and the 3-D anaglyph 5 in Appendix D show Asama-yama, one of Japan's most active and dangerous volcanoes, located on Honshu Island. Also view a recent satellite image of the volcano using Google Earth™ by typing the following coordinates in the search box: 36° 25′ 38.90″ N, 138° 31′ 46.24″ E. Start viewing from an Eye alt of 38,000 feet and use the zoom option to obtain both close-up and distant views.

(a) The photographs show evidence of three main stages in the history of the volcano. Locate and give grid coordinates for this evidence.

(b) What kind of volcano is Asama-yama?

(c) Did the newest cone of Asama-yama (D.7-1.4) form prior to or later than the most recent lava flow, which occurred in 1783? How can you tell? What relationship does this cone have to the main cone?

(d) Compare the photos in Fig. 5.4 (taken in 1947) and the 3-D anaglyph with the more recent image on Google Earth™. Why are some areas more highly dissected by streams than other areas? Does it appear that there have been any eruptions since 1947? Explain.

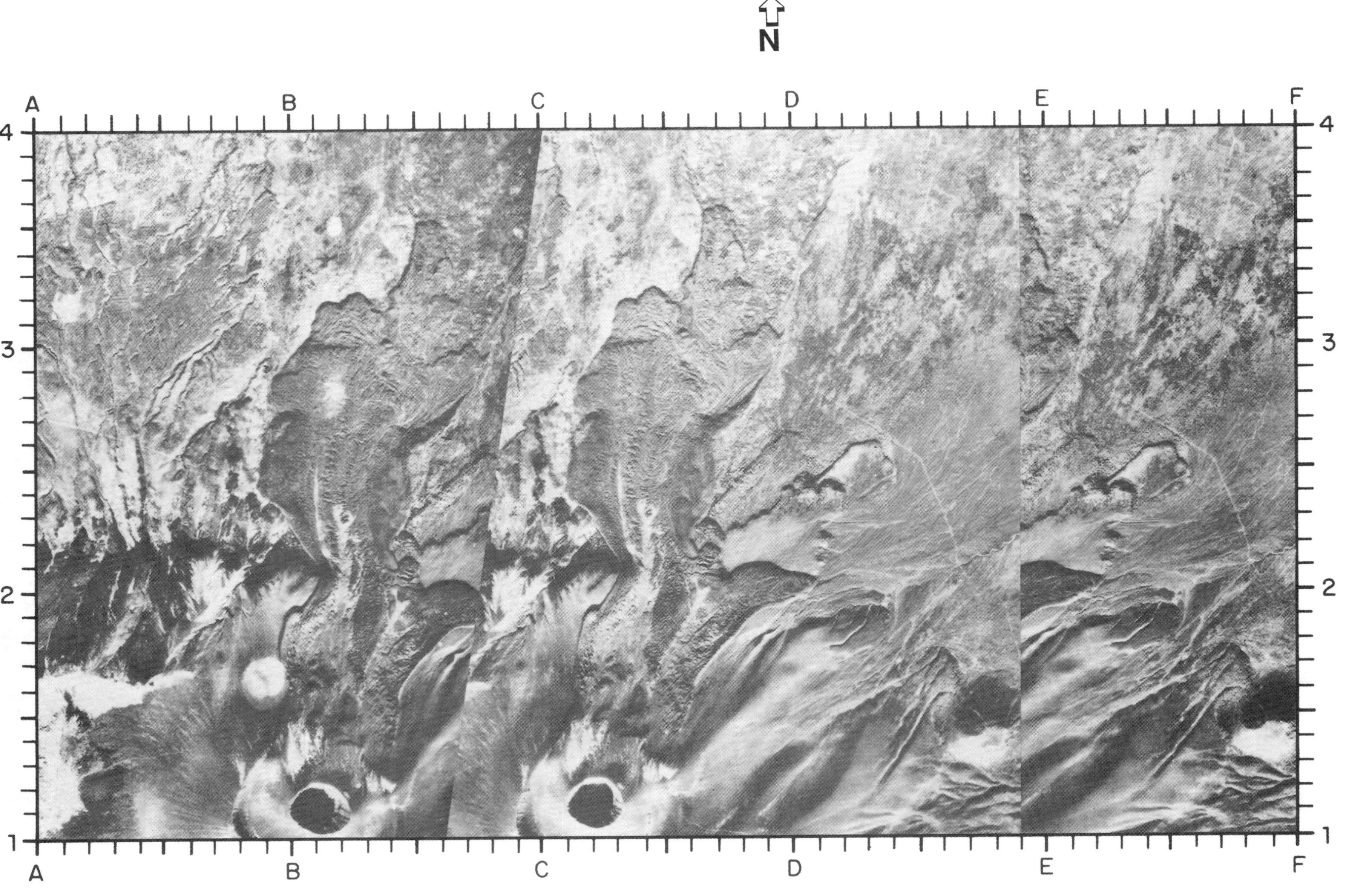

Fig. 5.4 Asama Volcano, Japan (1:52,800, A.0-1.0 in southwest corner).

5.3 Using Google Earth™ locate Mt. St. Helens, Washington by typing the following coordinates in the search box: 46° 13′ 18.63″ N, 122° 11′ 10.57″ W. Start viewing from an Eye alt of 20 miles. Also, locate Mt. St. Helens on the United States Geologic Survey (USGS) web Site:

(http://vulcan.wr.usgs.gov/Volcanoes/MSH/).

Once you are in the site scroll down to Maps, Graphics, and Images and select CVO Photo Archives - Mount St. Helens, 1980-2004 or type in the URL:

http://vulcan.wr.usgs.gov/Volcanoes/MSH/Images/MSH80/framework.html

Compare pre- and post-eruption photos of the volcano and, based on these images, outline what occurred during the eruption. Was it an explosive or effusive eruption?

5.4 Using the USGS web site (http://volcanoes.usgs.gov/activity/), list the three most recent volcanic eruptions anywhere in the world. Give the name of the volcano, its latitude/longitude, and when it erupted.

5.5 Hot spots are areas of unique volcanic activity where a source of magma or plume remains in the same approximate position over a long period of time. However, the features formed on the surface by plume activity move with the tectonic plate to which they are attached. Over time, a series of surface features may be created and this can give an indication of which direction the plate is moving relative to the plume. The Hawaiian Islands and Yellowstone National Park lie above two different hot spots. The islands of Hawaiian chain were all created above the same mantle plume, but have been carried away from the plume by movements of the Pacific Plate. Features created by the Yellowstone hot spot have also been transported from the plume by plate motions. Locate both of these areas using Google Earth™ and study the landforms that have formed above the plume. Using the USGS web site to help you, determine which direction the Pacific Plate moved to create the Hawaiian islands (also look at Fig. 4.3), and which direction the North American Plate moved to form the calderas in and near Yellowstone.

SECTION 2: *Intrusive Volcanic Landforms*

Magma within the Earth does not always reach the surface as it rises through the crust. Often it cools within the crust forming ***intrusive volcanic features*** that may be ***discordant*** or ***concordant*** (Fig. 5.1). Discordant features cut across existing strata and often replace these strata by melting the existing rock and forming new bodies of igneous rock. The largest of these is the ***batholith,*** which can cover thousands of square miles in area. The Sierra Nevada Mountains of California have formed from a series of exposed batholiths. Other discordant igneous bodies include ***stocks*** that extend upwards from batholiths and so are exposed by surface erosion of overlying rocks earlier than the main batholith structure. Also discordant are ***dikes,*** which are narrow, sub-vertical sheets of originally molten rock that cut across existing rock layers. ***Volcanic necks*** are the remnants of magma in the central feeder pipe of an ancient volcano and because these are often resistant to erosion they frequently rise sharply from the surrounding terrain. Concordant features generally form between rock layers. The two most common types are ***laccoliths*** (domes of magma between rock strata) and ***sills*** (narrow, sub-horizontal sheets of magma between rock layers). Laccoliths form near the surface and result in the doming upward of layered rocks. Sills develop at any depth and often intersect dikes. Stone Mountain near Atlanta, Georgia is an example of a smaller body of molten rock that migrated upward within a subduction zone due to melting of a subducting plate. Bodies of granite like Stone Mountain that are several kilometers in diameter are called plutons, and they are partly intrusive and partly originate by melting of the local rock.

QUESTIONS

5.6 Fig. 5.5 and 3-D anaglyph 6 in Appendix D show intersecting, narrow, linear features in Huerfano County, Colorado. Use Google Earth™ to obtain a recent satellite image of this area by typing the following coordinates in the search box: 37° 30′ 38.79″ N, 104° 50′ 18.23″ W. Start viewing from an Eye alt of 40,000 feet and view the area obliquely to get a 3-D look at the linear features. What volcanic landforms are they and why do they rise above the surrounding area?

5.7 Examine satellite images of the following places using Google Earth™ and give their latitude and longitude coordinates. By looking carefully at the images determine what type of intrusive volcanic structure you are looking at in each case.

Stone Mountain, GA ______________________________

Devils Tower, WY ______________________________

Shiprock, NM (2 features here) ______________________________

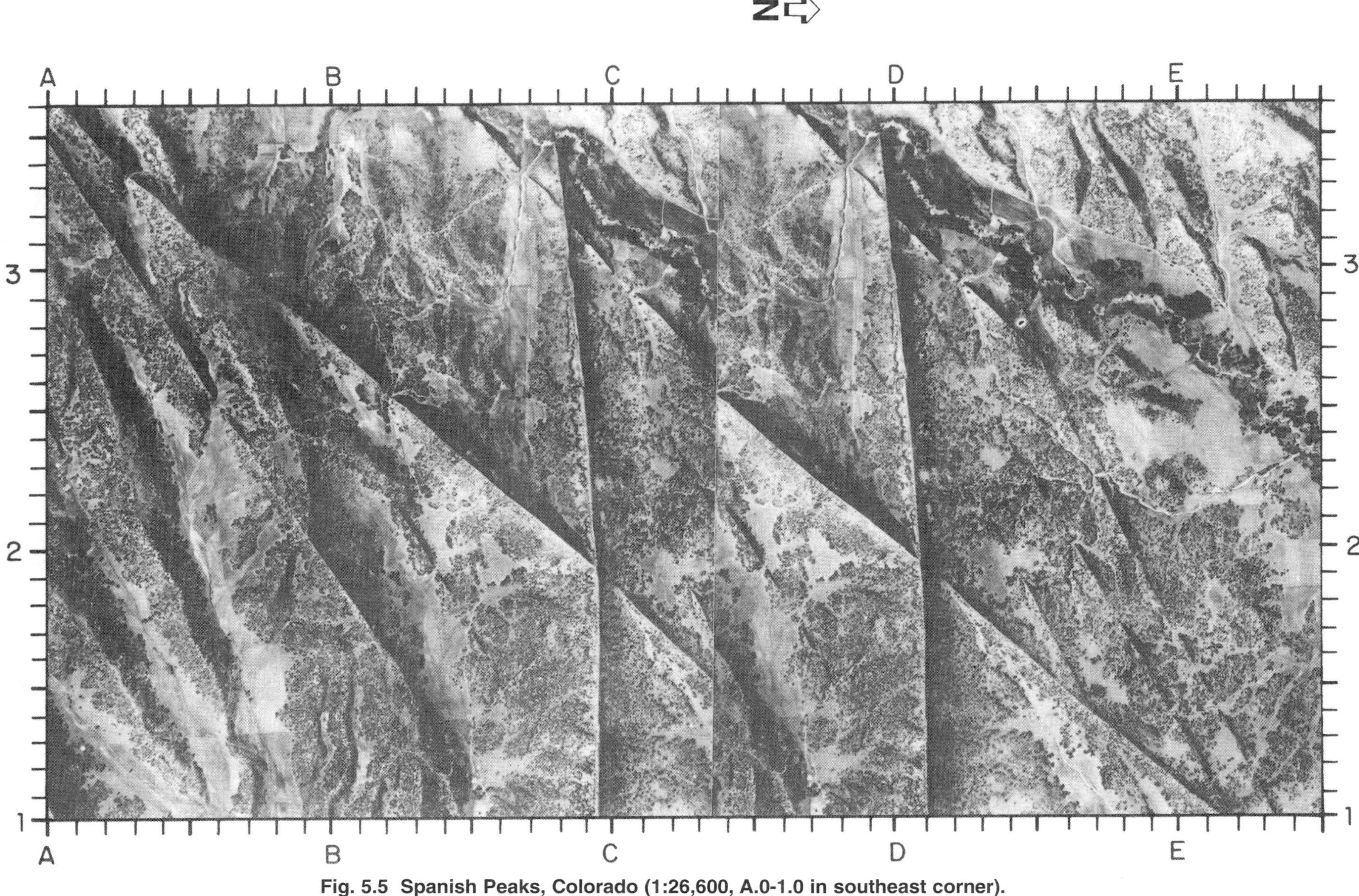

Fig. 5.5 Spanish Peaks, Colorado (1:26,600, A.0-1.0 in southeast corner).

Student Name________________________________

Exercise 6

STRUCTURAL LANDFORMS AND GEOLOGICAL MAPS

MATERIALS

Lens stereoscope (plastic), red/blue 3-D glasses, ruler, protractor, colored pencils, computer with Google Earth™ software and Internet access.

OBJECTIVES

1. Identify and determine the strike, dip and outcrops of the structures shown on a geologic map.
2. Recognize the relative ages of rock strata from their positions in a structure.
3. Recognize geological structures, including anticlines and synclines, on a geologic map, or on geological cross sections and block diagrams.
4. Recognize geological structures on air photos, topographic maps, and interpret how these structures have influenced topographic relief, drainage, and human activities.

INTRODUCTION

Variations in rock composition and structure are important in determining landform and landscape characteristics. Convergent tectonic forces produce ***fold*** structures in horizontally-bedded strata. Common fold structures include ***anticlines, synclines, monoclines, domes,*** and ***basins***. Vertical ***faulting*** due to compressive or tensional forces in the crust causes a relative displacement along the line of the fault with one side moving upward relative to the other. This results in the formation of ***fault scarps***, and in areas of multiple faults ***horsts*** and ***grabens*** may develop. Before they are modified by erosion, faults and folds impart ***primary relief*** to an area. As erosion progresses, areas underlain by weaker rocks (e.g. shale) are lowered more rapidly than areas underlain by more resistant rocks (e.g. sandstone or conglomerate) so that the resulting relief is determined by both structural and lithological characteristics. Over time, folds and faults are gradually reduced to surfaces of faint relief but, at all stages of evolution, the landscape reflects the underlying structure.

SECTION I: Geologic Maps and Sections

Whereas the topographic map shows both planimetric and hypsometric data for the Earth's surface, the primary purpose of a ***geologic map*** is to provide planimetric information about the outcrop of different rocks at the surface. In most cases, further structural information is given in the form of symbols. ***Geologic*** or ***structure sections*** show the subsurface configuration of rock bodies and layers as they would appear in the sides of a deep, vertical-walled canyon. The **dip** of a layer of rock or stratum (plural strata) is directed towards the maximum acute angle between the bedding and a horizontal plane. The acute angle itself is the magnitude of dip. The ***strike*** of a bed is the direction of a line formed by the intersection of the bedding and a horizontal plane. The directions of dip and strike are always at right angles to one another and on the map are indicated by the flattened T symbol: ⊢35. The long line indicates the direction of strike, the short line and number indicate the direction and magnitude of the dip in degrees. Vertical and horizontal beds are indicated by the symbols $+_{90^\circ}$ and ⊕ respectively, where the position of the 90° angle may be used to indicate the upper surface, or horizon, of the rock layer.

If rock strata are horizontal, each stratigraphic horizon is everywhere at the same elevation and will thus follow topographic contours. The width of the outcrop depends on the thickness of the bed, and where the thickness is constant the width will depend entirely upon the topographic slope, being greatest where slopes are gentle. The outcrop of a horizontal bed forms a V as it crosses a valley and the apex of the V points upstream. The top and bottom of a vertical bed will appear on a geological map as straight lines parallel to the strike of the layer. Topography has no control upon the outcrop pattern of vertically dipping structures such as dikes.

In areas of dipping beds where fold structures intersect a stream valley, the outcrop pattern of beds that dip upstream form a V that points upstream. The limits of the outcrop do not parallel the topographic contours. The outcrop pattern of beds that dip downstream at an angle greater than the stream gradient form a V with the apex pointing downstream. The outcrops of beds that dip downstream at an angle less than the stream gradient form a V that points upstream.

The outcrop pattern of any planar bed can be predicted if a topographic map is available, and if the dip and strike and the location of one exposure are known. For example, if a bed outcrops at X, and is known to strike east to west and dip north at 45°, it is possible to determine its position at any place in the area. The upper or lower surfaces of the bed can be represented by ***structure contours***, which like topographic contours, indicate the configuration of the surface. At each point where a structure contour intersects a topographic contour of the same elevation, the bed must outcrop. By connecting known outcrop points for the upper and lower horizons, an outcrop map can be prepared.

When preparing structure sections to illustrate the subsurface geological characteristics of an area, the first stage is to prepare a topographic profile. Normally, the vertical scale should be the same as the horizontal scale so that angular measurements are correct. If the outcrop pattern and rock dips are known, angles can be measured and rock layers plotted directly. If the strata are horizontal, it is sometimes necessary to exaggerate the vertical scale for the best presentation of the geological structure.

QUESTIONS

6.1 Examine Fig. 6.1. The dip of the strata in this diagram can be represented by the following symbol, ⊕.

(a) What is the dip of the sedimentary strata?

(b) Briefly describe the relationship between the outcrop pattern and the topography?

(c) Draw a topographic profile and geologic section along line A-B. Use the same horizontal scale as in the figure with a vertical exaggeration of 1 inch to 75 feet.

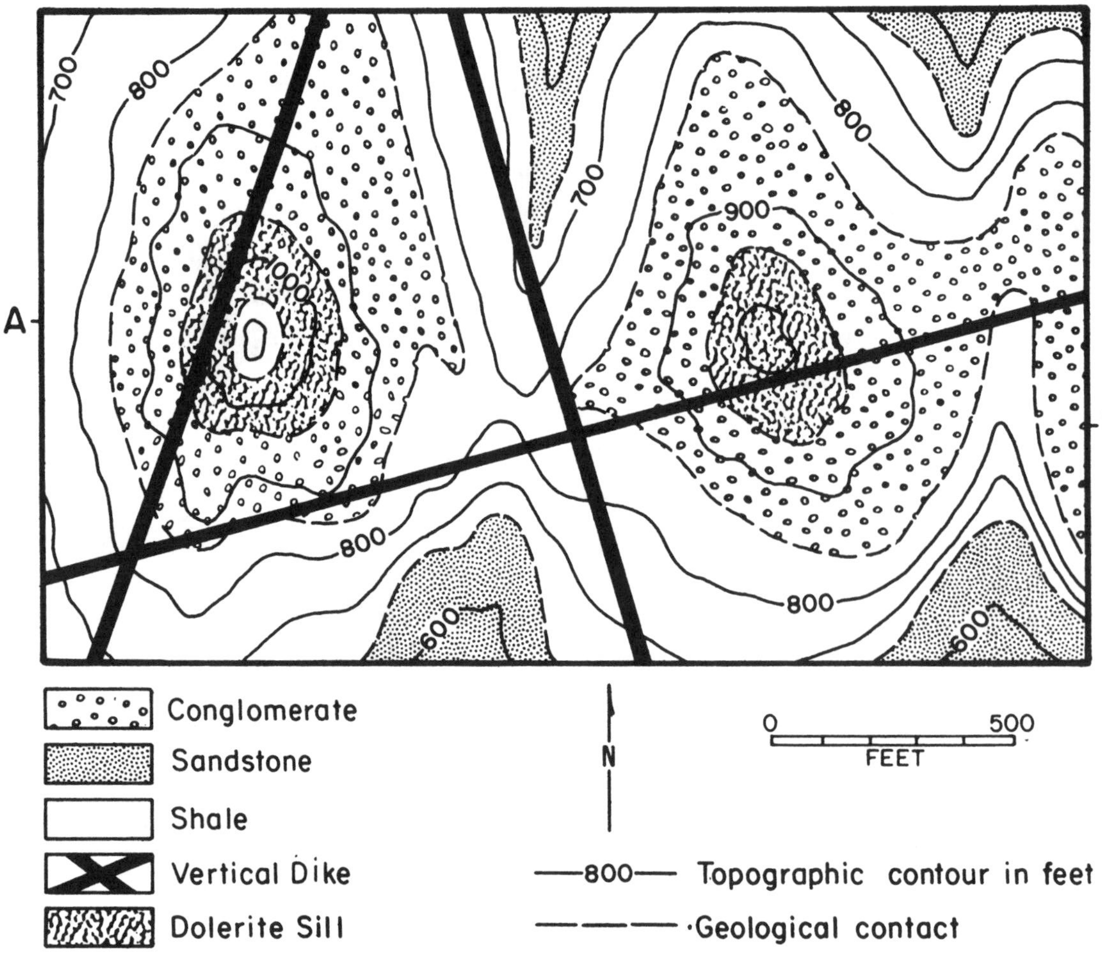

A
B
700
800
900
1000
800
700
800
600
800
600

Conglomerate
Sandstone
Shale
Vertical Dike
Dolerite Sill

N

0 500
FEET

—800— Topographic contour in feet
— — — Geological contact

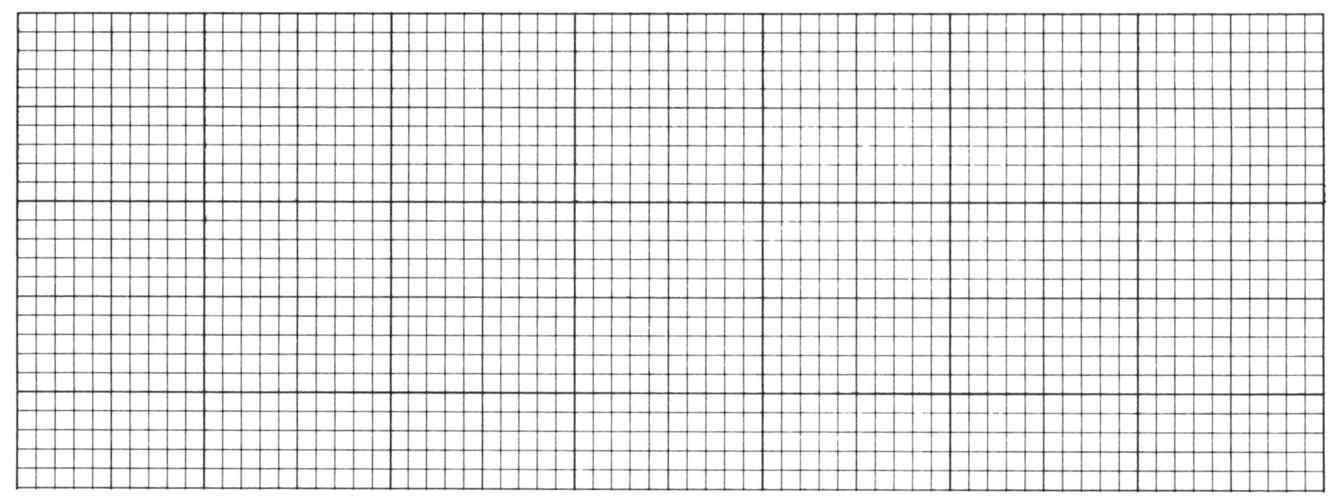

Fig. 6.1 Topographic map and geologic outcrop pattern.

6.2 Examine Fig. 6.2:

(a) What is the direction and magnitude of dip of the sedimentary strata?

(b) Assuming a horizontal but slightly irregular ground surface, draw a geologic section along line A-B. Use a horizontal scale of 1:6,000.

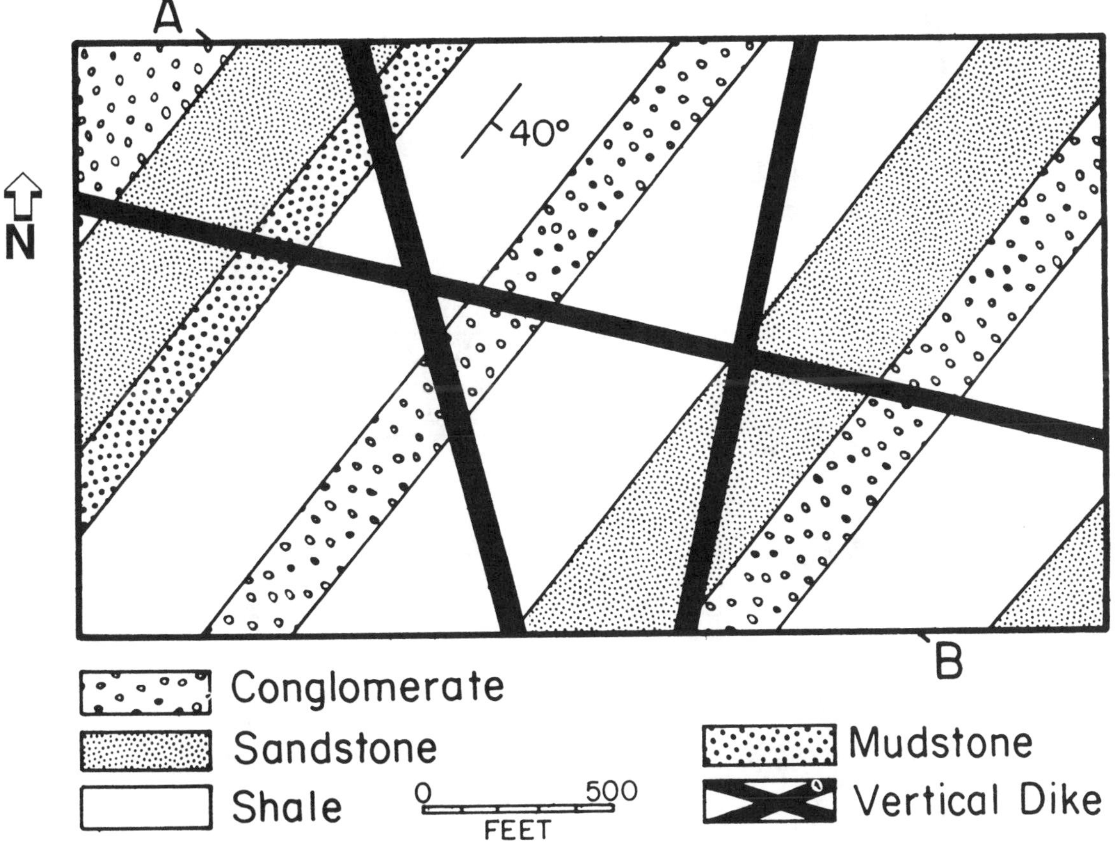

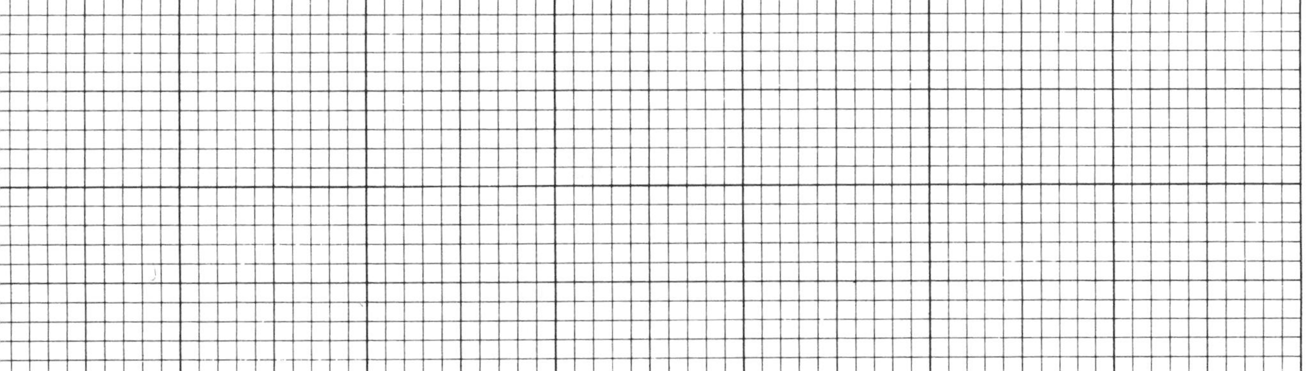

Fig. 6.2 Outcrop pattern of dipping rocks.

6.3 (a) In A of Fig. 6.3, the heavy line represents the outcrop of a thin layer of limestone. Where the layer intersects a contour line, we know the exact elevation of the layer at this point. If we join points on the layer at the same elevation we can produce a structure contour map of the layer (see dashed lines in Fig. 6.3A). When we do this we produce structure contours at 90, 80, and 70 feet elevation. It is clear from these structure contours that the bed is dipping toward the north. Over a distance of 100 feet, the elevation of the bed decreases from 90 feet to 70 feet (by 20 feet). The angle of dip is therefore tan 20/100 or tan 0.2, which is 11.3° or 11°18′.

Using a similar approach determine the angle and direction of dip of the thin layer of limestone in B, C, and D of Fig. 6.3.

(b) In E and F of Fig. 6.3, X and Y mark two points where a thin coal layer outcrops at the surface. In E the layer dips south at an inclination of 1 in 10. In F it dips east with an inclination of 1 in 5. Mark in the surface outcrop of the coal layer in each case.

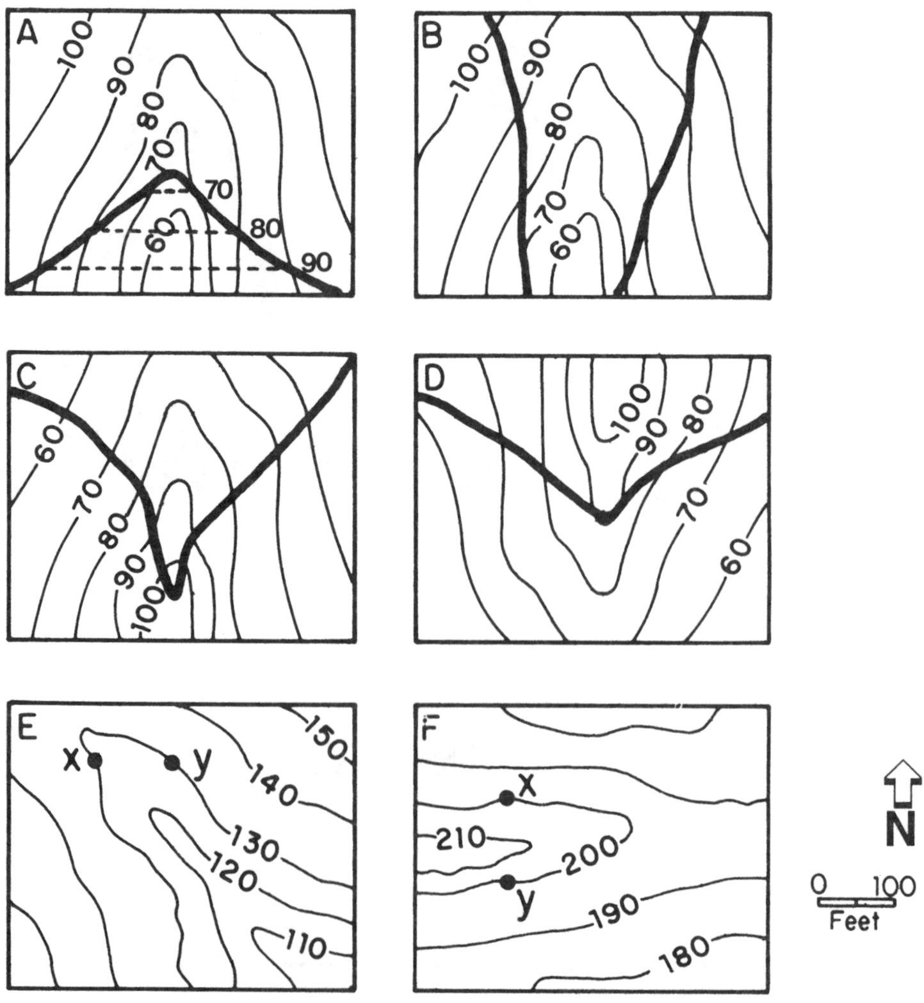

Fig. 6.3 The outcrop pattern of a thin rock layer in different topographic situations.

6.4 Examine Fig. 6.4:

(a) In the figure, the base of a horizontal bed of sandstone 150 feet thick is exposed at an elevation of 1950 feet on the northeastern slope of Long Ridge. Above the sandstone is a layer of shale and below it, 100 feet of conglomerate, 300 feet of limestone, and then a layer of dolomite. Produce a geologic map of the area, coloring or shading the various strata. Use the graph on the left-hand side to create a topographic profile of the area. The profile should go from south to north and cross through point X near White Mountain. Use a similar color or shading for the same beds in the map and profile.

(b) At point X northwest of White Mountain, the upper surface of a narrow dike is exposed at an elevation of 1700 feet. The dike dips at an angle of 60° to the north. Plot the outcrop of this dike on your topographic profile.

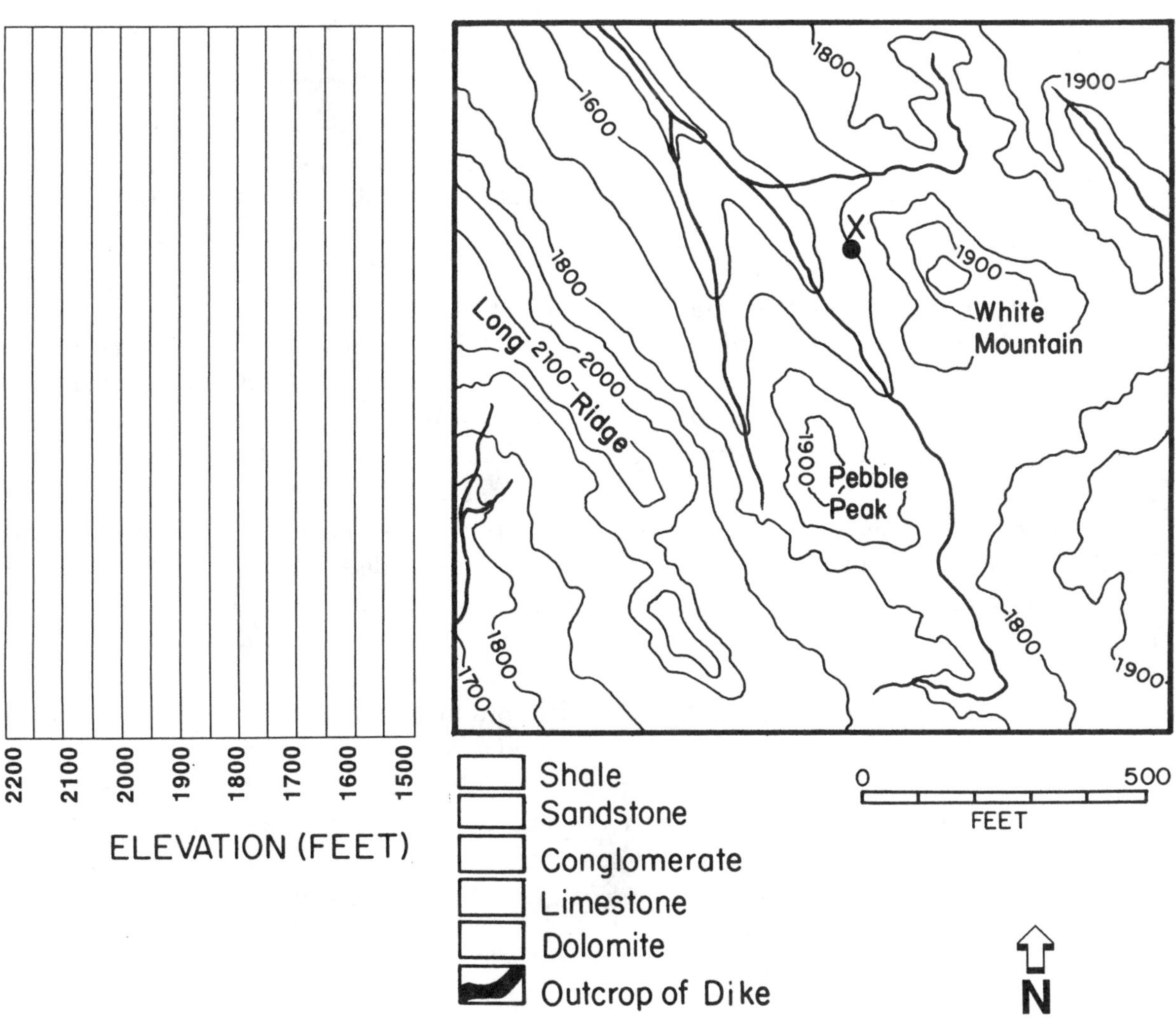

Fig. 6.4 Plotting the outcrop pattern of dipping rocks on a topographic map.

SECTION 2: Folds

Rock strata are commonly folded, tilted, or warped by tectonic forces creating domes, basins, monoclines, anticlines and synclines. Many mountain belts are little more than a series of parallel to sub-parallel folds. A ***syncline*** is a fold that is convex downward (shaped like the letter U), while an ***anticline*** is a fold that is convex upward (shaped like an upside down U, (∩)) (Fig. 6.5). Fold characteristics are indicated on a geologic map by the orientation of flattened T symbols. In an anticline they point away from each other on either side of the axis (Fig. 6.6B), while they point towards one another in a syncline. In a folded mountain belt, the anticlines may form ridges called ***anticlinal mountains***, and the synclines may form lowlands called ***synclinal valleys***. The ***axial plane*** of a fold divides it as symmetrically as possible so that the ***limbs*** dip evenly away from it. A symmetrical fold is one in which the axial plane is almost vertical, with the limbs dipping in opposite directions but by the same magnitude. In an asymmetrical fold, the axial plane is inclined and the limbs dip by different amounts.

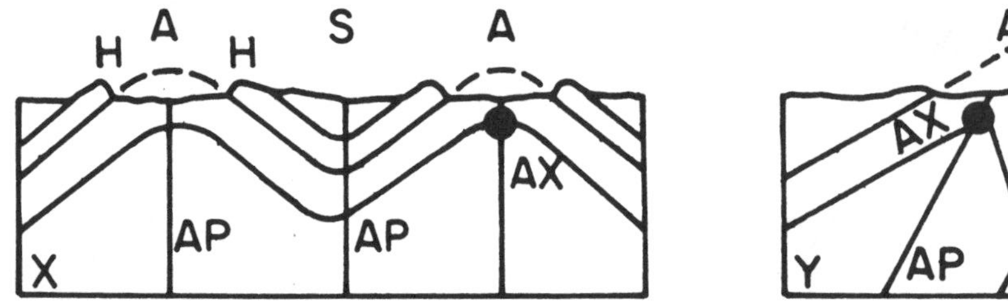

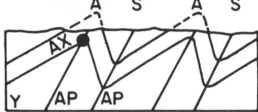

Fig. 6.5 **Eroded symmetrical (X) and asymmetrical (Y) anticlines and synclines (AP = axial plane, AX = axis, A = anticline, H = hogback ridge of hard rock).**

The ***axis*** of a fold is a line running along the flex of the fold (crest of an anticline, valley of a syncline). In some folds, the axis is horizontal, in others it is inclined and the folds are then said to ***plunge*** (Fig. 6.6A & C). When horizontal folds are eroded, the beds on opposite limbs are parallel to one another, and do not converge (Fig. 6.6B). When plunging folds are eroded, beds which outcrop at the surface converge in the direction of the nose (Fig. 6.6C). In an anticline, the nose points in the direction of the plunge and in the syncline, away from it. A ***double plunging fold*** is one that reverses its direction of plunge. ***Basins*** and ***domes*** are sub-circular, double plunging folds. When ***antiform*** structures are eroded, the oldest rocks are at the center of the outcrop pattern (Fig. 6.6B & C). In a ***synform*** structure, the youngest rocks occupy the center of the outcrop.

When ***fold mountains*** are eroded, streams cut into the flanks of the anticlines (which are frequently weakened by networks of open joints) and expose the underlying weaker rock layers. In some cases, a narrow valley may be incised parallel to the heavily fractured crest of the anticline and an ***anticlinal valley*** is formed. A synclinal valley on resistant rocks between two rapidly expanding anticlinal valleys cut in softer rocks may eventually become a ridge called a ***synclinal mountain***, and a ***reversal of topography*** will have occurred (Fig. 6.7).

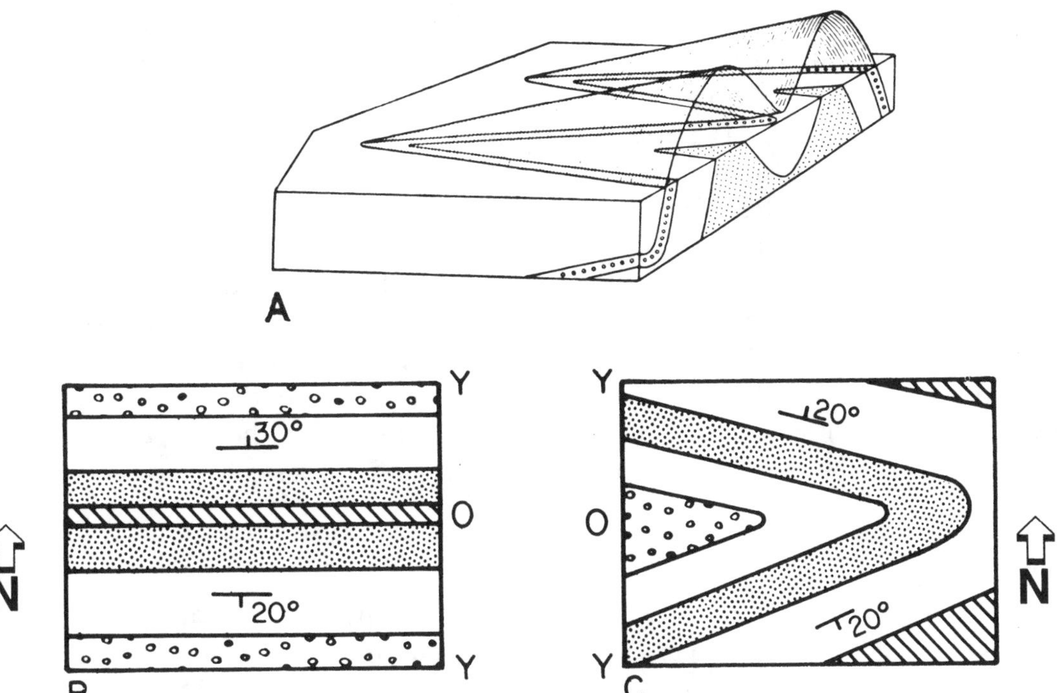

Fig. 6.6 Surface outcrop patterns of horizontal folds (B) and plunging folds (A and C). The outcrop patterns of B and C are of anticlinal structures. Y = youngest rock, O = oldest rock (diagram A from Billings 1954).

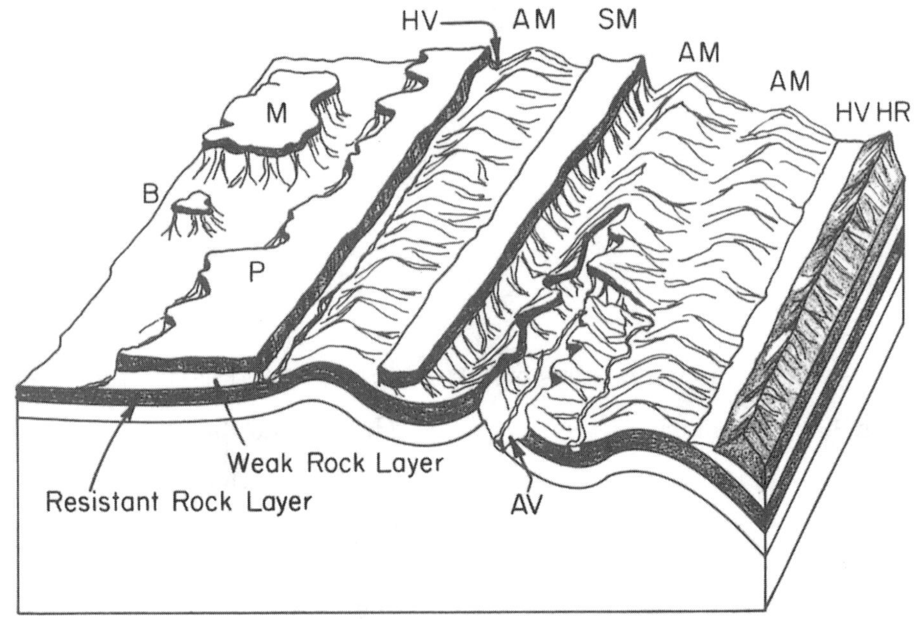

Fig. 6.7 Structural landforms of horizontal and folded sedimentary rocks (M = mesa, B = butte, P = stripped structural plateau, HV = homoclinal valley, HR = homoclinal ridge, AM = Anticlinal mountain, AV = anticlinal valley, SM = synclinal mountain).

Where folded rock structures are eroded and the strata exposed, denudation of the weaker layers is rapid, with the formation of lowlands separated by low ridges formed by the more resistant beds. Where the strata in a ridge dip is one direction only, as on the flank of an anticline or a syncline, the ridge is a ***homoclinal ridge***. Valleys cut in softer rocks which also dip in only one direction are ***homoclinal valleys***. If the beds dip at low angles (less than 10°), broad low ridges with one steep face and a gently sloping backslope develop. These are referred to as ***cuestas***. Where the strata dip at greater angles, sharp-crested ***hogback ridges*** form. These usually alternate with narrow valleys. A series of parallel ridges and valleys form where horizontal anticlines and synclines are eroded, while sinuous to zigzag ridges dominate landscapes cut across plunging folds (see Fig. 6.6). The hard rock ridges at the noses of eroded anticlines and synclines are called ***anticlinal*** or ***synclinal coves***. A concentric pattern of cuestas or hogbacks is typical of dissected domes and basins. In domes, the steeper faces of the upstanding ridges face the center of the structure. In basins, the reverse is the case.

QUESTIONS

6.5 The photos in Fig. 6.8a & b (3-D anaglyphs 7 and 8 in Appendix D) are along the same N-S flight path. The photo of Fig. 6.8a is north of the photo of Fig. 6.8b, with some overlap. Point E.2-2.8 in Fig. 6.8a is the same as B.2-2.8 on Fig. 6.8b. These photos show a folded sequence of Pennsylvania sandstone and shale on the boundary between the Ouachita Mountains and the Arkansas Valley in Oklahoma. Strip mines (C.7-3.2, page 6-12) have been opened up in the rocks on the top of the mountain that is bordered to the south by the Poteau River (E.0-1.6, page 6-12). The aerial photos were taken in 1955. Examine a recent Google Earth™ satellite image by typing the following coordinates in the search box: 34° 53′ 06.31″ N, 94° 39′ 03.56″ W. Start viewing from an Eye alt of 30,000 feet. Answer the following questions.

(a) Describe the geological structure of the area, noting anticlinal and synclinal structures and their direction of plunge.

(b) Locate the following features on the photographs and list their grid coordinates.

Synclinal Mountain ________________ Homoclinal Ridge ________________

Homoclinal Valley ________________ Hogback Ridge ________________

Synclinal Nose ________________ Anticlinal Nose ________________

(c) Does a weak or resistant rock underlie the valley of the Poteau River (E.0-1.6, page 6-12)? Why does the river follow the outcrop of this particular rock?

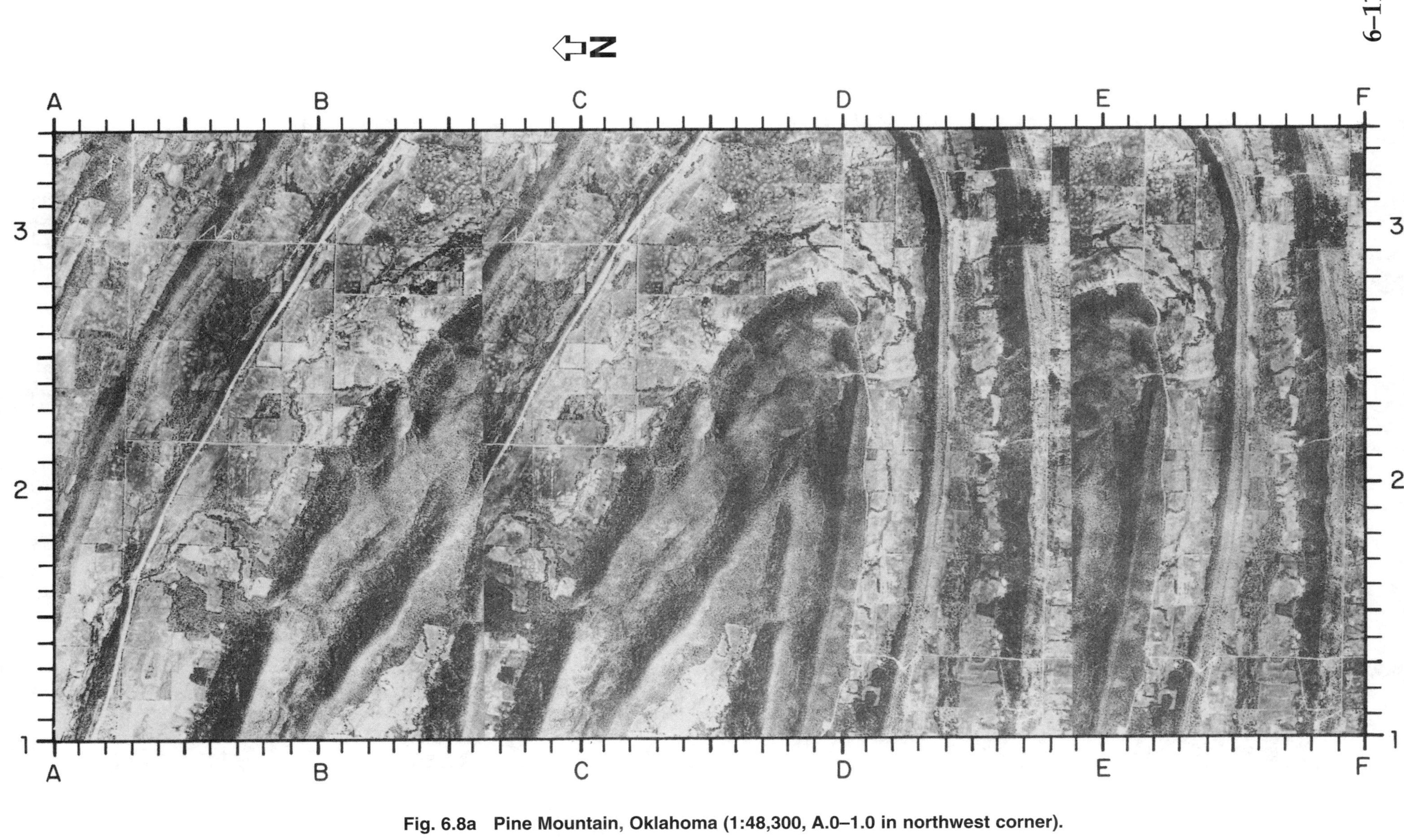

Fig. 6.8a Pine Mountain, Oklahoma (1:48,300, A.0–1.0 in northwest corner).

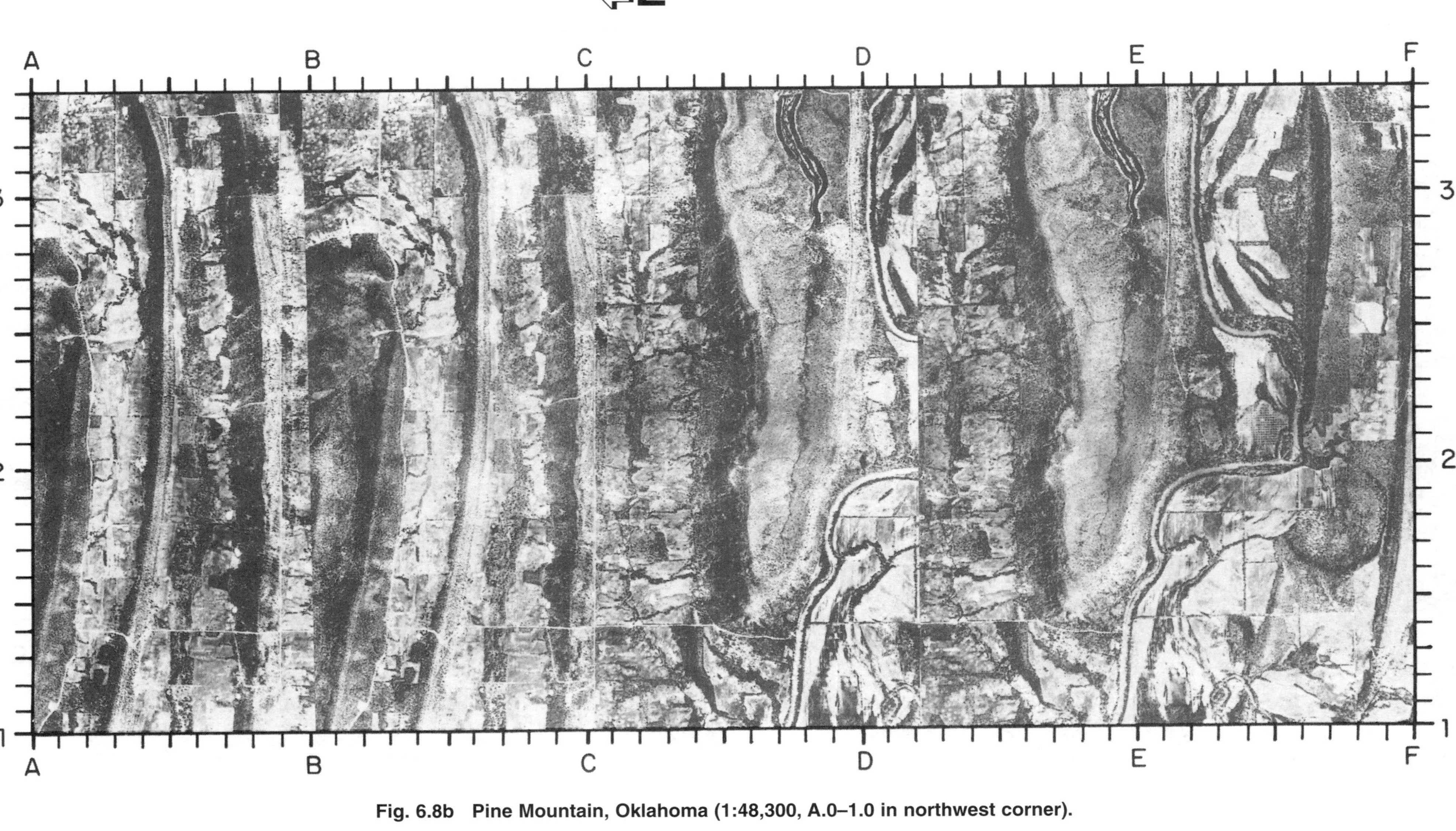

Fig. 6.8b Pine Mountain, Oklahoma (1:48,300, A.0–1.0 in northwest corner).

(d) How has the local structure of this area influenced human activities, such as transportation and agriculture?

(e) Compare the photos of Fig. 6.8, and anaglyphs 7 and 8, with the recent Google Earth™ image. Describe any changes in the area since 1955. For example, are strip mines still in operation, are there more roads, and has there been an expansion in agriculture? Explain your answers.

6.6 The central lowland of the geologic structure shown in the photos of Circle Ridge, Fremont County, Wyoming (Fig. 6.9 and 3-D anaglyphs 9 and 10 in Appendix D) is underlain by Triassic shale and sandstone and is surrounded by alternating sandstone and shale of Jurassic age. The aerial photo was taken in 1948. View a recent Google Earth™ satellite image (coordinates: 43° 31′ 46.64″ N, 109° 03′ 04.17″ W; starting Eye alt 30,000 feet) and answer the following questions.

(a) Locate the following features on the photographs and list their grid coordinates.

Hard Rock Layer ____________________ Soft rock Layer ____________________

Homoclinal Valley ____________________ Hogback Ridge ____________________

(b) Describe the geologic structure noting variations in the direction of dip of the strata. Is this a syncline, a dome, a basin, an anticline or some other structure?

(c) Compare a recent Google Earth™ image of this area with the 1948 photos shown in Fig. 6.9 and its anaglyph. Have there been any major changes to the area? Has the level of human activity increased or decreased? Explain your answer.

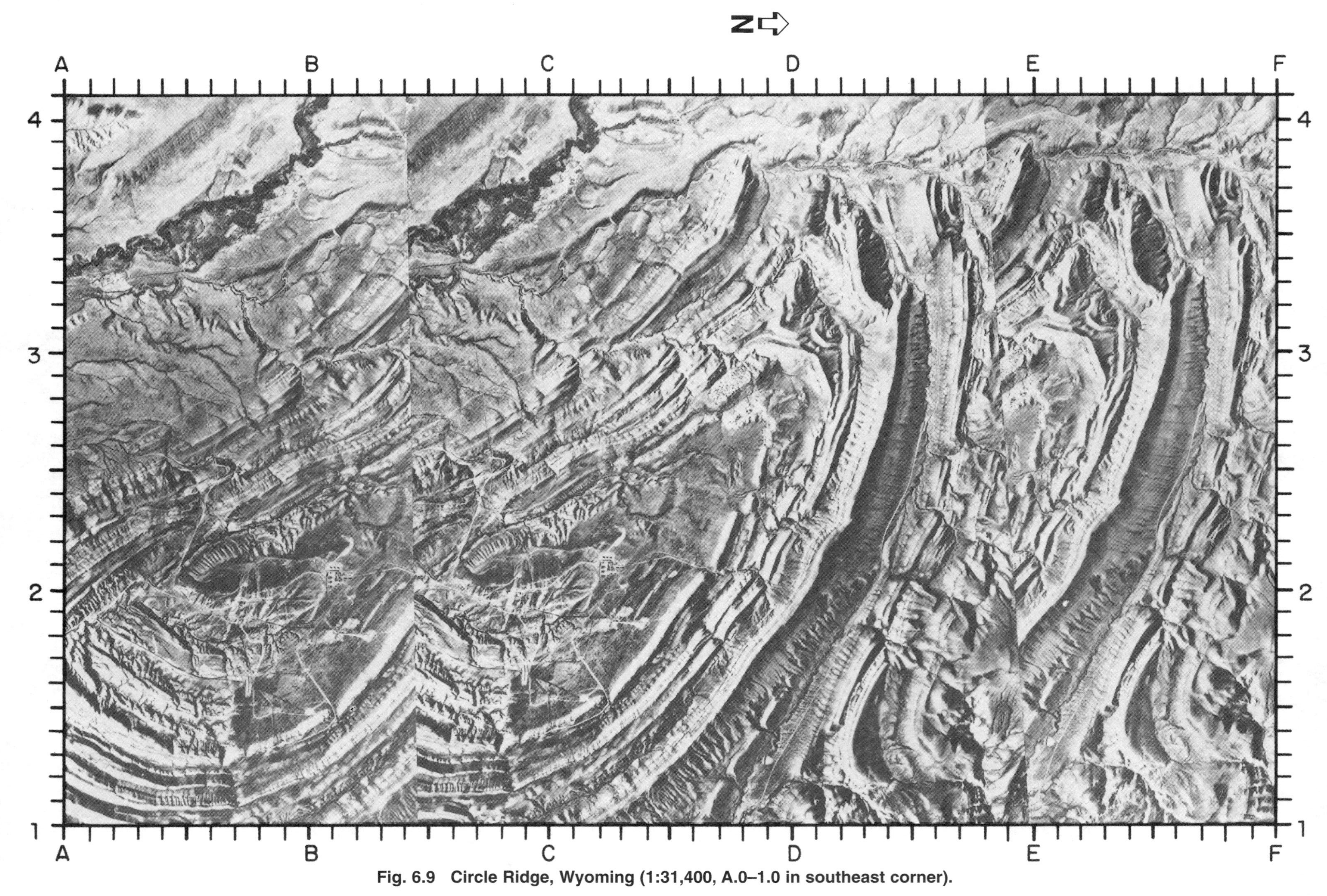

Fig. 6.9 Circle Ridge, Wyoming (1:31,400, A.0–1.0 in southeast corner).

6.7 The portion of the 1:250,000 scale Harrisburg, PA map (published in 1955) shown in Fig. 6.10 displays excellent examples of eroded plunging fold mountains in a variety of Pennsylvanian, Mississippian, Devonian, Silurian, and Ordovician rocks. The contour interval on the map is 100 feet and you are given that the town of Shamokin (D.5-4.1) occupies a synclinal structure. View a Google Earth™ satellite image of the area by typing the following coordinates in the search box: 40° 40′ 07.81″ N, 76° 49′ 46.44″ W. Start viewing from an Eye alt of 40 miles. Answer the following questions.

(a) Using the map and the satellite image, identify one further synclinal and two anticlinal structures, giving their grid coordinates, and directions of plunge.

(b) You will notice on the Google Earth™ image that a great deal of land in this area is used for agriculture. How has the nature of the landscape affected agricultural use and how has it influenced other human activities?

(c) How do you know that two of the rock types in the area are limestone and coal? (Consider clues provided by place names on the map.)

Next Page: Fig. 6.10 Harrisburg, Pennsylvania (1:250,000, A.0-1.0 in southwest corner).

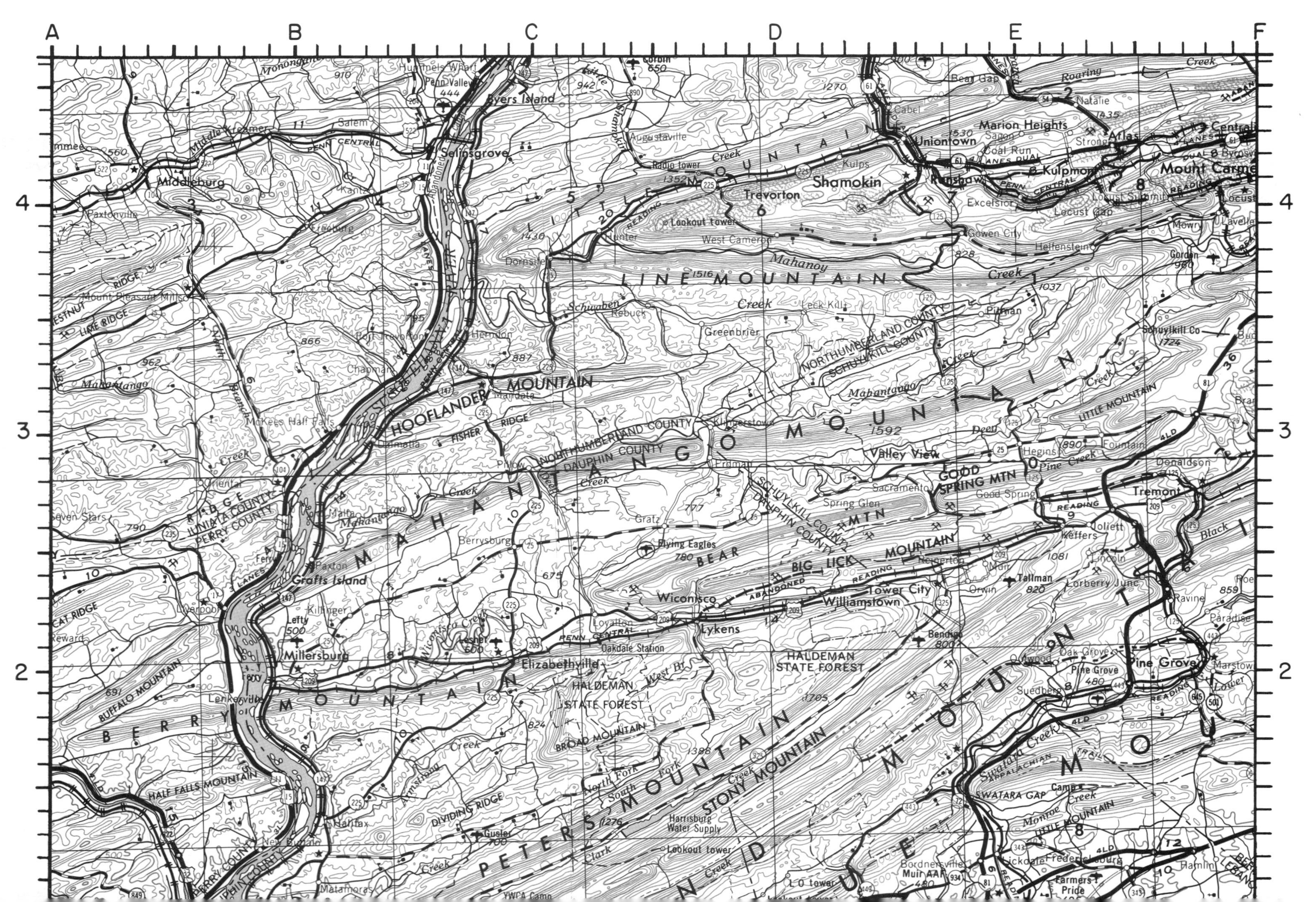

A
B
C
D
E
F
4
3
2
Shamokin
Mount Carmel
Kulpmont
Marion Heights
Uniontown
Trevorton
Selinsgrove
Middleburg
Herndon
Dornsife
Millersburg
Elizabethville
Lykens
Wiconisco
Williamstown
Tower City
Valley View
Gratz
Tremont
Pine Grove
Halifax
HALDEMAN STATE FOREST
LINE MOUNTAIN
MAHANTANGO MOUNTAIN
BERRY MOUNTAIN
PETERS MOUNTAIN
STONY MOUNTAIN
BIG LICK MOUNTAIN
GOOD SPRING MTN
HOOFLANDER MOUNTAIN

SECTION 3: *Faults*

Faulting is the rupturing of rocks and is always accompanied by a displacement along the plane of breakage. Where no such movement occurs, the plane is simply a ***joint***. The ***fault plane*** has a dip and strike, just like folds. Where the fault plane intersects the ground surface, it creates the ***fault line*** or ***fault trace*** (see FL in Fig. 6.11D). According to the nature and relative direction of displacement, several types of fault are recognized. Faulting that produces vertical displacement, one block being raised relative to the other block, produces a ***fault scarp*** at the surface (see FS in Fig. 6.11 A&B). When a fault scarp is eroded so that the base of the scarp no longer coincides with the fault trace, the scarp is called a ***fault line scarp*** (see FLS Fig. 6.11D).

A ***normal fault*** is formed when the fault plane dips in the direction of the block that is now relatively lower. This block is known as the ***downthrown block*** or ***hanging wall*** (Fig. 6.11A). The block that is relatively higher is known as the ***upthrown block*** or ***footwall***. It must be emphasized that up and down motions across fault planes are relative as both blocks may have moved upwards or both may have moved downwards. A ***reverse fault*** is formed when the fault plane dips towards the upthrown block or hanging wall (Fig. 6.11B). The fault scarps are also different, in that a reverse fault forms an overhanging fault scarp and a normal fault does not. When the dip of a reverse fault is less than 45°, both vertical and horizontal displacement of blocks takes place and the fault is known as a ***thrust fault***. A ***strike-slip or transcurrent fault*** is formed when the displacement is predominately horizontal and no fault scarp is produced (Fig. 6.11C).

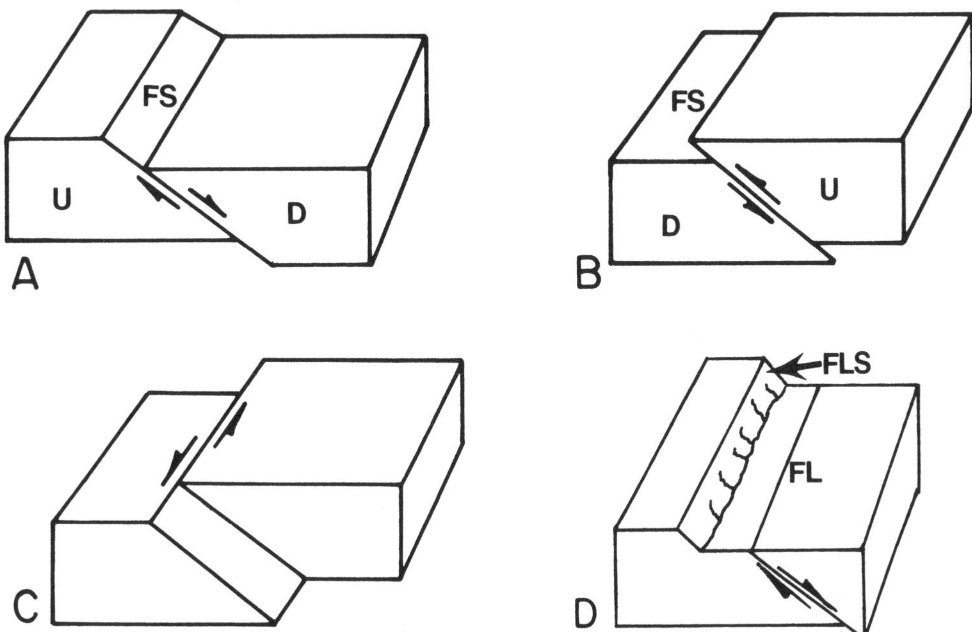

Fig. 6.11 Normal fault (A), reverse fault (B), and strike slip fault (C). A normal fault is shown in (D) with a fault line scarp (FLS). U = upthrown block, D = downthrown block, FS = fault scarp, FL = fault line.

The relative uplift of huge blocks of rock as a result of vertical faulting creates linear to slightly sinuous ***fault scarps*** in the landscape. These fault scarps are similar to those produced by monoclinal flexing. As streams dissect an upthrown fault block, the fault scarp is fretted by stream valleys and canyons. The portions of the fault scarp that remain intact have a triangular shape and are called ***triangular facets***. Ultimately, even these are destroyed and the eroded fault scarp becomes a ***fault line scarp***, located at some distance from the original fault but approximately parallel to it. Faults frequently occur in large numbers and it is common for huge blocks of rock to be raised or lowered between two faults. A narrow block dropped down between two normal faults is called a ***graben***. A block raised between two faults is called a ***horst***. When formed, grabens create topographic depressions. Where outlet streams do not develop they may remain depressions. Uplifted horsts form ***fault block mountains*** which, like grabens, have linear sides. The Basin-and-Range Province of the western United States is an erosionally-modified horst and graben terrain. Intersecting networks of faults and joints (fractures along which there has been no vertical or lateral displacement) represent weaknesses in the rock along which groundwater can penetrate. When these are etched out by chemical and mechanical weathering or by stream erosion, they impart a distinctive grain to the landscape and are normally responsible for ***lineations*** visible in aerial photographs and satellite images.

QUESTIONS

6.8 The photographs in Fig. 6.12 and 3-D anaglyphs 11 and 12 in Appendix D (taken in 1954) show the eastern half of the Santa Ana Mesa near the confluence of the Rio Jemez and the Rio Grande in New Mexico. The mesa is built of a series of basalt flows that issued from a north-to-south-trending string of vents to the west. Numerous faults displace the basalts with displacements ranging from a few feet to 150 feet. Examine the area on a recent Google Earth™ satellite image centered on the following coordinates: 35° 23′ 31.41″ N, 106° 31′ 19.45″ W. Start viewing from an Eye alt of 26,000 feet. Answer the following questions.

(a) Given that the faults dip toward the west, identify the upthrown and downthrown blocks and determine what kinds of faults they are.

(b) Using Fig. 6.12, its 3-D anaglyph, and the satellite image, identify a fault scarp and a fault line scarp. List their coordinates. Have the fault blocks been uplifted or depressed evenly, or are they tilted and, if so, in which direction?

(c) How has the faulting in this area influenced the stream drainage pattern? In answering consider the mass movement at D.1-3.0 and the clear stream erosion at B.0-3.0.

(d) Compare the photos in Fig. 6.12 with the recent Google Earth™ satellite image. What significant human structure can you see that has been erected since 1954?

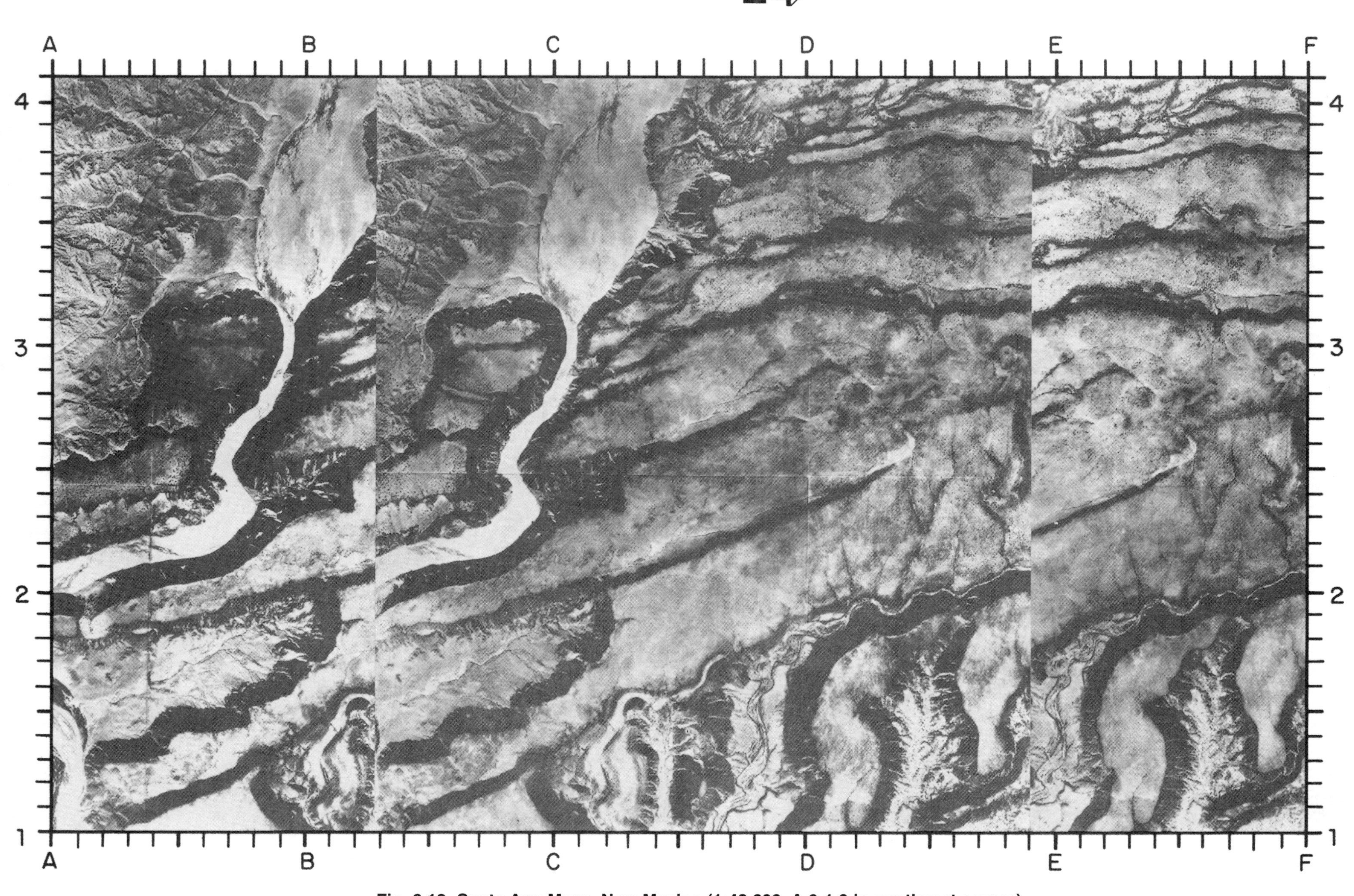

Fig. 6.12 Santa Ana Mesa, New Mexico (1:42,600, A.0-1.0 in southeast corner).

6.9 Figure 6.13 shows the outcrop pattern of a series of eroded and faulted plunging anticlines and synclines. Determine which features are anticlines and which are synclines and mark the direction of plunge. If one of the faults dips at 60° and the other is vertical, what kinds of faults are they and how do you know?

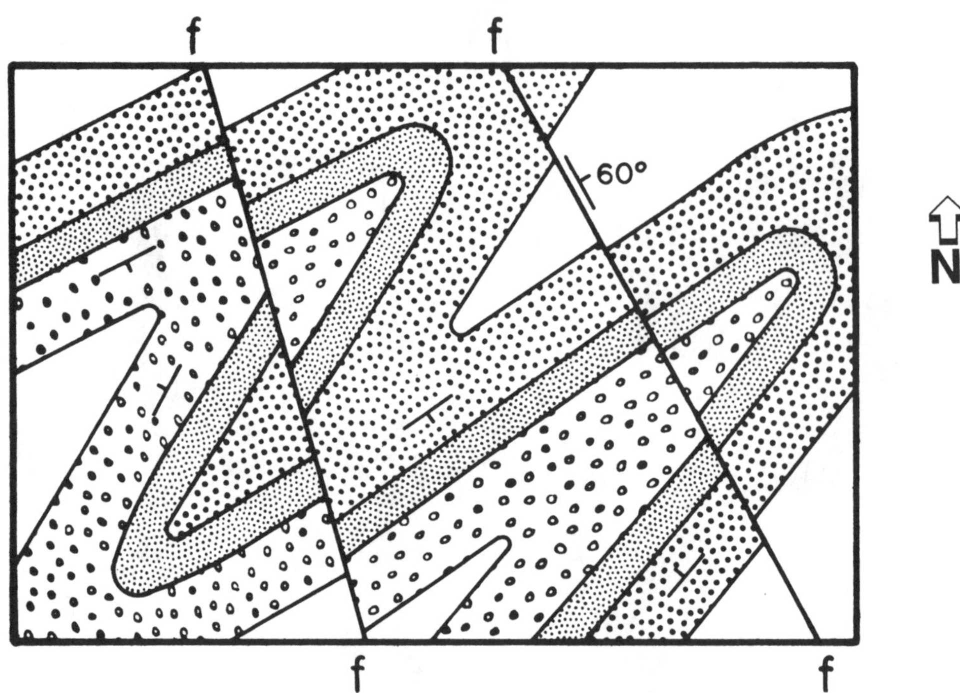

Fig. 6.13 Outcrop pattern of eroded and faulted fold structures.

6.10 (a) Name or describe the labeled geologic and topographic features A through M on Fig. 6.14.

LABEL	DESCRIPTION
A	
B	
C	
D	
E	
F	
G	
H	
I	
J	
K	
L	
M	

(b) Measure the magnitude and direction of dip of the faults at C and E and show the relative motions of the fault blocks.

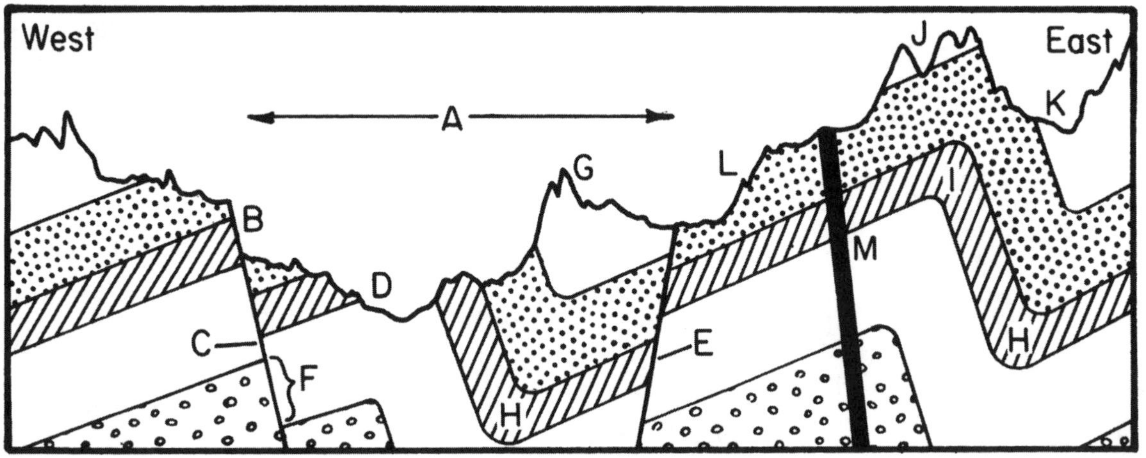

Fig. 6.14 Structural landforms of a hypothetical terrain.

Student Name________________________________

Exercise 7

HILLSLOPE FORM AND MASS WASTING

MATERIALS

Lens stereoscope (plastic), red/blue 3-D glasses, ruler, calculator, computer with Google Earth™ software and Internet access.

OBJECTIVES

1. Differentiate and describe the major forms of downslope mass movements.
2. Identify types of mass movement in block drawings, vertical air photos, oblique air photos, and on **Google Earth™** satellite images.
3. Relate mass movement features to other geomorphic processes and cultural activities.

INTRODUCTION

Hillslopes are that part of the landscape between the crests of hills and nearby drainage lines and therefore include the majority of the Earth's land surface. The form of any slope is ultimately determined by the relationship between the rate of weathering of the underlying rock and the rate of removal of rock debris from the surface. Movement of debris under the influence of gravity is called ***mass wasting*** and occurs when the downslope gravitational stress on the material exceeds its frictional resistance to movement. Hillslopes have four main elements, which are the ***crest***, the ***scarp***, the ***debris slope***, and the ***foot-slope*** (Fig. 7.1). One or more of these elements may be absent from any given hillslope.

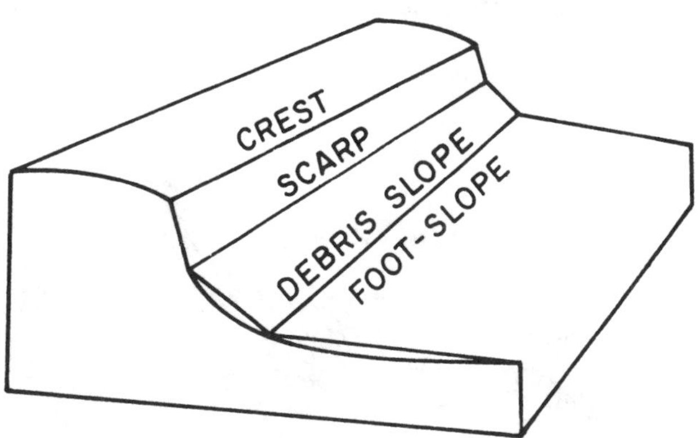

Fig. 7.1 The four main hillslope elements.

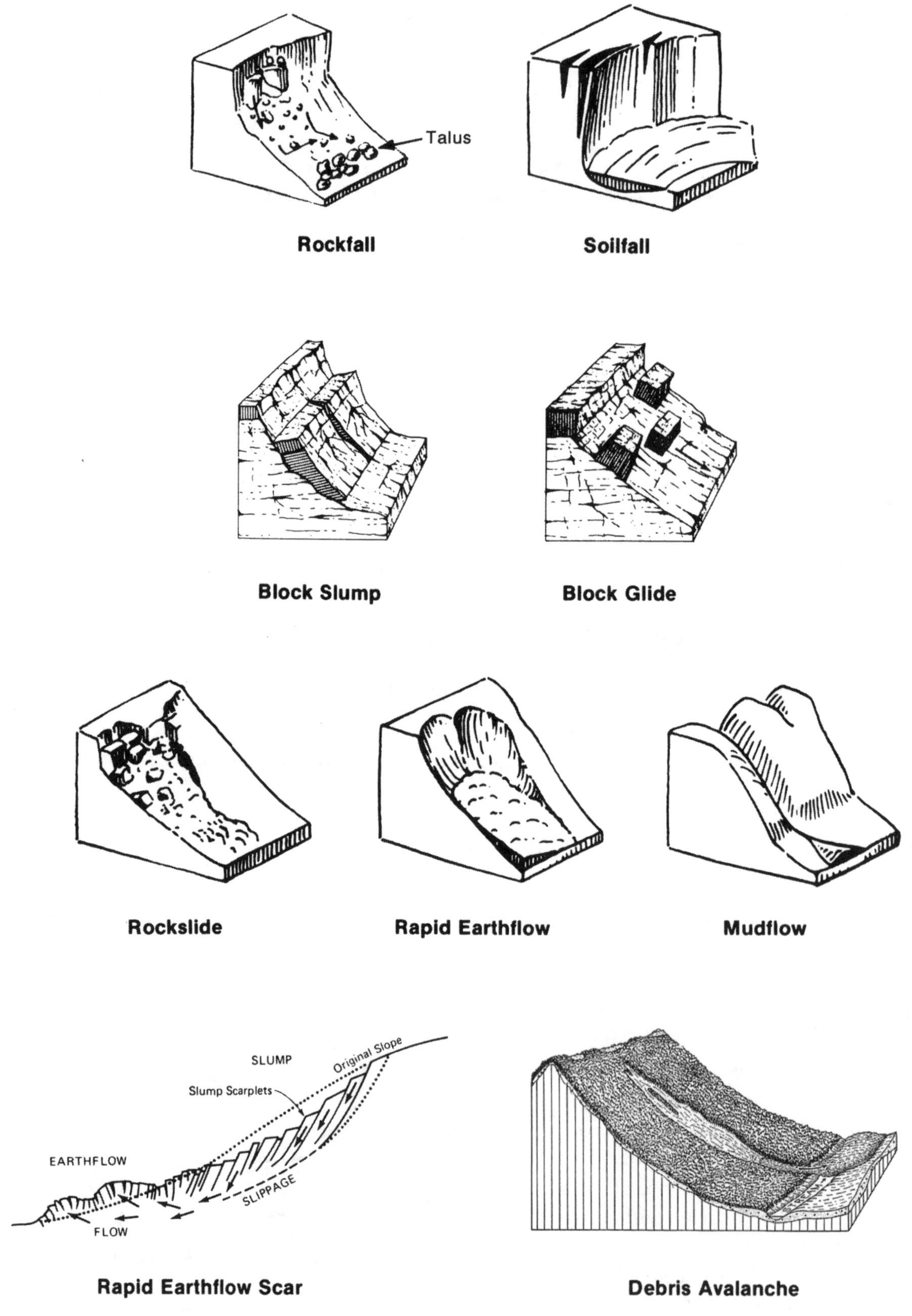

Fig. 7.2 Types of mass movement (after Leopold et al, 1964, Butzer, 1976 and Sharpe, 1960).

Mass movements are generally classified according to whether they involve compact rock or unconsolidated materials, the rapidity of movement, and whether the material slides or falls in discrete units or whether it flows and is thus deformed internally. The various types of mass movement are listed in Table 7.1, and the more important are illustrated in Fig. 7.2. Some mass movements occur suddenly and involve vast amounts of material, while others are barely perceptible. Catastrophic movements have blocked valleys with the formation of lakes, have diverted drainage, and have taken lives. Catastrophic and other mass movements occur more frequently where natural slopes have been undercut by groundwater seepage, rivers, waves, or human activities. Mass movements are often associated with seismic activity.

Table 7.1 Classification of mass movements.

Type of Movement	Type of Material	
	Bedrock	**Soil or Regolith**
Falls	Rockfall	Soilfall
Slides	Block Slump (rotational or translational)	Soil Slump
	Rockslide	Debris Slide or Avalanche
Slow Flows	Talus Creep	Soil Creep
	Block Streams	Solifluction
Rapid Flows		Rapid Earthflow
		Mudflow
Complex	Combinations of materials or type of movement	

SECTION I: Movements of Soil Material

Mass movements in soil or regolith usually involve some internal deformation or flow. However, occasionally a series of rigid units, or blocks is set in motion. Mass movements involving soil or regolith include soil creep, solifluction, earthflows and mudflows, debris slides, soil slumps, and soil falls.

The most ubiquitous of all mass movements is ***soil creep***, which occurs when particles of soil move progressively downslope. Contributing processes include raindrop splash, subsurface suffosion, wetting and drying, expansion and contraction, frost heaving, and biogenic disturbances. Movements are barely perceptible but over long periods a vast amount of material can be moved. Rates are quicker near the surface and diminish towards the bedrock-soil interface where the resistance to movement is greatest. ***Solifluction***, or soil flow, is gradual but more rapid than soil creep. It involves the plastic flow of water-saturated soil downslope in mountain or high-latitude areas. Solifluction is most common in areas of permafrost during the thaw period, when the shallow active layer becomes thoroughly saturated with water and cannot drain vertically due to the underlying frozen regolith. The process frequently forms ***lobate tongues***.

Rapid movements of unconsolidated material are either rapid earthflows or mudflows. ***Rapid earthflows*** occur in a matter of hours and involve the downslope flow of water-saturated regolith. These flows often leave concave scars with slump scarplets in more compact material at the head wall. ***Mudflows*** are produced when water is suddenly supplied to an area of thick soil or regolith. Mudflows move more rapidly than earthflows because of a higher water content and steeper gradient. They usually follow stream courses and only stop when their viscosity is too high for further flow. They frequently form lobate tongues at the mouths of mountain canyons. Mudflows are common in areas where there is little or no vegetation. Under such conditions, intense local storms may produce rain at a much faster rate than can be absorbed by the soil. These may also be described as ***debris flows*** depending on the composition of the material in the flow. Debris or mudflows associated with volcanic eruptions are called ***lahars***.

QUESTIONS

7.1 As can be seen in Fig. 7.3 and 3-D anaglyph 13 in Appendix D (taken in 1950), instability of the southern slope of a basalt-capped mesa north of the town of King Hill, Idaho (just off the photos to the south) and east of King Hill Creek (A.5-3.5) caused a major mass movement. The mesa has a local relief of approximately 1,000 feet. Also view the area on a Google Earth™ satellite image by typing the following coordinates in the search box: 43° 01′ 44.32″ N, 115° 13′ 04.04″ W. Start viewing from an Eye alt of 30,000 feet. Answer the following questions.

(a) What type of mass movement occurred and how did it happen. Did debris reach King Creek and, if so, where did this occur?

(b) On the photograph, outline the region covered by the collapse and calculate its approximate area in square miles. Note that agricultural fields at A.4-2.6 define the SE boundary of the mass movement).

(c) Three well-defined slump blocks are visible in the middle photograph. Give their grid coordinates.

(d) Compare Fig. 7.3 (taken in 1950) and its 3-D anaglyph with the recent Google Earth™ image. How has the area changed? Is there any evidence of mass movements in this area since 1950?

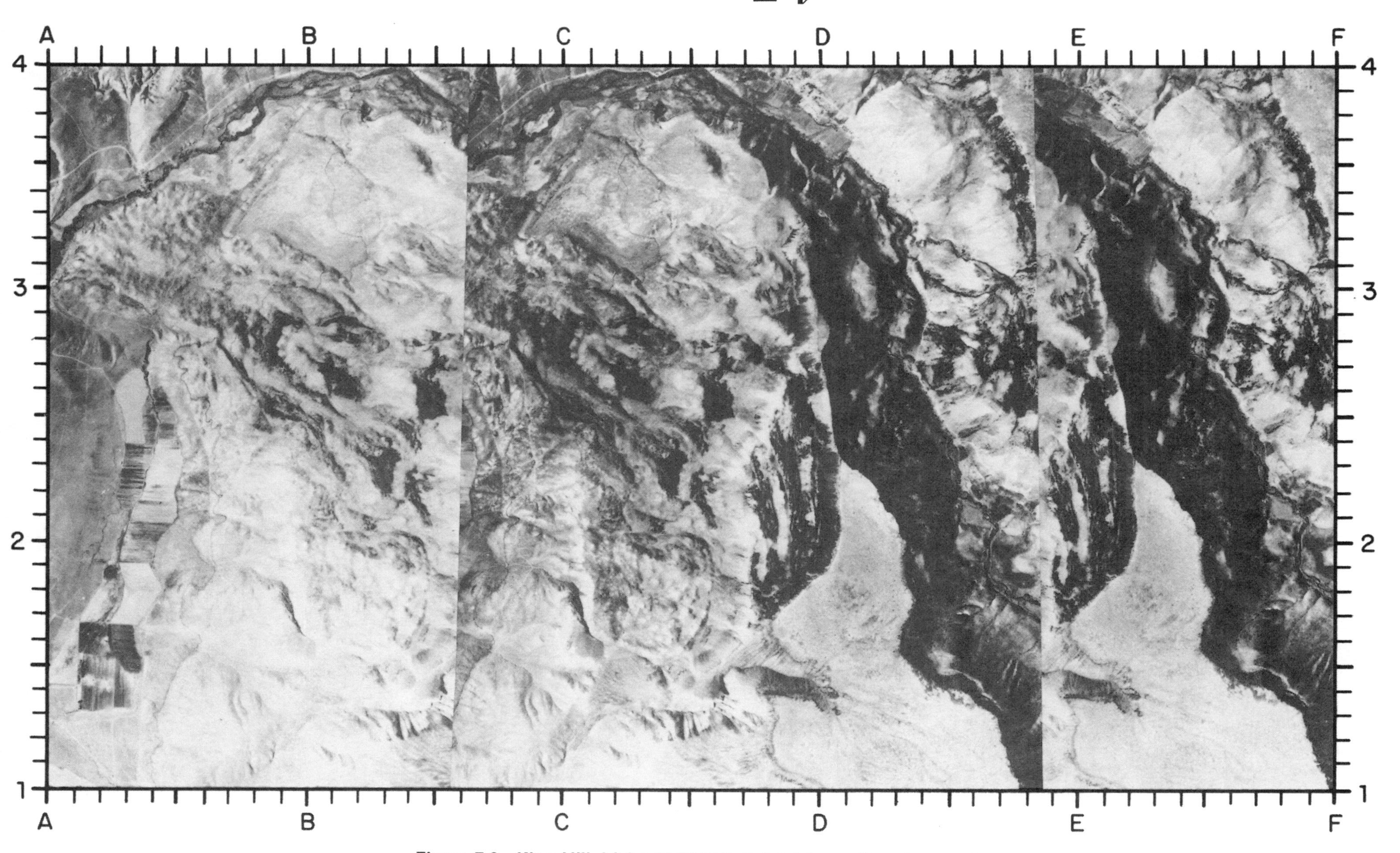

Figure 7.3 King Hill, Idaho (1:26,300, A.0-1.0 in southeast corner).

7.2 The aerial photographs in Fig. 7.4 and 3-D anaglyph 14 in Appendix D (taken in 1951) show a prehistoric mass movement (D.5-2.7) that affected the east slope of Lake Fork Gunnison River Valley. The lake in the photograph is Lake San Cristobal. View this area on a Google Earth™ image by typing the following coordinates in the search box: 37° 59′ 11″ N, 107° 17′ 38.80″ W. Start viewing from an Eye alt of 30,000 feet. Answer the following questions.

(a) What kind of mass movement occurred?

(b) What relationship is there between the moved material and Lake San Cristobal?

(c) The lower one-third of the debris is stable and contains wood that has a radiocarbon age of about 700 years. The oldest trees in the upper two-thirds of the debris are approximately 350 years old. What do these dates tell us about the age of the original mass movement and subsequent activity?

(d) Compare Fig. 7.4 (taken in 1951) and its 3-D anaglyph with a recent Google Earth™ image. Have there been any changes in the area? Is there any evidence of mass movements since 1950?

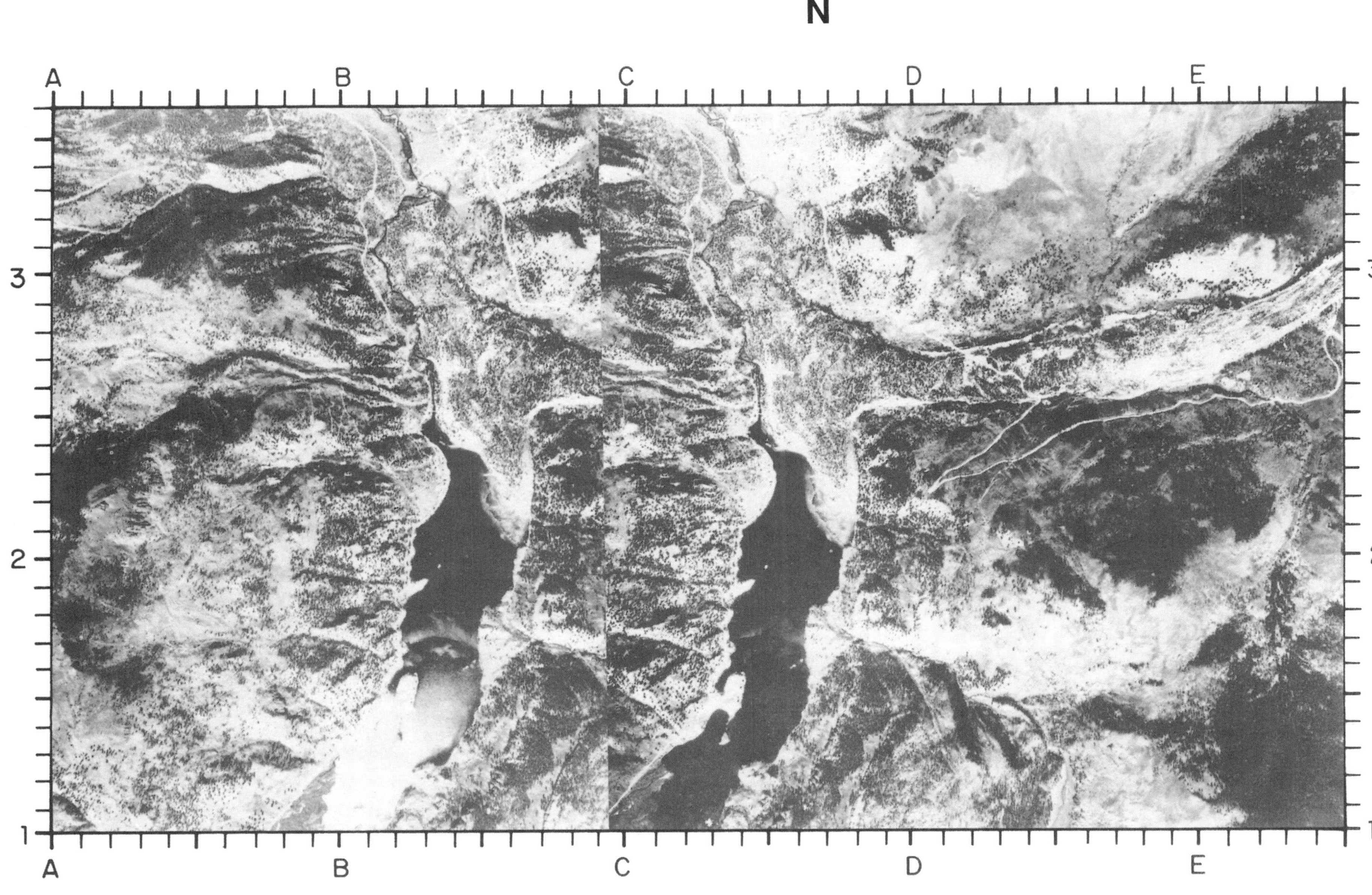

Figure 7.4 Slumgullion, Colorado (1:62,700, A.0-1.0 in southwest corner).

7.3 Among the geomorphic features that are visible in the aerial photographs of Fig. 7.5, taken in the southern Mackenzie Mountains region of Canada in the early 1970s, is a mass movement. What type of mass movement has occurred in the unconsolidated sands (D.1-2.0) in Fig. 7.5 and what could have triggered it? This general area can be viewed using Google Earth™ by typing the following coordinates in the search box: 61° 45′N, 124° 30′ W. Start viewing from an Eye alt of 45 miles.

7.4 Figures 7.6 and 7.7 show the results of two mass movements that occurred within the past 50 years in the Mackenzie Mountains region of northwest Canada. With reference to Table 7.1 and Fig. 7.2, classify these mass movements.

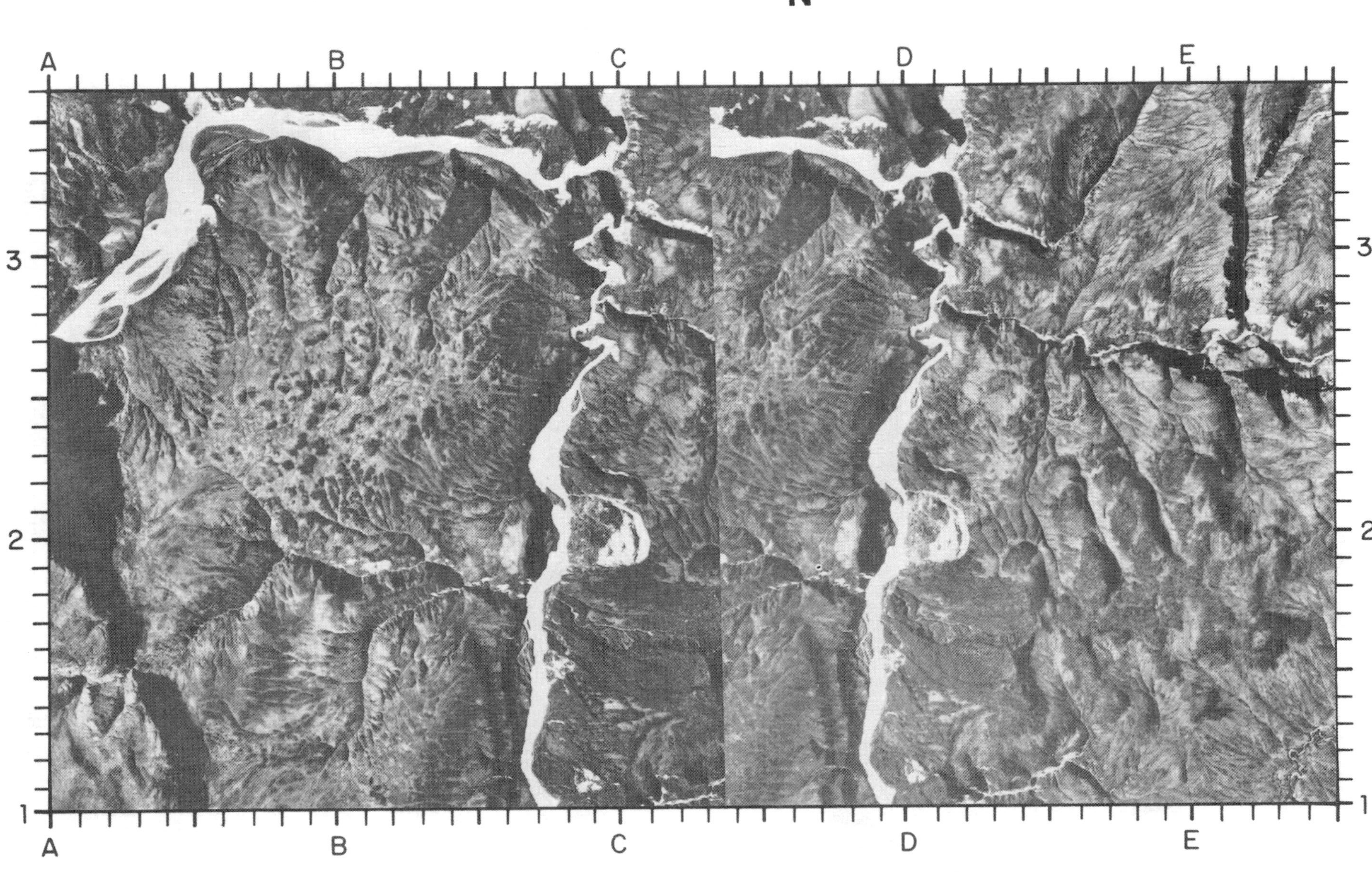

Figure 7.5 Sundog Basin, Canada (1:55,000 A.0-1.0 in southwest corner).

Fig. 7.6 Recent mass movement in Sundog, Basin, Mackenzie Mountains, Canada.

Fig. 7.7 Recent mass movement in Sundog Basin, Mackenzie Mountains, Canada.

SECTION 2: Movements of Rock Material

Mass movements involving solid rock include rockfalls, block slumps, rockslides, and talus creep. ***Rockfalls*** occur when segments of bedrock of any size are detached from a steep to vertical rock wall. Movement may be by vertical fall or by a series of leaps and bounds down a steep slope. If a block is large or its fall great, it may be completely shattered upon impact adding to the material that accumulates at the base of the slope in ***talus cones*** or ***talus aprons*** (also called ***talus slopes*** or ***scree slopes***). Talus cones develop where cliffs are notched by narrow ravines which funnel rock fragments along particular routes. A talus apron is formed when several cones coalesce laterally along a cliff face. The slow downslope movement of fragments in talus, known as ***talus creep,*** is most rapid in cold regions where the major trigger is the alternate freezing and thawing of ice in the interstices of the rock waste. The angle at which falling debris comes to rest is called the angle of repose. This angle usually varies from 25°–40°, depending upon the size, shape, and density of the debris, the roughness of particle surfaces, and how well-sorted the fragments are. In general, a decrease in fragment size or an increase in the height of fall reduces the angle of repose.

On moderately steep slopes, masses of bedrock may become dislodged and slide downslope. If the blocks move along a flat, inclined plane, then the movement is classified as a ***translational slide*** or ***slump***. If the blocks rotate backward on a concave-up slip plane, then the movement is classified as a ***rotational slide*** or ***slump***. Block slumping normally occurs intermittently over a long period although some movements are rapid and final. Movements are usually caused by the removal of support from beneath the toe of the slip block. The most destructive mass movements involving solid rock are rockslides, which occur on very steep bedrock slopes and so are most common in mountainous regions. Rockslides are downward and usually involve rapid movements of detached segments of bedrock, which slide on bedding, joint, or fault surfaces. Movements may involve thousands of tons of rock, and minor amounts of soil and other debris. Rockslides occur most frequently in soluble rocks, such as limestone and dolomites. These rocks are weakened by the action of solution, which gradually widens joint and bedding plane structures.

QUESTIONS

7.5 Given that the bedrock of the area shown in Fig. 7.8 is largely limestone and dolomite, explain what happened at C.0-1.9. To answer this question it will help to view a Google Earth™ satellite image by typing the following coordinates in the search box: 61° 45′ N, 124° 30′ W. Start viewing with an Eye alt of 45 miles and zoom in and out as needed.

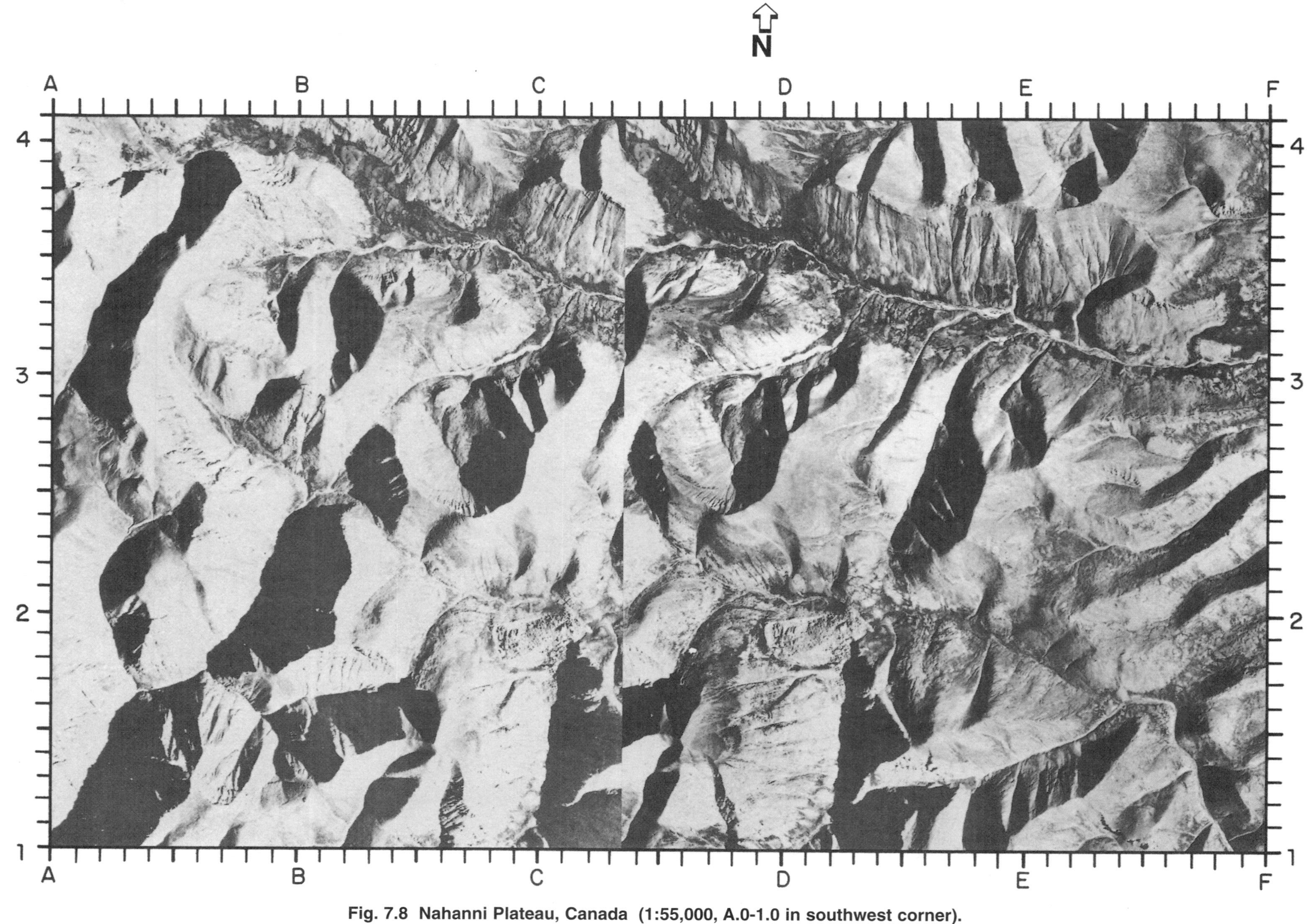

Fig. 7.8 Nahanni Plateau, Canada (1:55,000, A.0-1.0 in southwest corner).

7.6 Fig. 7.9 shows a 600-foot-high granite inselberg in Gauteng Province, South Africa. The domal form of this inselberg is due to curved sheeting structures that developed in the rock. These are clearly visible in the photograph. On the photograph, delimit and label the hillslope elements shown below. You can gain a better understanding of this remote area using Google Earth™ by typing the following coordinates in the search box: 24° 07′ S, 28° 32′ E. Start viewing with an Eye alt of 15 miles.

A Crest B Scarp C Debris slope D Foot-slope or Pediment

Fig. 7.9 Granite inselberg, Gauteng, South Africa

7.7 Fig. 7.10 is a view of Rio de Janeiro, Brazil, as seen from Sugar Loaf Mountain. The local bedrock is granite and sheeting structures frequently develop parallel to the hillslopes. In some cases, rock sheets may exceed 20 feet in thickness. In terms of slope stability, explain the presence of the white stone wall and white concrete pillars (structures are indicated by arrows) on the steep granite slope at the left of the photograph. It will help you to answer this question if you look at oblique views of the area using Google Earth™. To obtain an image, type the following coordinates in the search box: 22° 57′ 02.84″ S, 43° 09′ 50.05″ W. Start viewing from an Eye alt of 12,000 feet and zoom in as necessary to search for concrete pillars and walls on the mountain slopes. Are these structures still there?

Fig. 7.10 Rio de Janeiro, Brazil as seen from Sugar Loaf Mountain.

7.8 What evidence is there in Fig. 7.11 to indicate that here has been a relatively recent rockslide in Surprise Valley near Jasper, Alberta in the southern Canadian Rockies? Given that the local bedrock is limestone, briefly outline the events that probably preceded this catastrophic mass movement. In answering, consider that trees in the center of the photo are growing on a fresh debris pile. To help in answering also examine oblique views of a Google Earth™ satellite image. To obtain an image type the following coordinates in the search box: 52° 53′ N, 118° 05′ W. Start viewing from an Eye alt of 50 miles and zoom into the image as needed.

Fig. 7.11 Rockslide in Surprise Valley near Jasper, Alberta, Canada.

Student Name________________________________

Exercise 8

FLUVIAL LANDSCAPES

MATERIALS

Lens stereoscope (plastic), red / blue 3-D glasses, ruler, calculator, colored pencils, opsimeter (if available), transparent graph paper (in pocket), computer with Google Earth™ software and Internet access.

OBJECTIVES

1. Analyze a stream network using the rules developed by Horton and Strahler.
2. Understand the relationships between the various components of a drainage network.
3. Calculate the drainage density of a drainage basin.
4. Recognize structural controls on surface drainage by analyzing stream patterns.
5. Distinguish between youthful, mature, and old age streams on maps and photographs.
6. Recognize the landforms typical of a fluvial system.
7. Make observations of streams on maps and photographs, and use their characteristics to interpret stages of landscape change.
8. Calculate the cross sectional area and discharge of a stream, estimate runoff peaks and flood probabilities.

INTRODUCTION

Of all the processes that change the Earth's surface, the single most important is that of running water. ***Streams*** drain water from the land along valleys they create by water erosion. The process begins during a rain event as water that is not absorbed by the ground moves over the ground surface as ***sheet flow***. This water eventually collects in water channels varying in size from small rills to larger gullies and brooks, to even larger creeks, streams and rivers. Together, these channels make up a ***drainage system***. Most important is that as the water flows, it ***erodes, transports, and deposits*** earth material or sediment and thus changes the shape of the land, wearing it down in one place while building it up in another. The Mississippi River, the River Nile, and the Amazon are among the major fluvial or ***drainage***

systems of the world. Each has numerous tributaries within its ***drainage basin*** or watershed. A drainage basin is a network of water channels separated by ridges called ***interfluves*** that all drain to a major river. The perimeter of a drainage basin is the ***drainage divide,*** which is the high ground that separates one drainage basin from the one next to it (Fig. 8.1).

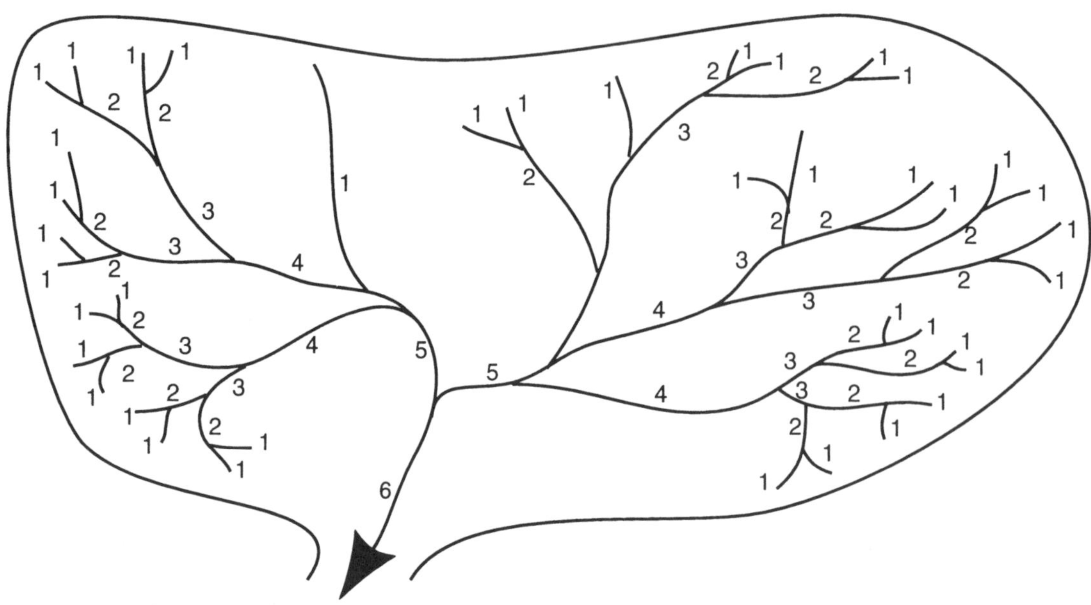

Fig. 8.1 Stream orders in a hypothetical 6th order basin. Each segment of given order is counted as *one* (number) until it joins a similar or higher order segment (e.g., the *number* of 3rd order segments is nine).

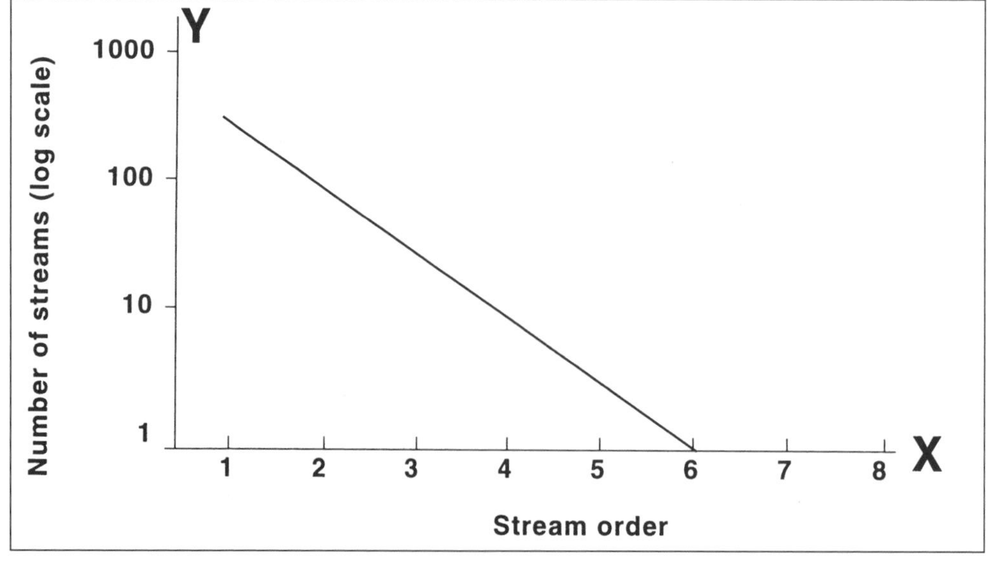

Fig. 8.2 Relationship between stream order and number (negatives).

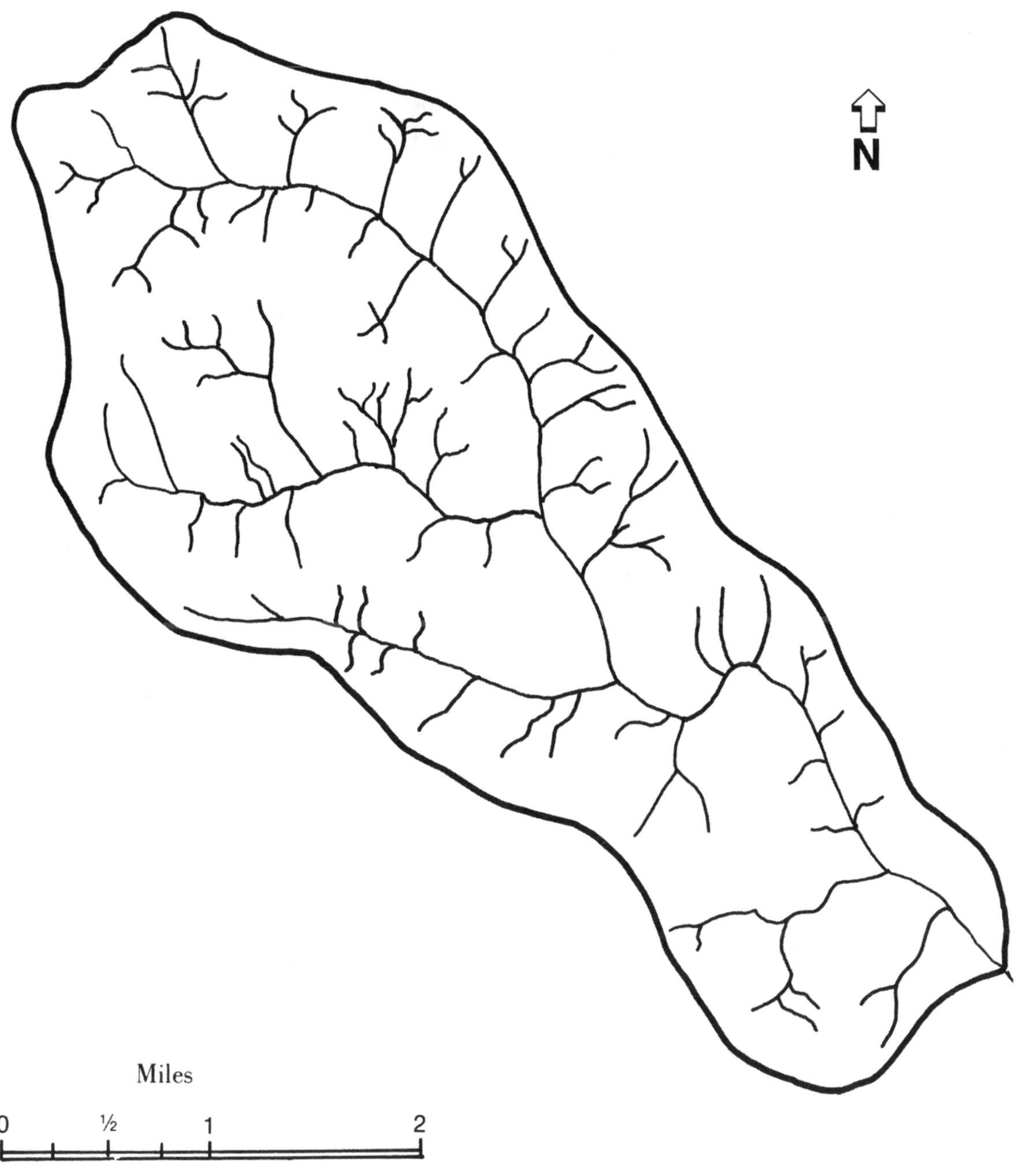

Fig. 8.3 Parks Creek, Georgia

SECTION I: The Drainage Basin

The work of Horton and Strahler has shown that a stream network is a hierarchy of ***channel segments*** of different importance, or ***order***. Using Strahler's method of subdivision, each fingertip tributary is a ***first order stream***. When two streams of similar order combine, the resulting stream has a higher order, so that two first order streams become a second order stream, and two fourth order streams become a fifth order stream, and so on. When a lower order stream joins one of higher order, there is no increase in order. Drainage basins are also ordered so that the ***trunk stream*** in a sixth orders basin is of order six.

Horton compared the characteristics of stream segments of one order with those of the next highest order in terms of a number of simple ratios, which he found remained almost constant from one stream order to the next within the drainage basin (Table 8.1). The next stage was the realization that stream order is related to number of streams, channel length, basin area and stream gradient by simple geometric relationships. In fact number of streams, stream length, basin area and stream gradient (the dependent variables – Y), are related to stream order (the independent variable – X) by either a positive or negative exponential function. Stream order (X), therefore, plots against these variables (Y) as a series of straight lines on semi-logarithmic graph paper (Fig. 8.2). Horton's exponential drainage basin laws are important because they demonstrate that, far from being chaotic, the fluvial landscape is very highly ordered (Table 8.2).

Channel density within a drainage basin depends upon the interaction between the eroding force of flowing water and the resistance of the soil to erosive channeling. The eroding forces increases with the increase in slope of the land and with the amount and intensity of precipitation. Variations in the permeability of rock and soil, vegetative cover, and soil cohesion are factors that determine resistance to erosion.

Table 8.1 Important ratios between streams of different order in a drainage basin.

Bifurcation Ratio	$R_b = \frac{N_\mu}{N_{\mu+1}}$
Length Ratio	$R_L = \frac{\bar{L}_\mu}{\bar{L}_{\mu-1}}$
Slope Ratio	$R_S = \frac{\bar{S}_\mu}{\bar{S}_{\mu-1}}$
Area Ratio	$R_a = \frac{\bar{A}_\mu}{\bar{A}_{\mu-1}}$

Table 8.2 Drainage basin network laws.

Law	Equation
Law of Stream Numbers	$N_\mu = R_b^{(k-\mu)}$
Law of Mean Stream Lengths	$\bar{L}_{\mu^*} = \bar{L}_1 R_L^{(\mu-1)}$
Law of Stream Gradients	$\bar{S}_\mu = \bar{S}_1 R_S^{(\mu-1)}$
Law of Basin Areas	$\bar{A}_\mu = \bar{A}_1 R_a^{(\mu-1)}$

μ stream order

N_μ number of streams of order μ

$\bar{L}_\mu$ mean stream length of order μ

$\bar{S}_\mu$ mean gradient of stream order μ

$\bar{A}_\mu$ mean area of basin of order μ

k is highest order of the basin

$\bar{L}_1$ mean length of first order segments

$\bar{S}_1$ mean slope of first order segments

$\bar{A}_1$ mean area of first order basins

$\bar{L}_\mu^*$ cumulative mean length of stream up to order μ

QUESTIONS

8.1 Order the stream network shown in Fig. 8.3 by color coding stream segments of the same order and providing a key. What order drainage basin is depicted?

8.2 Count the number of streams of each order. Add these to Table 8.3 and calculate the bifurcation ratios. In regions of uniform climate, rock type and relative relief, the value of R_b tends to remain constant from one order to the next. Values of R_b between 3 and 5 are characteristic of natural stream systems. In light of these comments, discuss your results.

Table 8.3 **Bifurcation ratios of streams in a hypothetical drainage basin.**

Stream Order	Number of Streams	Bifurcation Ratio
1		
2		
3		
4		

8.3 Plot the number of streams (logarithmic axis or Y-axis) against the stream order (arithmetic axis or X-axis) on semi-logarithmic graph paper. Does Horton's law of stream numbers hold for this drainage basin and, if so, is the relationship a positive or negative exponential one?

8.4 Measure the lengths of all streams, by order, and calculate the mean stream length for each order. Add these data to Table 8.4 and calculate the length ratios. (Use an opisometer if available, or measure approximate lengths with a strip of paper and a ruler.)

Table 8.4 **Length ratios of streams in a hypothetical drainage basin.**

Stream Order	Total Length of Streams	Mean Stream Length	Length Ratio	Cumulative Mean Stream Length
1				
2				
3				
4				

8.5 Plot cumulative mean stream length (logarithmic axis or Y-axis) against stream order (arithmetic axis or X-axis) on semi-logarithmic graph paper. The cumulative mean stream length of second order streams is the mean stream length of second order streams added to the mean stream length of first order streams. Does Horton's law of stream lengths hold for this drainage basin and, if so, is the relationship a positive or negative exponential one?

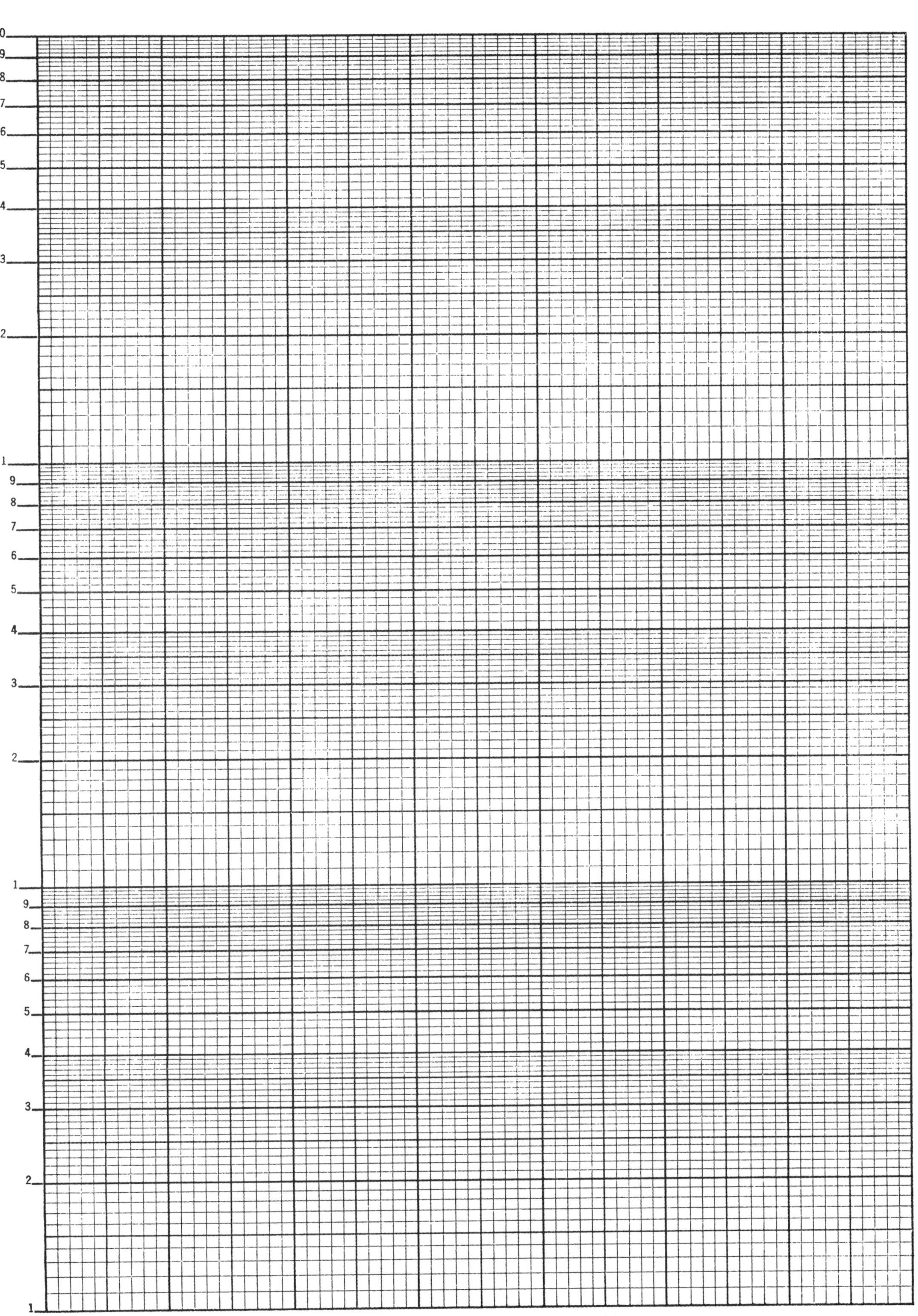

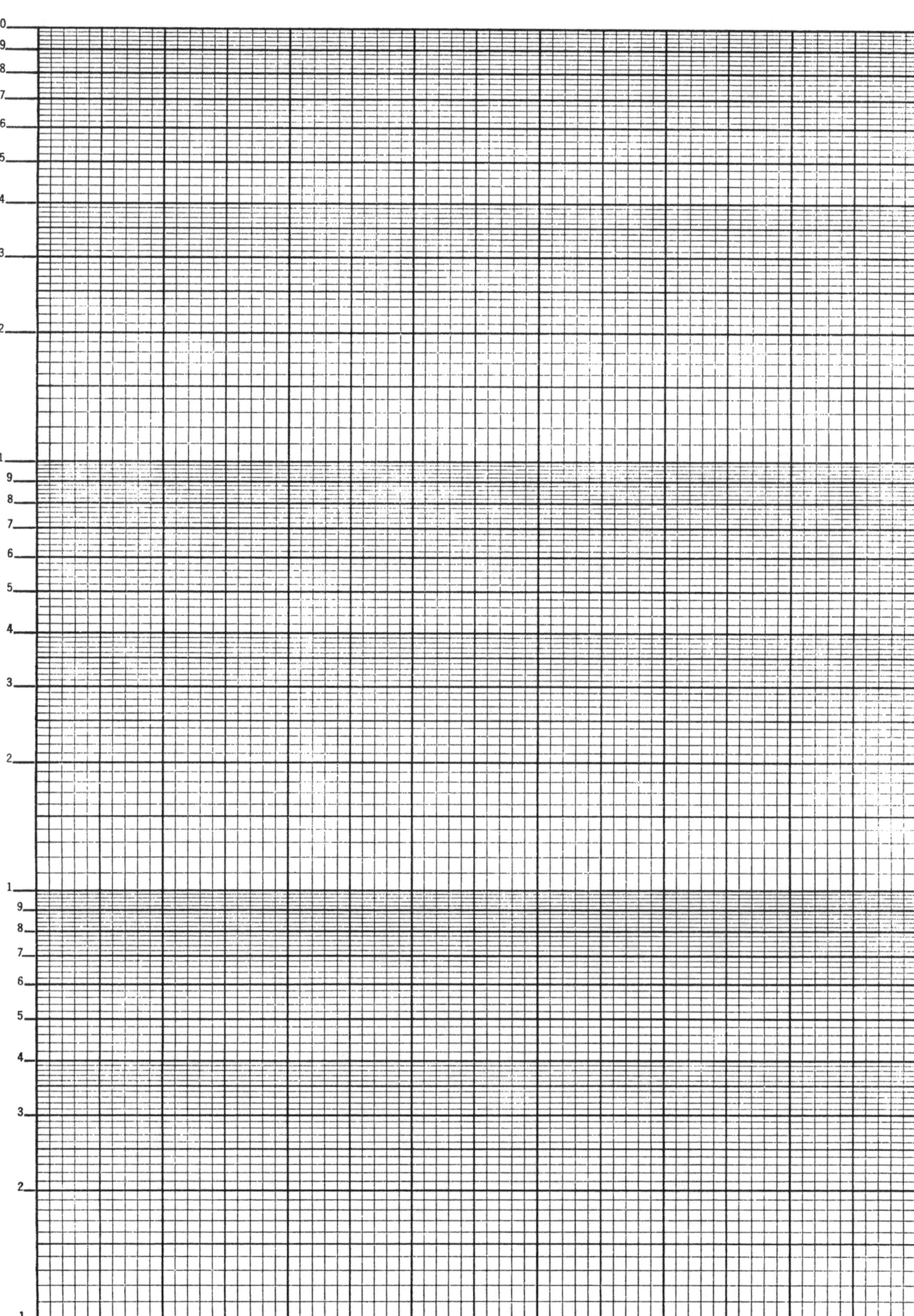
10
9
8
7
6
5
4
3
2
1
9
8
7
6
5
4
3
2
1
9
8
7
6
5
4
3
2
1

8.6 Drainage density is given by $D_d = \frac{\sum L}{A}$ where D_d is the drainage density in miles/square mile, $\sum L$ represents the total length of all channels of all orders, and A is the total basin area. Table 8.5 summarizes information contained in Strahler (1975) concerning ranges in drainage density and the texture of topography. The more highly dissected a terrain, the finer the topographic texture.

Using Fig. 8.3 and transparent graph paper, estimate the area of the basin. Using the total length of stream channels (Table 8.4) calculate the drainage density in miles/square mile. (One square on the graph paper grid is 0.8 x 0.8 mile = 0.64 square mile.) Examine Table 8.5 and determine the density class and texture class of this basin.

Table 8.5 Drainage density and texture classes of topography.

Drainage Density Class	Topographic Texture Class	Drainage Density (miles/sq. mile)
Low	Coarse	< 8
Medium	Medium	8 – 24
High	Fine	24 – 200
Badlands	Ultrafine	> 200

SECTION 2: *Drainage Patterns*

The arrangement of streams in a drainage system constitutes the ***drainage pattern***. The pattern will depend on a number of factors, including soil, geology, structure, tectonic history, climate, paleoclimate and human activity. Several geometric patterns are recognized (Fig. 8.4). Branching or tree-like ***dendritic*** drainage patterns are the most common and the result of random erosion on terrain of uniform lithology and slope. A ***trellis*** pattern is common in areas that have been folded and exhibit numerous anticline and syncline structures, or alternate weak and resistant beds. ***Rectangular*** patterns develop in areas where rocks are well jointed, the streams flowing along the joints. Volcanic cones produce ***radial*** drainage patterns as the streams flow down the slopes of the volcano away from the central crater. Structural domes can produce ***annular*** drainage patterns, which can look like broken, concentric circles when mapped. ***Parallel*** drainage develops due to structural control by the bedrock, or can evolve on steep, uniform slopes. The water channels of this drainage pattern are parallel to one another over considerable distances. A stream pattern is ***centripetal*** when streams drain radially inward toward a central area, sometimes with no outlet. Areas that have been affected by continental glaciation often show a ***deranged*** drainage pattern, with no discernable arrangement of the streams.

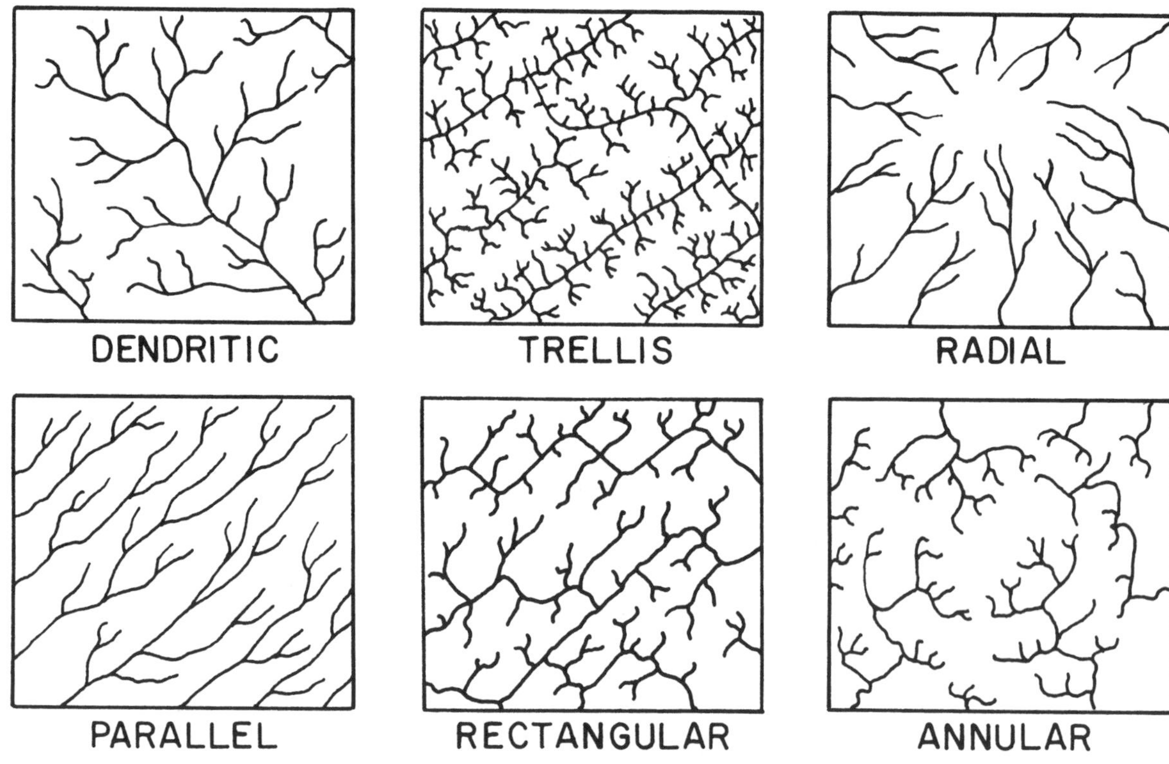

Fig. 8.4 Common stream drainage patterns.

QUESTIONS

8.7 Examine the figures in this manual that are listed below and classify the drainage pattern you see. Remember that these areas can also be viewed using **Google Earth**™ and this may help by giving you a more complete view of the drainage systems.

Fig. 5.3 ______________________ Fig. 6.10 ______________________

Fig. 8.3 ______________________ Fig. 10.4 ______________________

Fig. 6.9 ______________________ Fig. 13.3 ______________________

SECTION 3: Fluvial landscapes

As water flows over the surface and collects into streams it ***erodes, transports,*** and ***deposits*** sediments. It thus creates ***erosional landforms*** and ***depositional landforms***. Some fluvial features are primarily erosional others primarily depositional, while still others result from a combination of these two processes. The process of erosion includes ***hydraulic action, abrasion,*** and ***corrosion*** that often work together to wear down the landscape by ***downcutting, lateral erosion,*** or ***headward*** erosion.

The rate of stream erosion in an area is dependent on a number of factors including the geology, soil type, slope, climate, and vegetation, but two primary factors are the ***velocity and volume of water*** in the stream. Material transported by a fluvial system is called the ***load or stream load,*** and the size and volume of material transported is governed by two principles. The ***competence*** of a stream is a measure of the size of sediment particles that it can transport, and is controlled by the velocity of the flow. Stream ***capacity*** is a measure of the ***volume of***

material a stream can transport, and this is controlled by both the volume and velocity of stream flow. There are three classes of sediment in streams, the ***dissolved load, the suspended load,*** and the ***bedload***. The dissolved load is in ***solution*** and is dominated by easily soluble materials such as limestone. The suspended load consists of small silt and clay particles that travel in the stream in ***suspension*** and only fall out of the water column when still water is reached. The bedload of the stream moves by ***traction*** and ***saltation***.

Stream gullies, valleys and canyons are primarily erosional features as is the central channel of the stream or ***talweg***. However, over time a stream becomes sinuous and ultimately ***meanders*** may develop that are produced by a combination of erosion and deposition. A meander is a pronounced bend or curve in the course of a stream so that the flow of the stream may over some stretches be in the up-valley direction. Meanders are formed in sinuous streams where at bends there is more erosion on the outside (cut) bank or ***undercut slope*** of the stream, while deposition occurs on the inside of the curve where a ***point bar*** develops (Fig. 8.5). As a meander becomes more accentuated, its outside or undercut slope may intersect with an adjacent meander forming what is called a ***cutoff***. This creates a bypass or shorter path for the stream which may then abandon the ***meander loop***. If the isolated meander loop is dry it is called a ***meander scar***, and if wet an ***oxbow lake*** or ***swamp*** (Fig. 8.5). ***Waterfalls*** and ***rapids*** are also products of stream erosion and these often occur at ***nickpoints*** in the river system at the limit of ***headward erosion. Stream terraces*** may be ***erosional*** if they are produced by stream downcutting, or ***alluvial*** if they result from extensive infilling of the valley by sediment.

Deposition of sediment occurs when stream velocity falls below the minimum required for transport of particles of a particular size. Stream floodplains result from this process. ***Floodplains*** are the flat, low-lying areas on either side of a stream that are inundated periodically during floods. At these times water rises above the banks of the stream channel spilling on to the floodplain and forming ***overbank deposits***. The coarsest particles of the load are dropped close to the water channel on its bank, eventually building a low embankment or ***levee*** on either side. The finer particles are carried further from the stream and ultimately settle in low areas of the floodplain to form a cover of ***alluvium***. During floods, levees that develop may block the flow of small tributaries into the main channel. These streams must then flow parallel to the main stream until there is a break in the levee system that allows them to join the main flow. Such streams are called ***yazoo*** streams. When the sediment load carried by a stream is very high, sediment may be deposited in the middle of the channel creating sand bars or ***mid-stream bars***. These may cause a single stream to split into several smaller channels forming a ***braided stream***. When a stream flows into a lake or the ocean, water velocity is greatly reduced resulting in deposition of the sediment load and the formation of a ***delta,*** so named for the shape of the Nile River delta, which the Greeks first studied and thought resembled the Greek letter Δ.

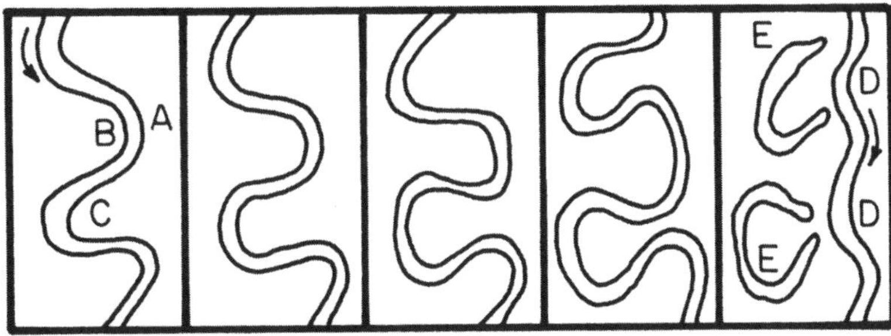

Fig. 8.5 The development of meanders and oxbow lakes (A = undercut slope, B and C = point bar, D = mander cutoff, E = oxbow lake).

QUESTIONS

8.8 The Philipp area shown in Fig. 1.4 is part of the Mississippi River floodplain, even though the Mississippi River is more than 100 miles to the west. The region is dominated by an indeterminate drainage with yazoo streams. Look at a Google Earth™ satellite image of the Philipp, MS map (published in 1957) by typing the following coordinates in the search box: 33° 48′ 32.77″ N, 90° 07′ 36.11″ W. Start by viewing from an Eye alt of 40,000 feet. Answer the following questions.

(a) On the map, draw the boundary between the alluvial floodplain of the Mississippi River and the ancient river bluff (cliff indicated by closely arranged contour lines), and calculate an average east- to-west gradient for the floodplain in this region.

(b) Identify and explain the existence of alluvial fans at the base of the ancient Mississippi bluff.

(c) Why do elevations on the east side of the Tallahatchie River (A.2-1.2) increase towards the stream channel?

(d) Identify the following features and give their grid coordinates:

Large meander ____________________ Small meander ____________________

Meander cutoff ____________________ Meander scar ____________________

Point bar ____________________ Undercut slope ____________________

Oxbow lake ____________________ Oxbow swamp ____________________

(e) Compare Fig. 1.4 with the recent Google Earth™ satellite image and describe any changes in the area since 1957. For instance, are there any new meanders, or oxbow lakes, or indications of additional human activities?

8.9 The map in Fig. 8.6 shows the West Branch of the Susquehanna River in Pennsylvania and two of its tributaries, Kettle Creek and Sinnemahoning Creek. The stream valleys are cut largely in bedrock and the stream pattern traverses the geologic structure. A recent satellite image of the Renova West, PA map (published in 1946) area can be viewed using Google Earth™ by typing the coordinates 41° 19′ 54.58″ N, 77° 49′ 52.45″ W into the search box. Start with an Eye alt of 50,000 feet. Answer the following questions.

(a) On the map, identify two abandoned, entrenched meander loops, their respective meander cores, the points of cutoff, and list their respective grid coordinates below.

(b) Mark on the map the former courses of the Sinnemahoning Creek around Little Round Top and the Susquehanna River around Round Top Mountain. Measure how much each stream was shortened by the cutoffs.

(c) Draw a topographic profile that is 7 inches in length from A.3-2.9 (BM 719) and passes through the top of Round Top Mountain (B.4-2.5). Label your diagram and comment on the asymmetry of the valley sides in the Susquehanna Valley and the marked change in elevation across Kettle Creek.

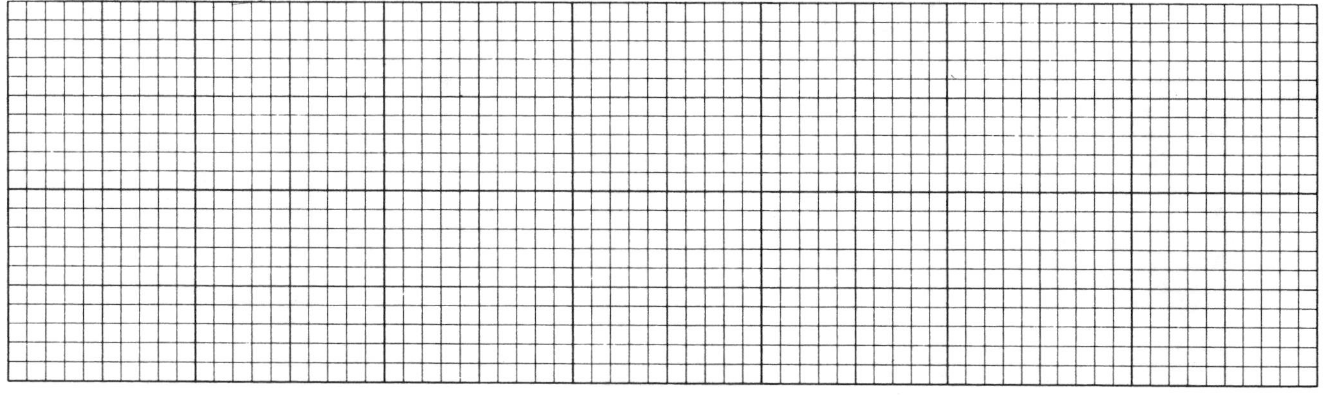

Next Page: Fig. 8.6 Renova West, Pennsylvania (1:62,500, A.0-1.0 in southeast corner).

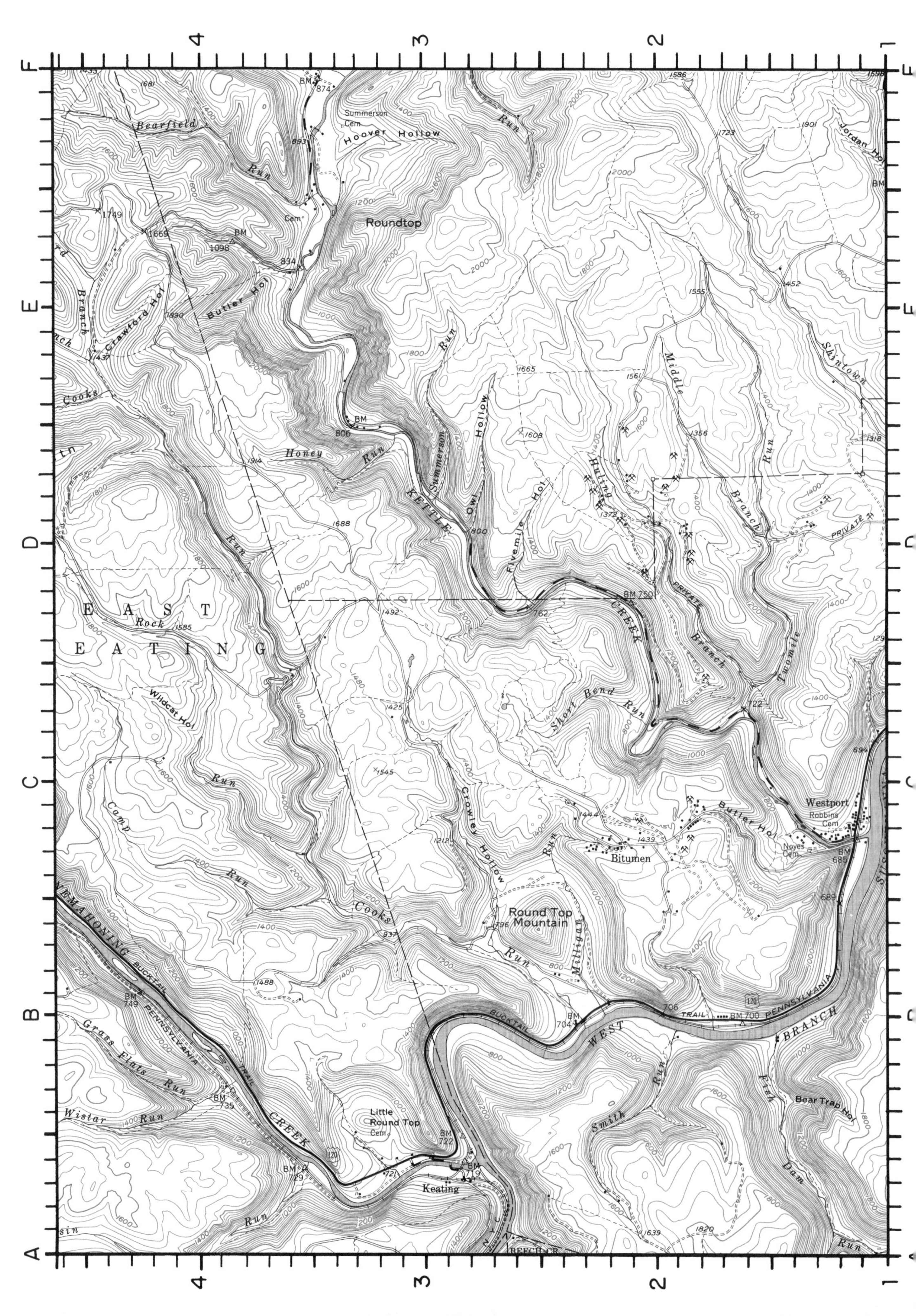

Bearfield Run
Summerson Cem
Hoover Hollow
Roundtop
Butler Hol
Crawford Hol
Cooks
Honey Run
Summerson
Owl Hollow
Fivemile Hol
Huling
Middle Branch
Run
Shintown
Jordan Hol
KETTLE CREEK
EAST EATING
Rock
Wildcat Hol
Short Bend Run
Branch
Twomile
Westport
Robbins Cem
Noyes Cem
Butler Hol
Bitumen
Crowley Hollow
Camp Run
Round Top Mountain
Milligan
Cooks Run
SINNEMAHONING
BUCKTAIL PENNSYLVANIA TRAIL
WEST BRANCH
Grass Flats Run
Wistar Run
CREEK
Little Round Top Cem
Keating
Smith Run
Fish Dam Run
Bear Trap Hol
BEECH CR
PRIVATE

(d) Compare Fig. 8.6 with a recent Google Earth™ satellite image of the area and describe any changes that have taken place. Are there any new meanders, or have any oxbow lakes developed? Are there any indications of changes due to human activities?

8.10 A large percentage of the sediment transported by streams is carried in suspension or in solution.

(a) Examine Table 8.6 and determine the relative importance of the suspended and dissolved loads of streams. Do most streams have more suspended load or more dissolved load? Of the 12 streams listed, which have more dissolved load than suspended load?

Table 8.6 Dissolved and suspended load in selected rivers in different climatic regions of the United States (modified after Leopold et al. 1964).

River and Location	Drainage Area (sq mi)	Average Discharge, Q (cfs)	Discharge ÷ Drainage Area (cfs/sq mi)	Average Suspended Load (millions of tons/yr)	Average Dissolved Load (millions of tons/yr)	Total Average Suspended and Dissolved Load (millions of tons/yr)	Total Average Load ÷ Drainage Area (tons/sq mi/yr)	Dissolved Load as Percent of Total Load (%)
Little Colorado at Woodruff, Arizona	8,100	63.3	.0078	1.6	.02	1.62	199	1.2
Canadian River near Amarillo, Texas	19,445	621	.032	6.41	.124	6.53	336	1.9
Colorado River near San Saba, Texas	30,600	1,449	.047	3.02	.208	3.23	105	6.4
Bighorn River at Kane, Wyoming	15,900	2,391	.150	1.60	.217	1.82	114	12
Green River at Green River, Utah	40,600	6,737	.166	19	2.5	21.5	530	12
Colorado River near Cisco, Utah	24,100	8,457	.351	15	4.4	19.4	808	23
Iowa River at Iowa City, Iowa	3,271	1,517	.464	1.184	.485	1.67	510	29
Mississippi River at Red River Landing, Louisiana	1,144,500[b]	569,500[b]	.497	284	101.8	385.8	337	26
Sacramento River at Sacramento, California	27,000[c]	25,000[c]	.926	2.85	2.29	5.14	190	44
Flint River near Montezuma, Georgia	2,900	3,528	1.22	.400	.132	.53	183	25
Juniata River near New Port, Pennsylvania	3,354	4,329	1.29	.322	.566	.89	265	64
Delaware River at Trenton, New Jersey	6,780	11,730	1.73	1.003	.830	1.83	270	45

(b) In Table 8.7, the discharge per square mile within a drainage basin is listed as a climatic indicator. As can be seen in Table 8.6, low discharges occur in arid and semiarid areas and higher discharges in humid, temperate areas. Why is the dissolved load in streams less important in arid and semiarid terrains than in humid, temperate regions?

Table 8.7 Variation with climate of ratio of dissolved load to total load (after Leopold et al, 1964)

Climatic Indicator: Discharge per Square Mile (cfs./sq. mi.)	Dissolved Load as a Percentage of Total Load
0 – 0.1	9
0.1 – 0.3	16
0.3 – 0.7	26
> 0.7	37

SECTION 4: *Life Cycle of a Stream*

All land masses are subject to weathering and erosion and may be worn down to the universal base level, sea level, if they remain undisturbed for tens of millions of years. In 1899, William Morris Davis argued that as upland landscapes are reduced to low-relief, low-elevation erosion surfaces, they progress through three stages of development he called ***youth, maturity***, and ***old age*** (Fig. 8.7). This life cycle idea was also applied to the gradual evolution of streams and their valleys. A ***youthful stream*** is one characterized by narrow V-shaped valleys with a small, if present, floodplain and steep, irregular gradients. A ***mature stream*** has a broader, more U-shaped valley with meanders and oxbow lakes and an extensive floodplain. An ***old age stream*** is characterized by very wide floodplains, (up to several miles in width), large meanders, and numerous oxbow lakes and meander scars. It should be kept in mind that these terms are merely descriptive and often have no relationship to the actual age of the stream. For example, the Colorado River where is flows through the Grand Canyon is classified as a youthful stream, even though it has been flowing in this area for over 20 million years.

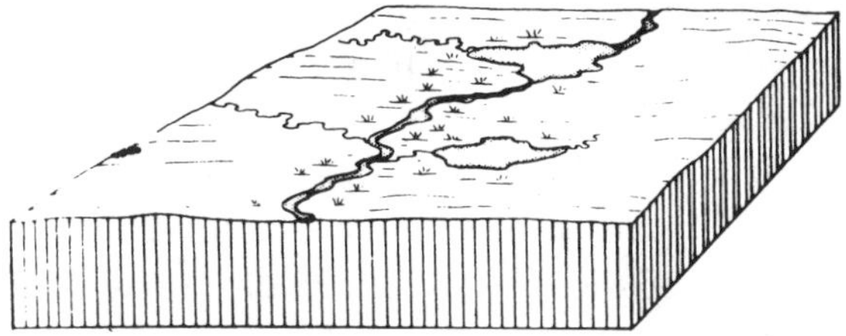

A. In the initial stage, relief is slight, drainage poor.

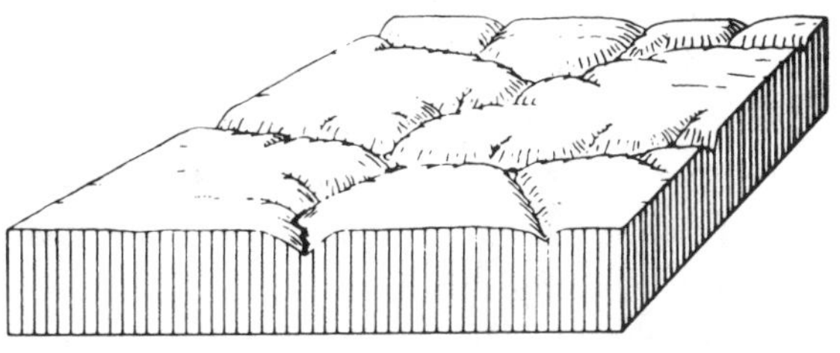

B. In early youth, stream valleys are narrow, uplands broad and flat.

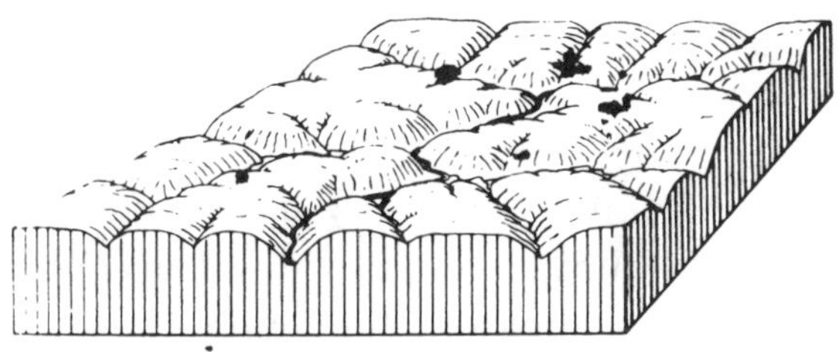

C. In late youth, valley slopes predominate but some interstream uplands remain.

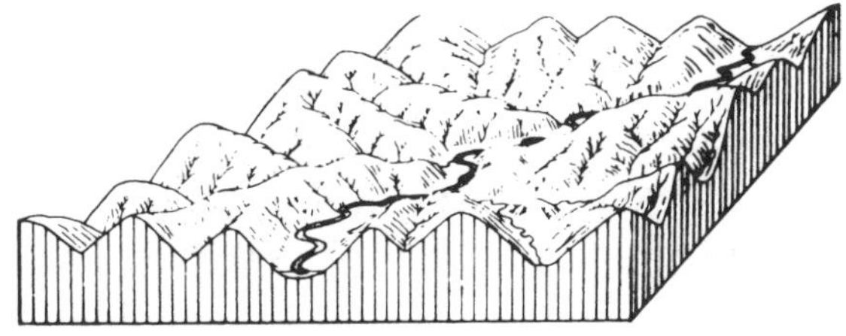

D. In maturity, the region consists of valley slopes and narrow divides.

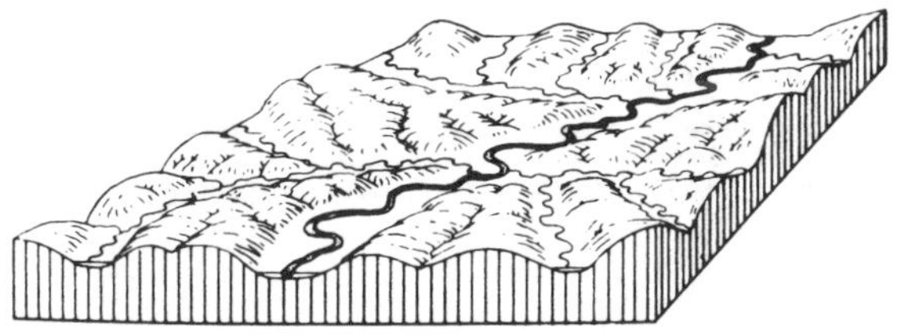

E. In late maturity, relief is subdued, valley floors broad.

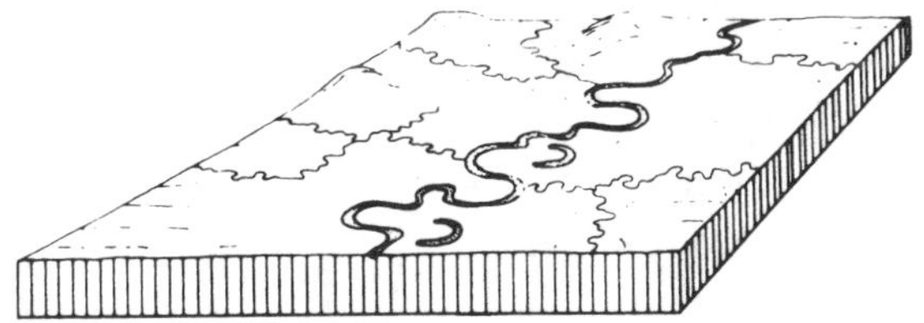

F. In old age, a peneplain with monadnocks is formed.

Fig. 8.7 The cycle of land mass denudation in a humid climate (from Strahler 1975).

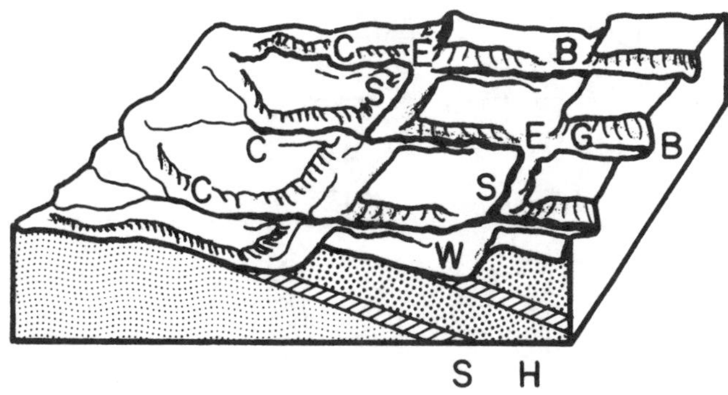

Fig. 8.8 Stream capture in an area of gently dipping hard and soft rocks (C = consequent stream, S = subsequent stream, E = elbow of capture, W = water gap, G = wind gap, B = misfit stream, (and below the diagram) S = soft rock layer, H = hard rock layer).

When an old age landscape is uplifted at the end of an erosion cycle, the streams begin rapid downcutting towards the new lower base level. This process is called ***rejuvenation***. If an old age stream is uplifted but not tilted, it may cut a deep gorge into its former floodplain and carry meanders into bedrock as ***entrenched meanders***. Entrenched meanders also produce cut-offs, the abandoned meander loop being characterized by a central ***meander core*** of solid rock. A drainage pattern inherited from a former structural or erosional land surface and impressed on underlying older rocks is said to be ***superimposed***. A pattern that existed prior to mountain building and was little changed by it is said to be ***antecedent***. A stream whose course developed when water first flowed down a newly-created surface is a ***consequent stream***, and normally parallels rock dip (Fig. 8.8). Streams which later adjusted their courses to weak rock belts or fracture lines by differential erosion are ***subsequent streams*** and frequently these parallel the direction of strike.

If rates of erosion in the headwaters of different drainage systems are not the same, ***stream capture*** may take place (Fig. 8.8). Capture occurs when a stream in one system captures or diverts part of the drainage in another system. In areas of alternate hard and soft rock layers, it is common for a subsequent stream that is eroding its course in less resistant rock to capture part of the drainage of a consequent stream that is flowing across resistant rock ridges through ***water gaps***. At the elbow of capture, the consequent stream meets the subsequent stream, forming a sharp bend in the course of the new trunk river. The consequent stream down-valley of the point of capture is said to be beheaded and, because it is deprived of much of its drainage, it appears too small for the valley it occupies and is called a ***misfit stream***. The deep gorge cut by the consequent stream is left virtually dry when drainage is diverted and becomes a ***wind gap***.

QUESTIONS

8.11 Look at the maps and aerial photographs of the following areas and determine which stage in the life cycle of a stream (youthful, mature, old age) best describes each area. Remember that these can be viewed obliquely in Google Earth™ and this may help in your determination.

(a) Harrisburg, PA (Fig. 6.10) ________________________

(b) Philipp, MS (Fig. 1.4) ________________________

(c) Renova, PA (Fig. 8.6) ________________________

(d) Sacaton Mountains, AZ (Fig. 13.3) ________________________

(e) Pine Mountain, OK (Fig. 6.8) ________________________

(f) Circle Ridge, WY (Fig. 6.9) ________________________

(g) Mackenzie Mountains, Canada (Fig. 7.8) ________________________

8.12 Examine the Harrisburg, PA area shown in Fig. 6.10. Also view a Google Earth™ satellite image by typing the following coordinates in the search box: 40° 40′ 07.81″ N, 76° 49′ 46.44″ W. Start viewing from an Eye alt of 40 miles. Answer the following questions.

(a) Is the Susquehanna River an antecedent, a consequent, or a superimposed stream?

(b) Identify and give the grid coordinates of good examples of a water gap and a subsequent stream.

(c) What has controlled the course of Mahantango Creek (A.3-3.2) in the west of the map area?

SECTION #5: Measuring Stream Meanders

Meandering streams are highly sinuous channels in which the curves are nearly symmetrical. Measures that are commonly used to describe river meanders are illustrated in Fig. 8.9 and Table 8.8. Sinuosity, or tightness of bend, is the ratio of the length of the channel in a given curve to the wavelength of the curve (L/λ), and the higher the value, the more sinuous the channel. It has been found that in many meandering streams the ratio of radius of curvature to width (r_c/w) lies in the narrow range of 2 to 3, with the median value being 2.7. This explains why meandering streams closely resemble one another even though they may vary considerably in size.

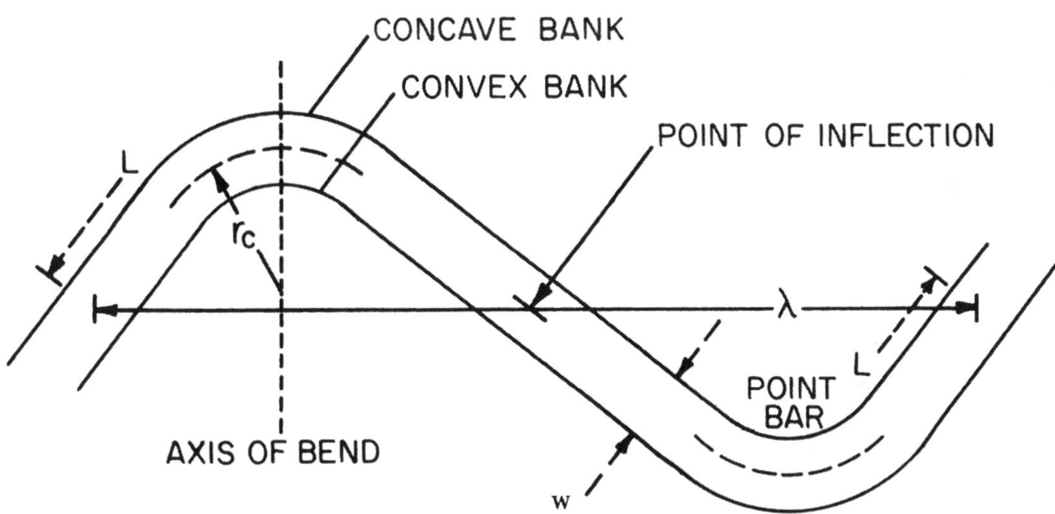

Fig. 8.9 Common measures used to describe river meanders.

Table 8.8 Properties used to describe river meanders (after Leopold & Langbein, 1966)

Common Measures	Ratio	Typical Figures
Length of channel to wavelength (sinuosity)	L/λ	1.3 to 4.0
Length of channel to width	L/w	7 to 10
Radius of curvature to width	r_c/w	2 to 3
Wavelength to radius of curvature	λ/r_c	Average of 4.7

8.13 Using Fig. 8.10, measure the meander properties of the streams and complete Table 8.9. (Use the average of several measurements of each property.)

Table 8.9 Meander Characteristics of Selected Streams

River	λ	L	r_c	w	L/λ	L/w	r_c/w	λ/r_c
Arkansas								
Missouri								
Kaskaskia								
Souris								
Mississippi								

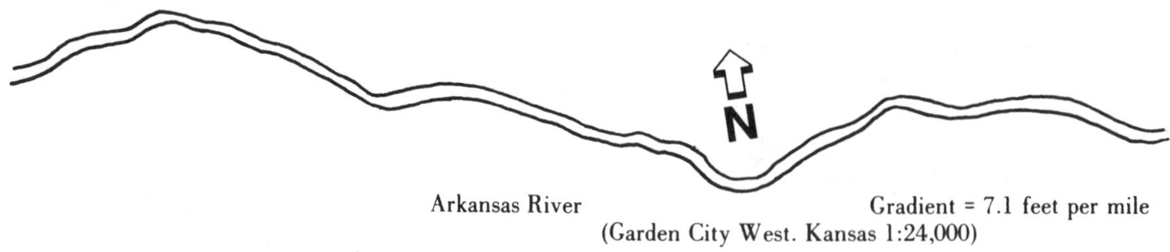

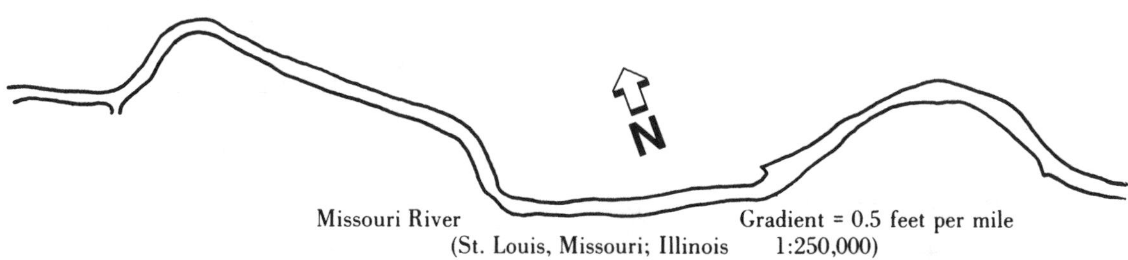

Fig. 8.10 Examples of meandering streams taken from topographic maps. **(Continued on next page.)**

Fig. 8.10 Examples of meandering streams taken from topographic maps. (Continued from previous page.)

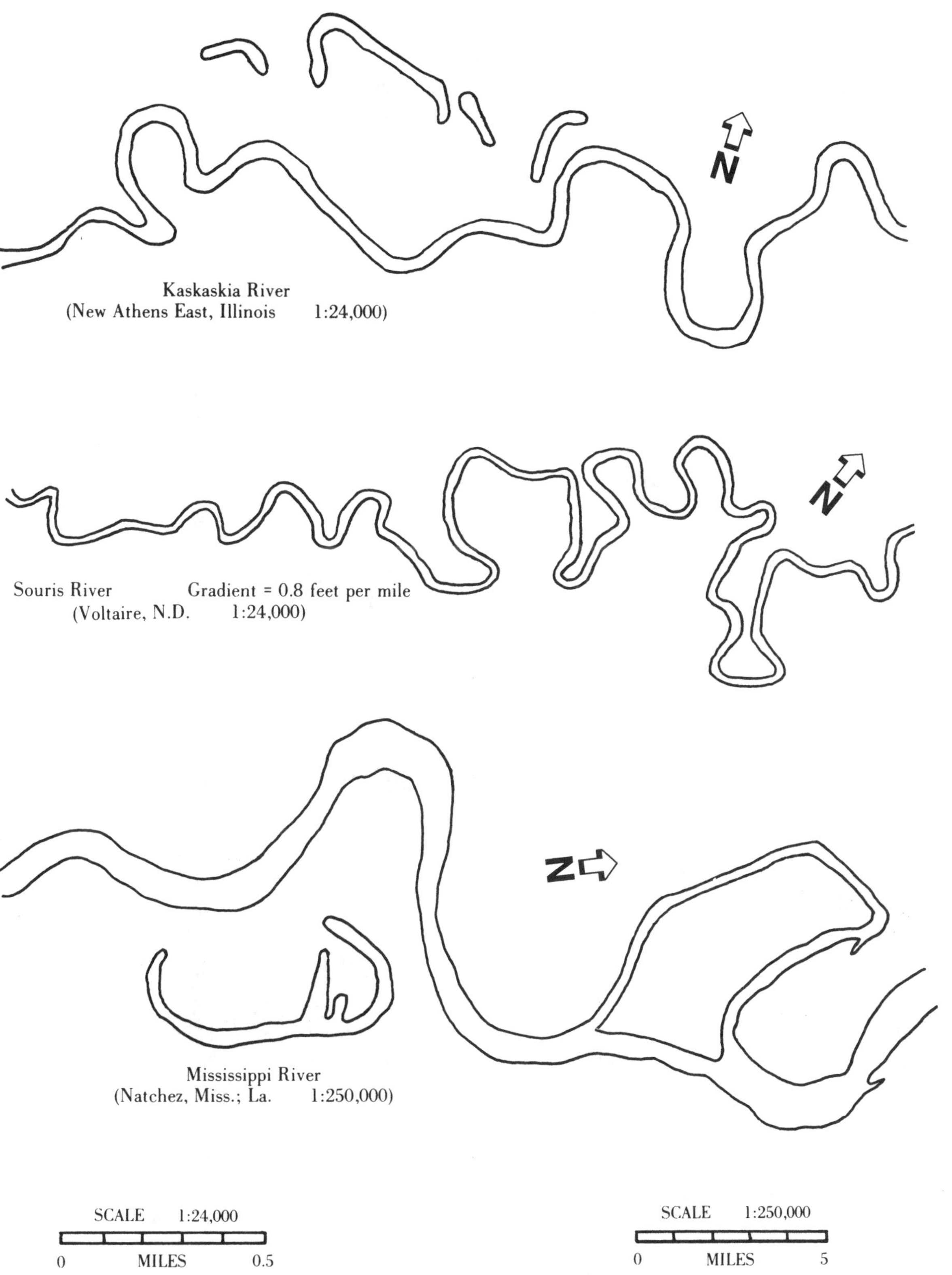

SECTION #6: Stream Discharge

The ***discharge*** of a stream is the volume of flow per unit of time. Normally, this flow is expressed in cubic feet per second (cfs). At any point along the stream channel, the discharge (Q) in cubic feet per second is given by **Q = A • V**, where A is the cross sectional area of the stream in square feet and V is the mean velocity in feet per second. When a stream is at the brink of overflowing its bank, discharge is ***bank full***. When the flood spills over the river bank, this is called ***overbank flow***. On average, the bank full stage occurs 1.5 times a year in humid mid-latitudes, with the typical range of variation lying between 1 and 4 times. Generally, channel banks without vegetation delimit the bank full level.

The force of gravity propels water in a stream channel down slope. Flow is retarded by friction between the moving water and the floor and sides of the channel, and by internal friction between water particles. As the discharge of a stream increases, the cross sectional area increases at a rate more rapid than the ***wetted perimeter***, resulting in a relative decrease in frictional retardation by the floor and banks of the channel (Fig. 8.11). For this reason, the velocity of flow increases with discharge. At any given point, the ***mean velocity*** occurs at approximately 0.6 of the distance from the surface of the stream to the bed. Velocities vary considerably with the maximum velocity usually near the middle of the channel just below the surface. It is common for this value to be 0.5 to 0.25 greater than the average velocity of a cross section.

Most rivers show a seasonal variation in flow that is largely a reflection of climatic conditions. This pattern, which tends to be repeated year after year, is the ***regime*** of the river or stream. ***Floods*** occur when high discharges cause inundation of adjacent floodplains. They are almost always caused by intense rainfall, snow melt, or a combination of the two. In analyzing the occurrence of floods, the underlying assumption is that the available stream discharge record is a sample of an infinitely large population in time. The ***recurrence interval*** of a flood of given magnitude is the average time within which that flood will be equaled or exceeded once. For example, if the largest flood recorded at a gauging station during the last 50 years is 200,000 cfs, it is expected that a flood of equal or greater magnitude will occur at least once in the next 50 years. ***Flood frequency*** can be calculated by tabulating and ranking the highest discharge in each year of record (Table 8.12). The recurrence interval of a particular flow is then given by the formula:

$$\textbf{Recurrence interval} = \frac{\mathbf{n+1}}{\mathbf{m}}$$

where **n** is the number of years of record and **m** is the rank of the particular discharge. The mean of the sample of maximum discharges is the ***mean annual flood***.

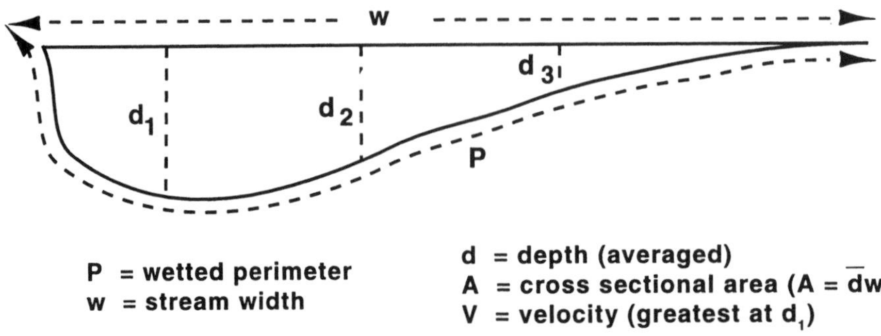

Fig. 8.11 Parameters of a stream cross section.

QUESTIONS

8.14 The discharge of a stream in a remote location was measured on June 22. At the same time, data were collected to allow the bank full discharge to be estimated.

(a) The width of the stream at bank full stage when measured with a tape was found to be 120 feet. The depth of water in the stream was measured with a wooden rod at intervals across the channel. Using the data shown in Table 8.10, draw a cross section of the stream channel marking in the bank full and June 22 levels. Use a horizontal scale of 1 inch represents 20 feet and a vertical scale of 1 inch represents 10 feet.

Table 8.10 Cross sectional data of a hypothetical Stream Channel.

Distance from left bank at bankfull stage (feet)	Height above water level (*) or depth of water (feet and inches)	Comments
0	3 ft. 1 inch (*)	Left bank at bankfull
6	0	Left bank of present stream
10	2 ft. 2 inches	
20	3 ft. 3 inches	
30	6 ft. 4 inches	
34	6 ft. 8 inches	
40	10 ft.	
50	13 ft. 1 inch	
60	13 ft. 4 inches	
70	12 ft. 1 inch	
80	8 ft. 7 inches	
84	3 ft. 9 inches	
90	2 ft. 5 inches	
100	1 ft.	
105	0	Right bank of present stream
110	1 ft. 1 inch (*)	
120	3 ft. 1 inch (*)	Right bank at bankfull

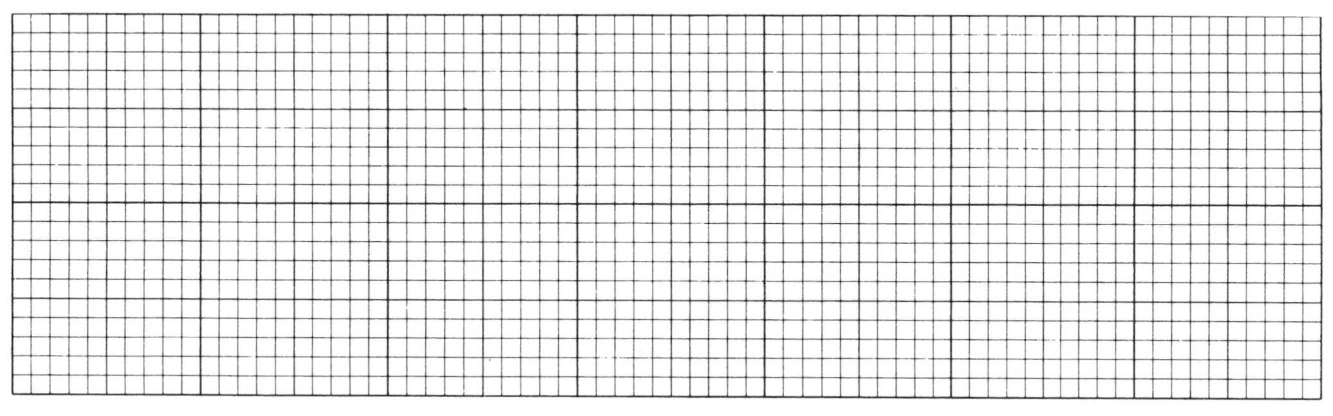

(b) A number of velocity readings were taken across the channel width. Sites were chosen carefully and, in particular, were located where flow velocities appeared to change substantially. In any depth of water the mean velocity is determined by measuring the speed of flow with a current meter at 0.6 of the depth. On the basis of these results, the channel cross section can be divided into four sub-areas or velocity domains, in which the rate of water flow is approximately constant. Using information given in Table 8.11, mark the four velocity domains on the stream cross section from part (a). Using graph paper divisions, measure the area for each. Add these values to the table and calculate the discharge through each sub-area. What is the discharge of the stream and what is it's average velocity?

Table 8.11 Velocity and discharge characteristics of a hypothetical stream.

Area	Location of velocity domains in terms of distance from the left bankfull position	Average Velocity (ft/sec)	Cross Sectional Area (square ft)	Discharge (A_xV_x) (c.f.s.)
1	6 ft. to 34 ft.	V_1 0.93	A_1	A_1V_1
2	34 ft. to 60 ft.	V_2 3.07	A_2	A_2V_2
3	60 ft. to 84 ft.	V_3 3.14	A_3	A_3V_3
4	84 ft. to 105 ft.	V_4 0.51	A_4	A_4V_4

Total Discharge Q = $A_1V_1 + A_2V_2 + A_3V_3 + A_4V_4$ = ________ c.f.s.

Average Velocity = $\dfrac{\text{Total Discharge (Q)}}{\text{Cross sectional area } (A_1+A_2+A_3+A_4)}$ = ____ feet/sec.

(c) The hydraulic radius (R) of a stream is equal to the cross sectional area of the stream (A) divided by its wetted perimeter (P). Determine the wetted perimeter from the stream cross section and calculate (R) for June 22, and for bank full stage. Your answers will be in feet.

(d) To determine bank full discharge, use the ***Manning Equation***, which expresses an empirical relationship. This is:

$$\mathbf{V} = \frac{\mathbf{1.49}}{\mathbf{n}} \times \mathbf{R}^{2/3} \times \mathbf{S}^{1/2}$$

where **n** is roughness, **R** is the hydraulic radius, and **S** is the slope of the stream surface. The slope of the stream on June 22 was determined by measuring the elevation of the stream at two widely separated locations. At each site the elevation was taken as the mean of measurements on the two sides of the channel. On June 22, the slope of the stream surface was 0.4% or 0.004 (this last figure is used in the Manning Equation). Estimate the roughness (n) of the stream channel using the values of (V) and (R) already calculated.

(e) Assume that the slope of the stream surface remains at 0.004 during bank full stage. Substitute the relevant values of (n), (R), and (S) into the Manning Equation. Calculate the expected mean velocity of the stream at bank full stage and determine the mean discharge.

8.15 The discharge of a stream has been monitored over a period of 24 years and, every time the flow exceeded 115,000 cfs a small settlement on the river floodplain near the gauging station was flooded.

(a) From the data given in Table 8.12, estimate the percentage probability of runoff in order 2 through 24 and add these figures to the table.

Table 8.12 Annual runoff peaks for a hypothetical stream arranged in descending order of magnitude.

Runoff Peak (thousands of cubic ft. per second)	Order of Magnitude (m)	% Probability of runoff being equalled or exceeded $(\frac{m}{n+1} \times 100)$*
149.0	1	4
134.0	2	
127.0	3	
118.0	4	
113.0	5	
109.0	6	
104.0	7	
102.0	8	
100.0	9	
96.5	10	
94.5	11	
91.5	12	
88.0	13	
85.5	14	
82.0	15	
79.5	16	
78.5	17	
76.0	18	
73.0	19	
71.5	20	
67.0	21	
64.0	22	
57.5	23	
55.0	24	

* n is the number of years of record (24)

(b) Calculate the mean annual flood and estimate its recurrence interval.

(c) What is the percentage probability of flooding in the settlement and how many times can it be expected to flood in the next 20 years if measures to reduce flooding are not taken?

(d) Plot the discharge-probability data on log-probability graph paper. Connect the points with a straight line and extend it to cover the range of probabilities from 0 to 100%. This line can be used to estimate the probability of annual runoff peaks outside those recorded in the 24 years that records have been kept. From this graph, estimate the probability of an annual flood peak of 200,000 cfs. Discharge should be plotted along the vertical axis.

8.16 Using the USGS web site (http://waterdata.usgs.gov/ga/nwis/rt) determine the most recent discharge for a river near your campus or hometown. List the name of the river, the location of the monitoring station you used, and the magnitude of discharge.

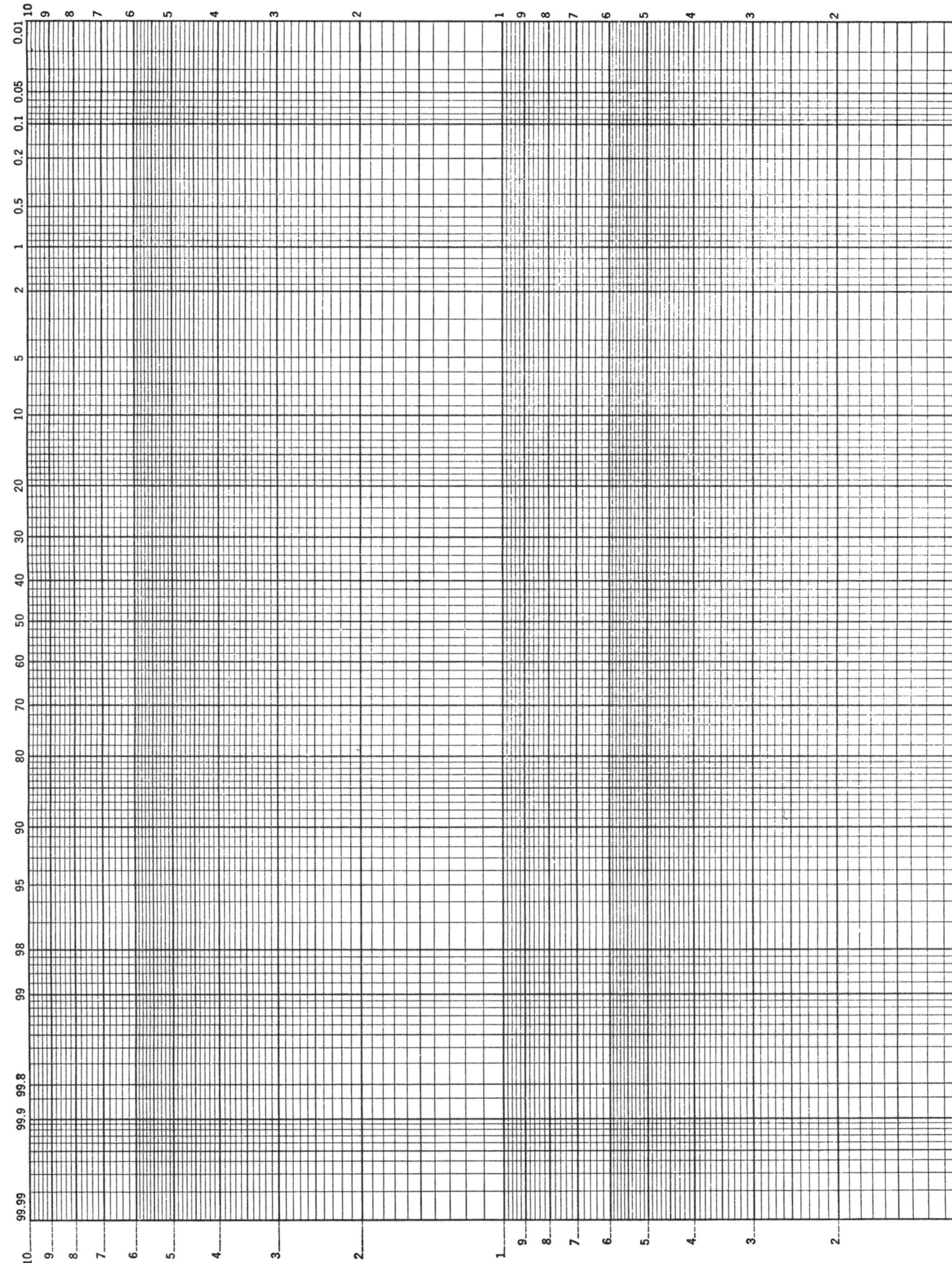

Student Name________________________________

Exercise 9

KARST LANDSCAPES

MATERIALS

Lens stereoscope (plastic), red/blue 3-D glasses, calculator, computer with Google Earth™ software and Internet access.

OBJECTIVES

1. Understand the basic processes involved in solution weathering, particularly carbonation.
2. Recognize landforms produced by solution weathering.
3. Understand how climatic factors and human activities have affected karst landscapes.

INTRODUCTION

The German term ***karst*** is derived from the Slav word "krš", meaning "crag". It refers to terrain that has largely been molded by the action of solution. Solution is never the only process that has fashioned a karst landscape but it is always the most important one. The most common karst rocks are ***limestones*** ***($CaCO_3$)*** and dolomites ($CaMg(CO_3)_2$). ***Evaporites,*** such as halite (NaCl), anhydrite ($CaSO_4$), and gypsum ($CaSO_42H_2O$), also form karst landscapes but these are less common.

Pure water containing no carbon dioxide (CO_2) will dissolve approximately 15 mg/l (or parts per million (ppm)) of limestone. Water in contact with the atmosphere is capable of dissolving 65 mg/l, but waters in contact with the soil are capable of dissolving 100-300 mg/l. This difference is due to different levels of CO_2 in the materials the water has been in contact with and thus in the water. The atmosphere contains about 0.03% CO_2 by volume whereas the soil contains about 0.1 – 1.0% CO_2 by volume. Enrichment of the soil in CO_2 is due to decomposition of organic matter in the soil by biogenic and microbial action. The importance of carbon dioxide in the dissolving of limestone stems from the fact that, when mixed with water, it produces a weak solution of ***carbonic acid***. This acid attacks the ***calcium carbonate*** ($CaCO_3$), to chemically break the bonds holding the substance together and form a different compound, ***calcium bicarbonate*** ($Ca(HCO_3)_2$). This is known as the chemical weathering process of ***carbonation***. The basic chemical equation for this process is:

$$CaCO_3 + H_2O + CO_2 \leftrightarrow Ca(HCO_3)_2$$

The most important effect of solution weathering lies in its enlargement of subsurface voids causing a steady increase in ***secondary permeability*** or the ability of water to flow through the rock material below ground. This enables underground channels (which are called ***caves*** when they are large enough for a human to enter) to transmit water out of the karst area. Rainwater falling on limestone will rarely flow over the surface for any great distance before sinking underground. As secondary permeability increases, enabling the limestone to transmit large amounts of water underground, surface drainage systems are disrupted and streams entering a karst area are likely to lose all or part of their water. Underground water moves through caves, which commonly form in the ***phreatic zone*** or ***zone of saturation***. If a lowering of the water base level or ***water table*** occurs, these caves come into the ***vadose zone*** or ***zone of aeration*** and may often by occupied by free-flowing streams. These underground streams often reappear on the surface as ***springs***. The two longest cave systems in the world are the Mammoth-Flint Ridge system in Kentucky, USA, (120 miles long) and the Hollach system in Switzerland (40 miles long).

SECTION 1: Dolines, Uvalas, Poljes and Sinking Streams

In rocks of low solubility, the characteristic surface landform is the stream valley. In karst areas the rocks are of high solubility, and because of rapid underground drainage and localized surface solution, the characteristic landform is the ***closed depression***, the smallest variety of which is called a ***doline*** or ***sinkhole.*** Several different types of dolines are recognized and the most important of these are shown in Fig. 9.1. ***Solution dolines*** are produced in bedrock by the action of solution from the surface down, while ***collapse*** and ***subjacent karst collapse dolines*** are formed by the collapse of a cave ceiling and thus from below the surface upward. ***Suffosion*** and ***subsidence depressions*** are developed in surficial, unconsolidated, non-soluble material and are not in bedrock. Suffosion dolines, which are usually funnel-shaped, are formed as particles of soil are gradually washed into an underground cave. Subsidence depressions develop by the gradual subsidence of regolith, due to collapse or compaction, into a subsurface cavity or depression.

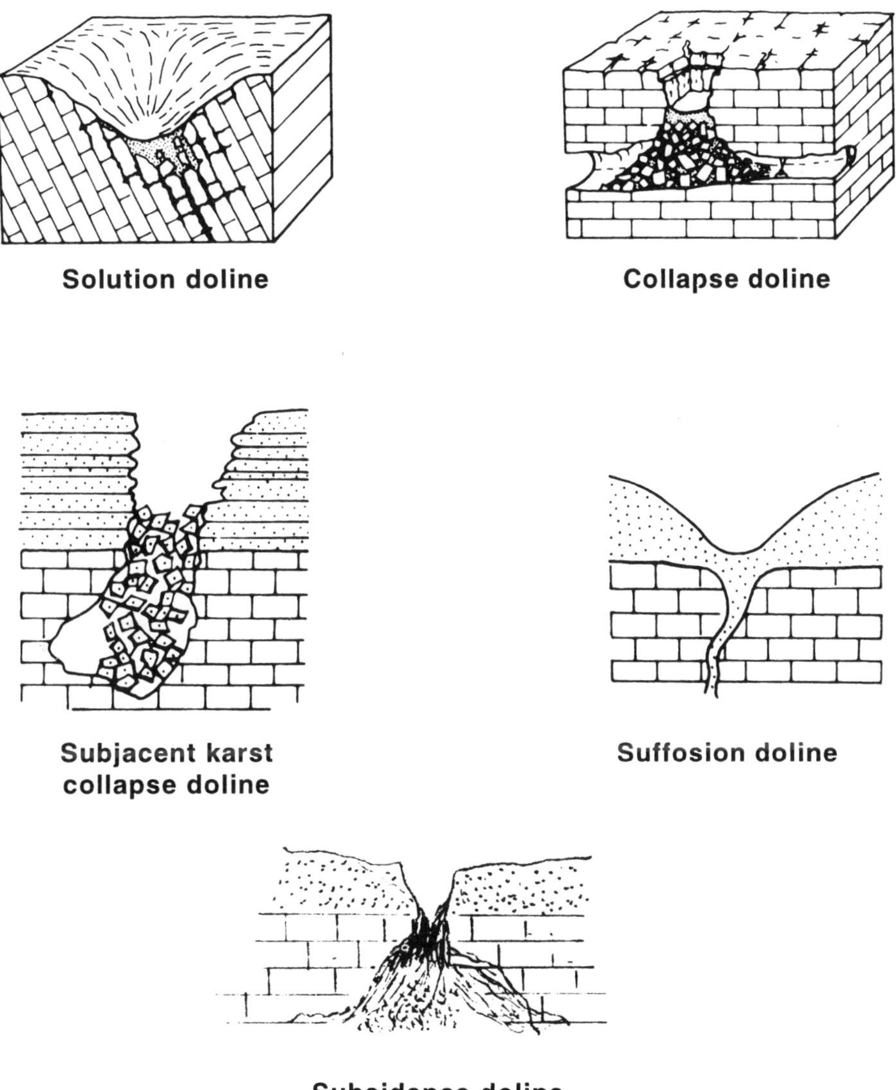

Fig. 9.1 Five common varieties of doline to be found in karst areas (modified after Jennings, 1971).

Next Page: Fig. 9.2 Mammoth Cave, Kentucky (1:62,500, A.0-1.0 in southeast corner).

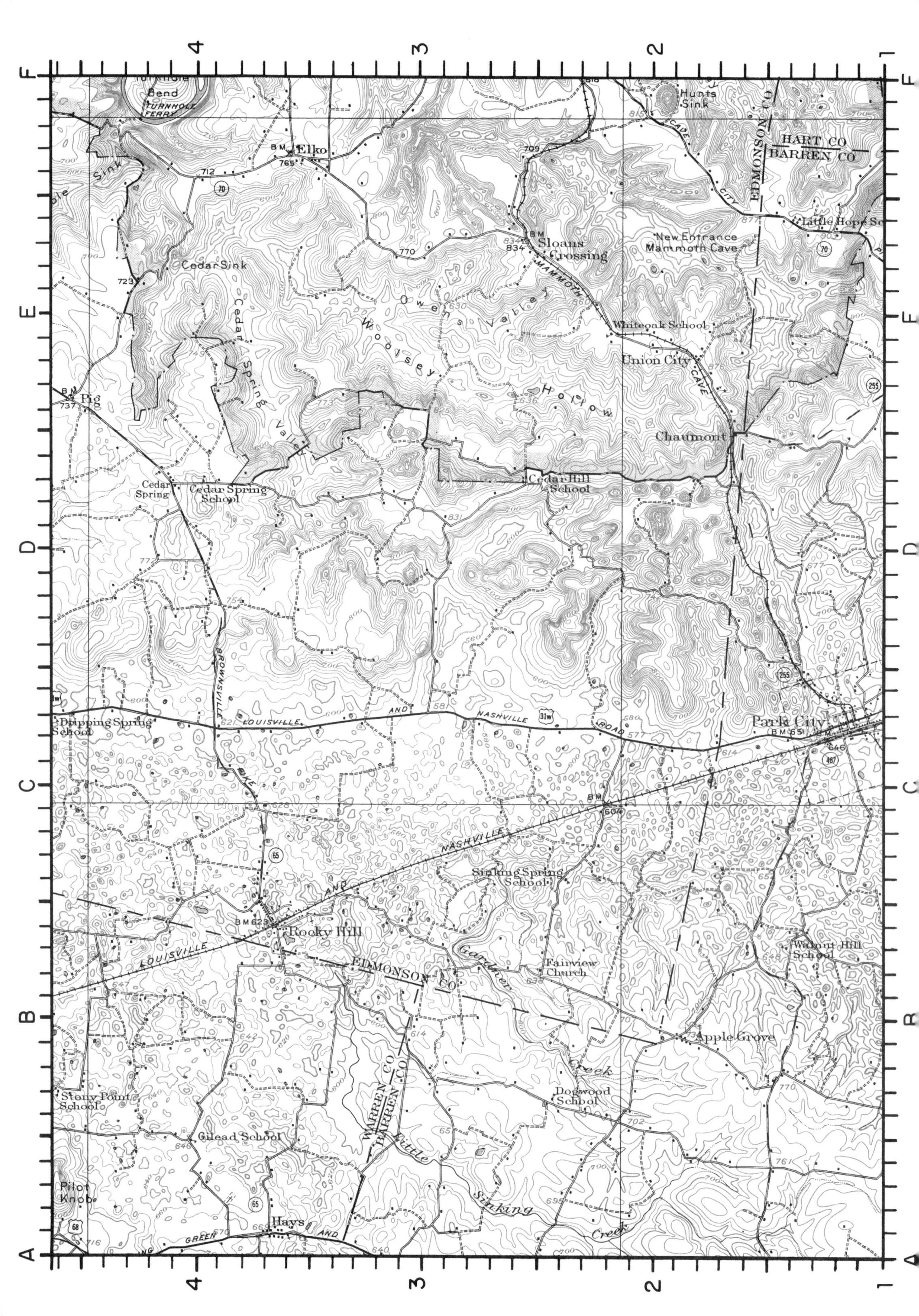

Turnhole Bend
TURNHOLE FERRY
Elko
Hunts Sink
EDMONSON CO
HART CO
BARREN CO
Sloans Crossing
New Entrance Mammoth Cave
Little Hope Sc
MAMMOTH CAVE
Cedar Sink
Cedar Spring Valley
Owens Valley
Woolsey Hollow
Whiteoak School
Union City
Chaumont
Pig
Cedar Spring
Cedar Spring School
Cedar Hill School
BROWNSVILLE PIKE
Dripping Spring School
LOUISVILLE AND NASHVILLE ROAD
Park City
LOUISVILLE AND NASHVILLE
Sinking Spring School
Rocky Hill
EDMONSON CO
Gardner Creek
Fairview Church
Walnut Hill School
Apple Grove
Dogwood School
Stony Point School
Gilead School
WARREN CO
BARREN CO
Little Sinking Creek
Pilot Knob
Hays
GREEN
A
B
C
D
E
F
1
2
3
4

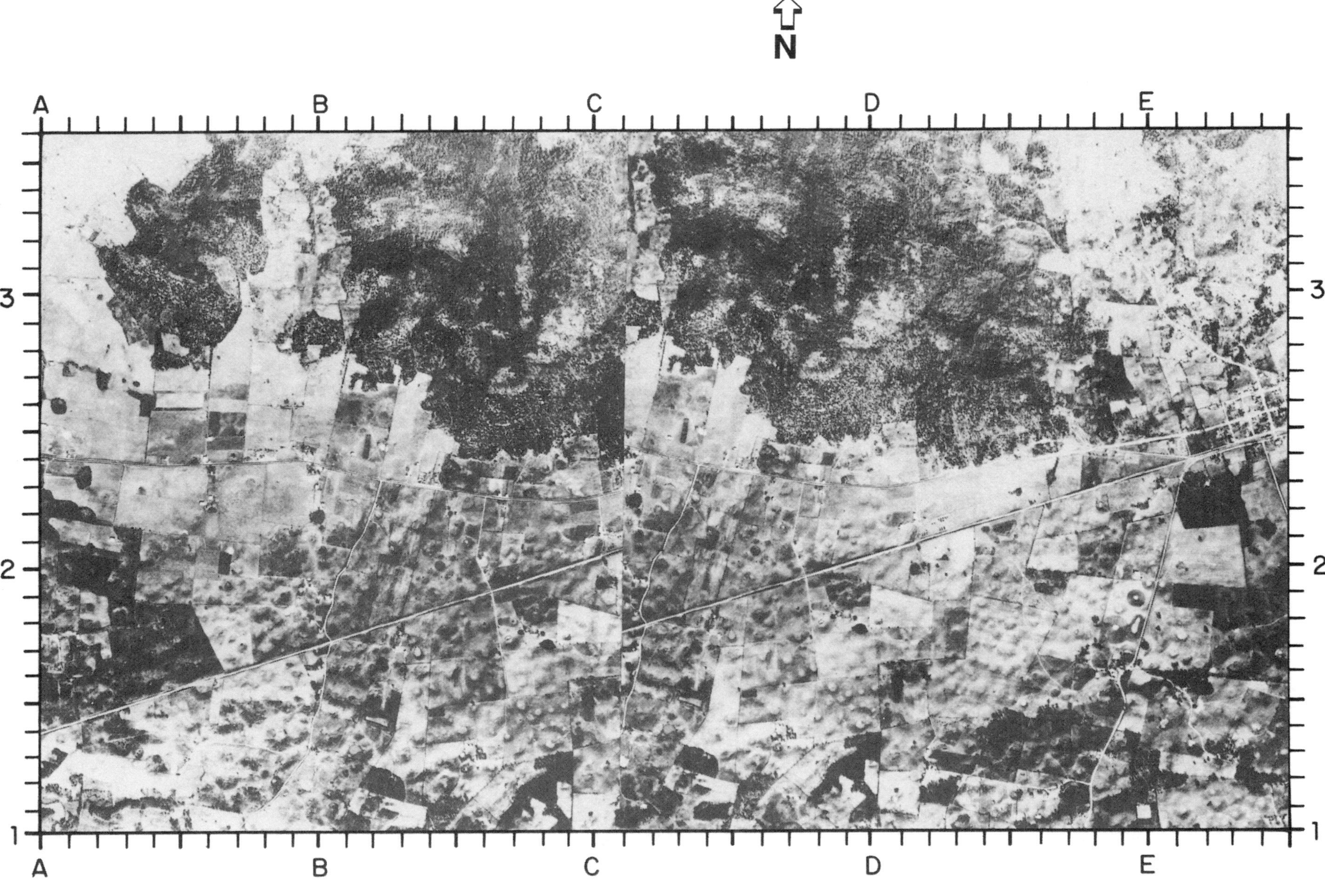

Fig. 9.3 Park City, Kentucky (A.0-1.0 in southwest corner).

When two or more dolines of any type enlarge and coalesce at the surface, larger complex depressions, called ***uvalas***, are formed. The largest closed depressions characteristic of karst terrains are ***poljes***. These may be of structural origin (originally synclinal or fault depressions) or they formed by the gradual coalescence of dolines and uvalas. In a closed polje, water entering the depression via surface streams and springs flows across the flat and often sediment-covered floor before sinking into cavities or sinkholes called ***ponors***. In many depressions, the ponors cannot carry away the runoff fast enough after heavy rains, making them susceptible to flooding. It is this frequent inundation that leaves many polje floors treeless and entirely grass-covered when dry. The Slav word "polje" means "field" and was used because of the meadows covering the floors of these depressions. Poljes are common in Croatia, Serbia, and surrounding countries. The largest polje in the world is the Livanjsko Polje in Bosnia and Herzegovina, which is 70 km long and an average of 10 km wide.

Persistent sinking at a point on a stream's course leads to the development of a ***streamsink*** and the differential lowering of the stream bed by solution. Upstream of the streamsink the flow is greater than it is downstream of it, so that a threshold develops in the stream profile immediately downvalley of the streamsink. As subsurface voids continue to enlarge, the streamsink will absorb more and more of the stream's flow. Eventually, it may capture all of the streamflow, even during periods of flood. When this happens, there is no further surface flow in the valley downstream of the streamsink and this abandoned channel becomes a ***dry valley***. The channel upstream of the sink, which still has surface flow, is then known as a ***blind valley***. The stream itself is usually called a ***sinking*** or a ***disappearing stream***.

QUESTIONS

9.1 In the southern half of the Mammoth Cave map and in the aerial photograph of the same area (Fig. 9.2 and 9.3, and 3-D anaglyph number 15 in Appendix D)), the St. Louis Limestone underlies a well-developed karst area. This area is called the Pennyroyal Plain and it has abundant small closed depressions. Larger depressions to the north in the Mammoth Cave Plateau region have formed in the overlying Ste. Genevieve Limestone. These limestones are of Mississippian age. The wooded hills have sandstone caps of Big Clifty Sandstone. Separating the Pennyroyal Plain and the Mammoth Cave Plateau is the Dripping Springs Escarpment. In the extreme northwest of the map area is a bend of the Green River. Also view the area on a Google Earth™ satellite image before answering the questions. Remember you can view the landscape from an oblique angle and this may help you to see the landscape more clearly. You can obtain an image in Google Earth™ by typing the following coordinates in the search box: 37° 05′ 31.11″ N, 86° 04′ 00.25″ W. Start viewing from an Eye alt of 20,000 feet.

(a) On Fig. 9.3, draw in the boundary between the St. Louis and Ste. Genevieve Limestones and identify (with an S) a hill capped with sandstone and give its grid coordinates. Also identify on both the photos and the map, the Pennyroyal Plain, the Dripping Springs Escarpment, and the Mammoth Cave Plateau and give grid coordinates for the center of each feature.

(b) Identify the following karst features and give their grid coordinates. Look at a Google Earth™ satellite image as this will help you locate the landforms.

Doline ____________________ Uvala ____________________

Dry Valley ____________________ Blind Valley ____________________

Disappearing Stream ____________________

(c) Carefully examine Cedar Sink (E.2-4.1), Cedar Spring Valley (D.8-3.8), Owens Valley (E.0-2.8), and Woolsey Hollow (D.7-3.0), in the northern portion of the map. How have these features developed and what relationship is there between them and the Green River (F.0-4.0)?

(d) The level of the groundwater in this area, the karst water table, is not close to the surface, yet some of the depressions contain water for long periods of time. What may account for this?

(e) Examine the photograph shown in Fig. 9.3, taken in 1954 and its 3-D anaglyph. Also examine the topographic map of this area (Fig. 9.2) published in 1948, and a recent Google Earth™ satellite image. What natural and human-induced changes have occurred in the area since 1948?

9.2 Fig. 9.4 is a portion of the 1:24,000-scale Lake Wales Quadrangle of central Florida (published 1952). This area is underlain by up to 1,000 feet of Tertiary limestones that are covered by 100-200 feet of unconsolidated Miocene and Pleistocene sands and clays. The contour interval is 5 feet. Also view a Google Earth™ satellite image of this area by typing the following coordinates in the search box: 27° 53′ 39.58″ N, 81° 34′ 38.42″ W. Start viewing from an Eye alt of 20,000 feet. Use the oblique viewing option to get a different perspective of the landforms.

(a) What type of karst depression does each of the following lakes occupy? Refer to Fig. 9.1 and be as specific as possible.

Lake Alta ____________________ Crystal Lake ____________________

Twin Lakes ____________________ Lake Serena ____________________

Lake Belle ____________________

Next Page: Fig. 9.4 Lake Wales, Florida (1:24,000, A.0-1.0 in southwest corner).

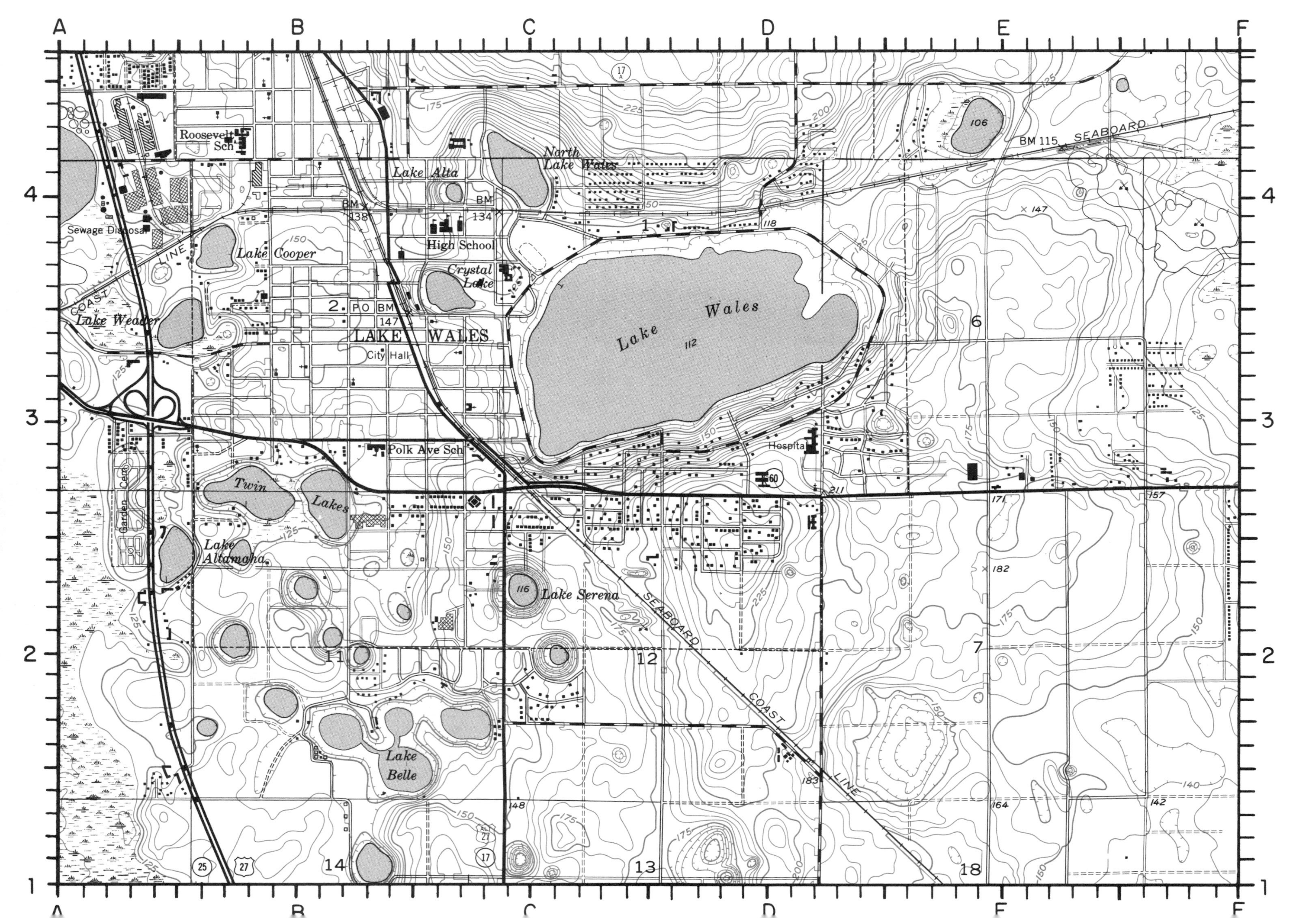

LAKE WALES
Lake Wales
North Lake Wales
Lake Alta
Lake Cooper
Crystal Lake
Lake Weader
Twin Lakes
Lake Altamaha
Lake Serena
Lake Belle
Roosevelt Sch
High School
Polk Ave Sch
City Hall
PO
Hospital
Garden Cem
Sewage Disposal
SEABOARD
COAST LINE
BM 115
BM 138
BM 134
BM 147

(b) If lake levels are an indication of ground water table elevation, use the lake levels in this area to determine the gradient of the water table and the direction in which it slopes. In what direction will groundwater move? North is to the top when you turn the map sideways to read the names.

(c) What is the most likely reason why some closed depressions contain water and others do not, and why are there no surface streams marked on the map?

(d) Note the facility located at A.2-3.8. What problems are posed for this activity by the groundwater situation here? By looking at a recent Google Earth™ image, determine if this facility is still in operation?

(e) Describe the changes that have taken place in the Lake Wales area since 1952 (the map date). Are all the lakes still there and are they the same size? What changes do you see that are due to human activities?

9.3 Locate the Livanjsko Polje in Bosnia and Herzegovina on a Google Earth™ satellite image by typing the following coordinates in the search box: 43° 48′ 25.99″ N 16° 54′ 40.66″ E. Start viewing from an Eye alt of 40 miles and look at the area both vertically and from an oblique angle for best understanding. The polje is oriented approximately NW-SE. Which end (NW or SE) seems to have more surface water and why? What other karst features can you see in this area, for instance near 43° 44′ 41.33″ N 16° 54′ 27.58″ E? Looking elsewhere in this region (in Croatia for example) can you see other poljes?

SECTION 2: Cockpit Karst

In humid tropical areas where high rainfall and dense vegetation produce great volumes of biogenic CO_2, karst landscapes are extremely accentuated and varied in nature. Solution is frequently so intense that the landscape is one closed depression after another in all directions. These depressions, called ***cockpits***, are separated by narrow ridges or ringed by 4-5 hills which may dominate the landscape. The cockpits are often deep, steep-sided depressions and the hills may take on more of a ***cone*** or ***tower*** shape. In Puerto Rico the towers are called ***mogotes***. In southern China and Southeast Asia, vertical-walled karst towers may rise more than 2,000 feet above the surrounding terrain.

QUESTIONS

9.4 Both the Utuado (Fig. 9.5) and Manati (Fig. 9.6 and 3-D anaglyph 16 in Appendix D) areas of north-central Puerto Rico contain highly-developed karst terrains. Both have excellent examples of cockpit and mogote karst. They also have ***oriented karst***, where the long axes of depressions and ridges are distinctly aligned (e.g. N-S, E-W). For maximum understanding of these landscape styles look at satellite images of these areas using both the vertical and oblique viewing options. A Google Earth™ satellite image of Fig 9.5 can be obtained by typing the coordinates 18° 21′ 06.65″N, 66° 40′ 39.55″ W in the search box. Type the following coordinates in the search box: 18° 24′ 13.29″ N, 66° 27′ 09.08″ W for a satellite image of Fig. 9.6. Start viewing from an Eye alt of 20,000 feet.

(a) On Fig. 9.5 identify and give the grid coordinates of areas of cockpit karst, oriented karst and mogote karst. Do the same for Fig. 9.6.

(b) Why does oriented karst develop in some areas and not in others?

(c) Compare the photograph in Fig. 9.6 (taken in 1963) and its 3-D anaglyph, with a recent Google Earth™ satellite image. Describe how the area has changed.

Next Page: Fig. 9.5 Utuado, Puerto Rico (1:20,000, A.0-1.0 in southwest corner).

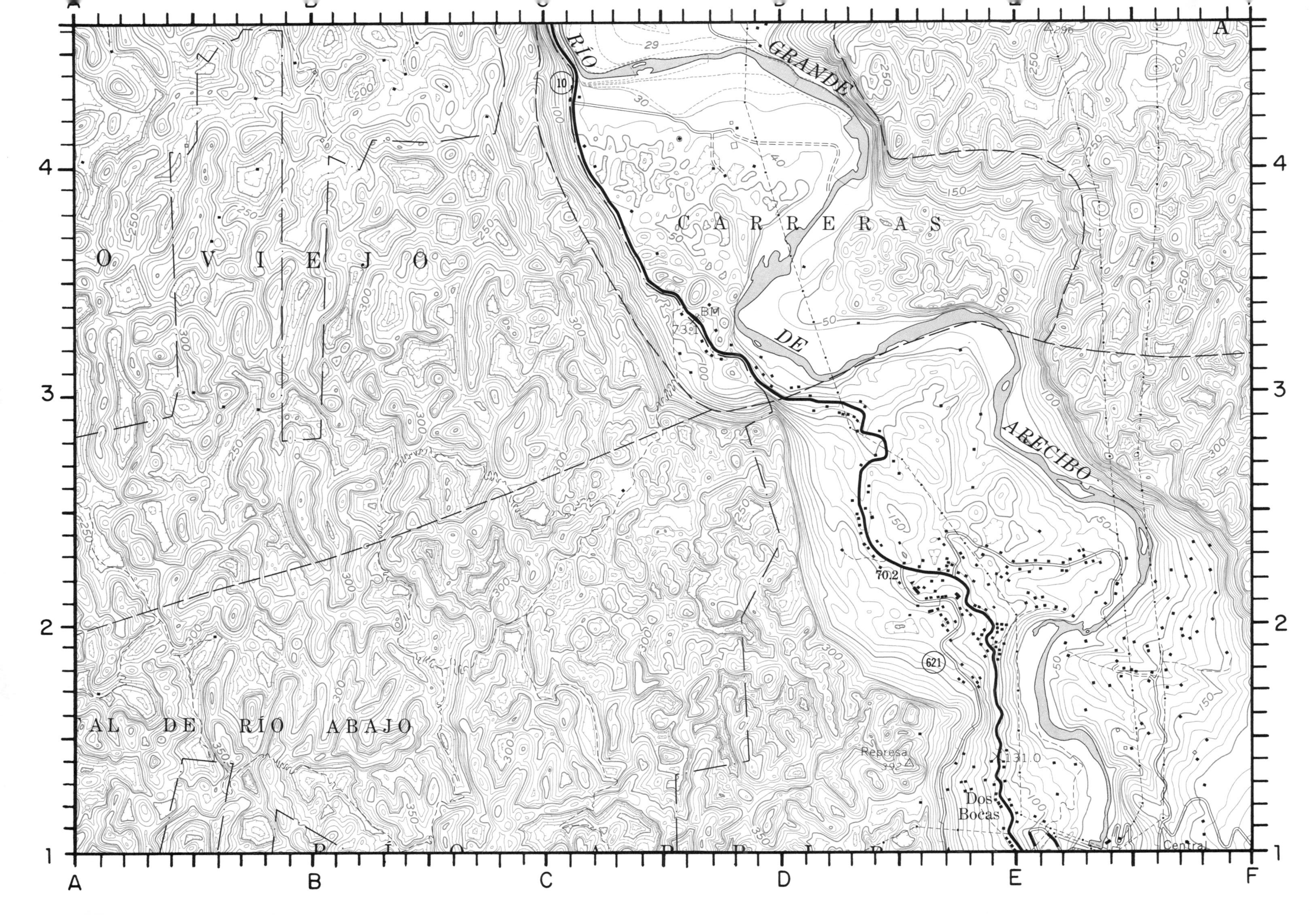
RÍO GRANDE DE ARECIBO
CARRERAS
VIEJO
AL DE RÍO ABAJO
Dos Bocas
Represa
Central
10
621
BM
73.1
70.2
131.0
392
296
A
B
C
D
E
F
1
2
3
4

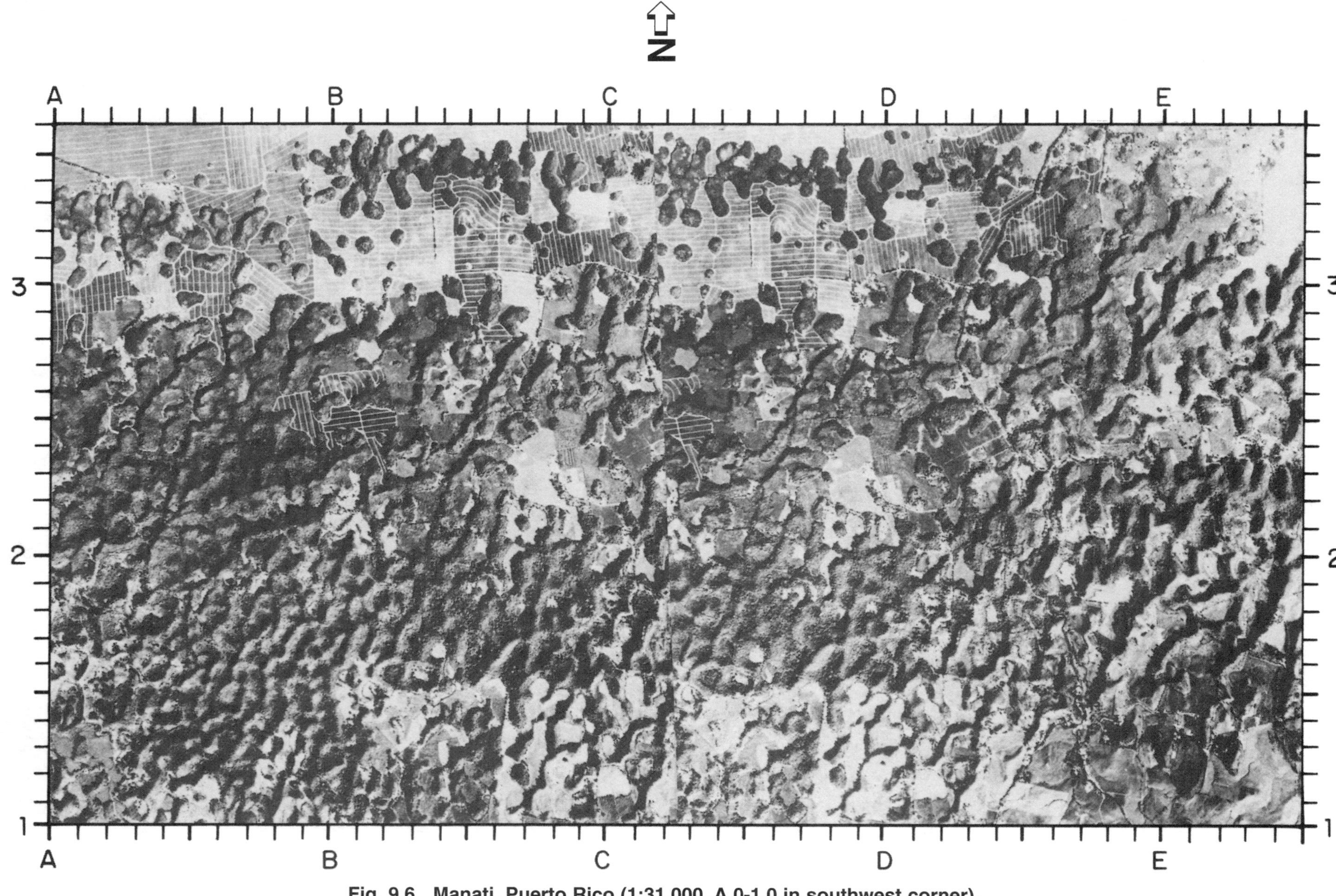

Fig. 9.6 Manati, Puerto Rico (1:31,000, A.0-1.0 in southwest corner).

(d) Examine a satellite image of the Arecibo Observatory by typing the coordinates, 18° 20′ 39.10″ N, 66° 45′ 10.06″ W, into the Google Earth™ search box. The Observatory is located in what type of karst depression? What do you think the Observatory does and why do you think it was located here?

(e) The mean annual precipitation in the Mammoth Cave area is approximately 47 inches. The annual rainfall in north-central Puerto Rico is 80 inches. Compare and contrast the landforms in these two karst areas. Bearing in mind that rainfall might affect the rate of solution and thus the rate of karst landform development, why do you think these two areas are so different?

SECTION 3: Estimating Karst Denudation

9.5 The catchment of a spring is 100 square kilometers in area and there is no surface flow out of it. On average, the spring has a discharge of 50 m^3/sec and carries 200mg/l of limestone in solution. If the density of the limestone is 2.5 g/cm^3, calculate the weight (in kilograms) and the volume (in m^3) of rock removed in solution from the catchment each year. If all this material were removed from the surface of the catchment, what would be the amount of surface lowering (in cm)?

9.6 The average annual precipitation in a one-square-kilometer limestone area is 80 cm. Approximately 15 cm of this is lost to evapotranspiration and the rest drains underground. Chemical analysis of cave drip waters in the area reveals that these contain 150 mg/l of limestone and are saturated. The density of the limestone is 2.5 g/cm^3. Calculate the weight and volume of rock removed by ground waters annually. If half of the solution occurs at the surface and the rest forms a single, large cave one kilometer long with a square cross section, what will be the dimensions of this cave after 5 years?

Student Name ________________________________

Exercise 10

GLACIAL LANDSCAPES

MATERIALS

Lens stereoscope (plastic), red/blue 3-D glasses, computer with Google Earth™ software and Internet access.

OBJECTIVES

1. Learn the four most recent stages of glaciation.
2. Describe the unique ways that ice alters landscapes through erosion and deposition.
3. Recognize specific glacial landforms shown on maps and air photos.
4. Identify the different types of glacier.
5. Recognize the effects of climate change on glacial systems.

INTRODUCTION

Glaciers are masses of ice that under the influence of gravity flow out from the snowfields where they originate. Much of North America, Europe, parts of northern Asia, and southern South America were covered by enormous ***continental ice sheets*** during the ***Pleistocene Epoch***. Ice sheets, which are continental in size, may cover millions of square miles and be up to 4 miles thick. Only the Greenland and Antarctic Ice Sheets remain today. ***Ice caps*** and ***ice fields*** drape mountainous regions or occur at very high latitude; they are tens of thousands of square miles in area. ***Outlet valley glaciers*** form where an ice sheet, ice cap or ice field spills ice into an adjacent valley. ***Cirque*** and ***alpine valley glaciers*** occupy stream valleys and are not fed by larger masses of ice. They vary from one to a few hundred square miles in area and are 100-200 feet thick. As cirque glaciers grow in size as the snowline falls, they extend down valley and become ***alpine valley glaciers. Piedmont glaciers*** form where a valley glacier passes from a restricted trough to a more open lowland and then spreads out. If an alpine glacier or a section of an ice sheet reaches the sea, this section is called a ***tidal glacier***. Large pieces of the tidal glacier may break off in a process known as ***calving***, creating ***icebergs***.

The loss of snow and ice from a glacier as a result of melting, wind action, or sublimation, is called ***ablation***. The addition of snow and ice to a glacier is called ***accumulation***. The ***zone of accumulation*** of an alpine glacier occurs at higher elevations where all of the winter snow does not melt during the summer months. At lower elevations is the ***zone of ablation***, where all the winter snow and some of the underlying glacial ice melts during the summer months. Between these two zones, the ***firn line*** defines the line along which all of the winter snow melts but none of the underlying glacial ice melts (Fig. 10.1). Glaciers are composed of three types of frozen water, snow, ***firn*** (compacted snow but not yet ice), and glacial ice. If the loss of snow and ice from the ablation zone is balanced by an equal amount of flow of ice from the accumulation zone, then the ***snout*** of the glacier neither advances nor retreats. An increase in accumulation over ablation causes the snout to advance, while a decrease in accumulation compared to ablation causes it to retreat. As the glacier moves downvalley, the flow rate is not constant everywhere. Surface ice in the center of the glacier moves faster than ice at the margins or base of the glacier due to higher friction between ice and bedrock in these last two locations. In addition, some sections of a glacier may move more quickly than nearby sections because of differences in friction due to irregularities in the valley walls and floor. These differences in flow rate create fissures or ***crevasses*** in the upper brittle part of the glacier. In valley glaciers, ***marginal crevasses*** open up because of friction between the glacier and the valley walls, while ***transverse crevasses*** form across a glacier because of increased flow rates towards the glacier snout. ***Longitudinal crevasses*** run approximately parallel to the direction of flow of the glacier and form because the glacier widens and cracks as the valley increases in size downvalley. Near the snouts of valley glaciers, longitudinal crevasses transition into ***radial crevasses*** as the ice thins and spreads out into a lobe.

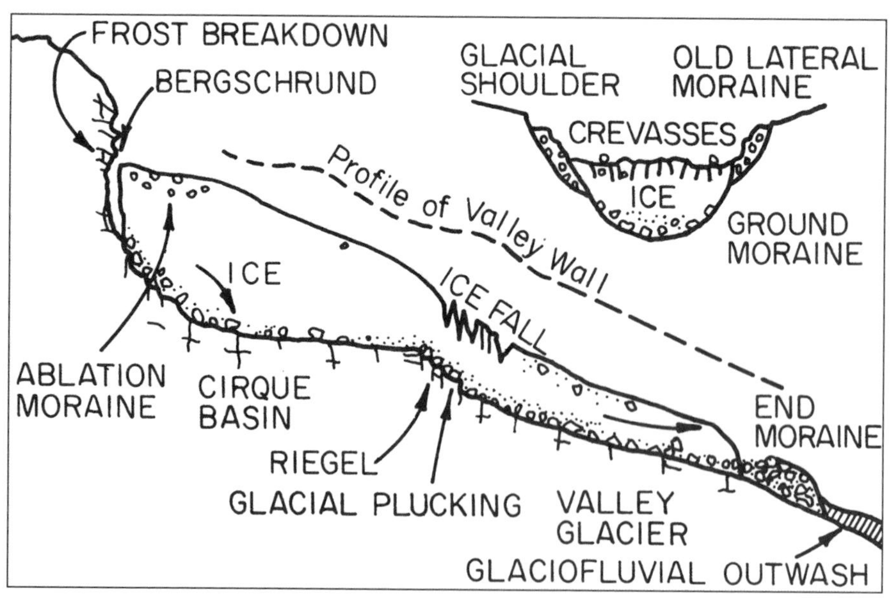

Fig. 10.1 Characteristics of the alpine valley glacier.

Glaciers erode and also deposit sediment on the areas they cover. Glacial erosion occurs primarily by ***abrasion*** and ***plucking***. Abrasion will smooth rock surfaces creating a ***glacial polish*** while at the same time scratching the rock surface along the direction of flow with the formation of ***striations***. ***Plucking*** occurs where ice moves over uneven terrain and freezes onto the bedrock pulling pieces of bedrock away as it moves. By abrasion and plucking, alpine glaciers scour out stream valleys changing them from V-shaped features in cross section to U-shaped valleys called ***glacial troughs***. Plucking and abrasion by continental glaciers may form hills called ***roche moutonnées*** that are asymmetrical in long section. The material transported by a glacier and subsequently deposited, the ***glacial drift*** or ***glacial till***, varies in thickness and composition. It is an unsorted mixture of soil, rocks, and boulders. ***Stratified drift*** consists mainly of sand and silt carried by ice that has been reworked by meltwater streams. Such deposits are known as ***glaciofluvial deposits***. ***Ground***, ***terminal***, ***medial***, and ***lateral moraines*** are common depositional features of glaciated terrain.

SECTION 1: Alpine Glaciers

Alpine or mountain glaciers create both erosional and depositional landforms. The glacial trough is ubiquitous in glaciated alpine areas. During ice ages, when the sea level was much lower, valley glaciers cut troughs below present sea level. When the glacial period ended rising sea level flooded the troughs to form inlets of the sea called ***fjords*** with almost vertical walls. In mountainous areas outlet and alpine glaciers in the main valleys erode much deeper troughs than smaller glaciers in the tributary valleys. After the glaciers melt, the floors of the tributary valleys are left high above the floors of the main valleys leaving a series of ***hanging valleys*** in the landscape. Where alternating layers of hard and soft rock are exposed, valley floors are deepened unevenly, forming ***rock basins*** or ***rock steps***. After the valley glaciers melt, a series of such basins may form a string of lakes called ***paternoster lakes***. In the highest parts of mountain valleys scouring by cirque glaciers has left bowl-shaped depressions called ***cirques***. The floors of these depressions are frequently occupied by lakes or ***tarns*** after the glacier melts. Several cirque glaciers on the same mountain may erode the mountain peak into a pyramid shape or glacial ***horn***, and the area between the cirques is often carved into steep-sided, knife-edge ridges called ***arêtes***.

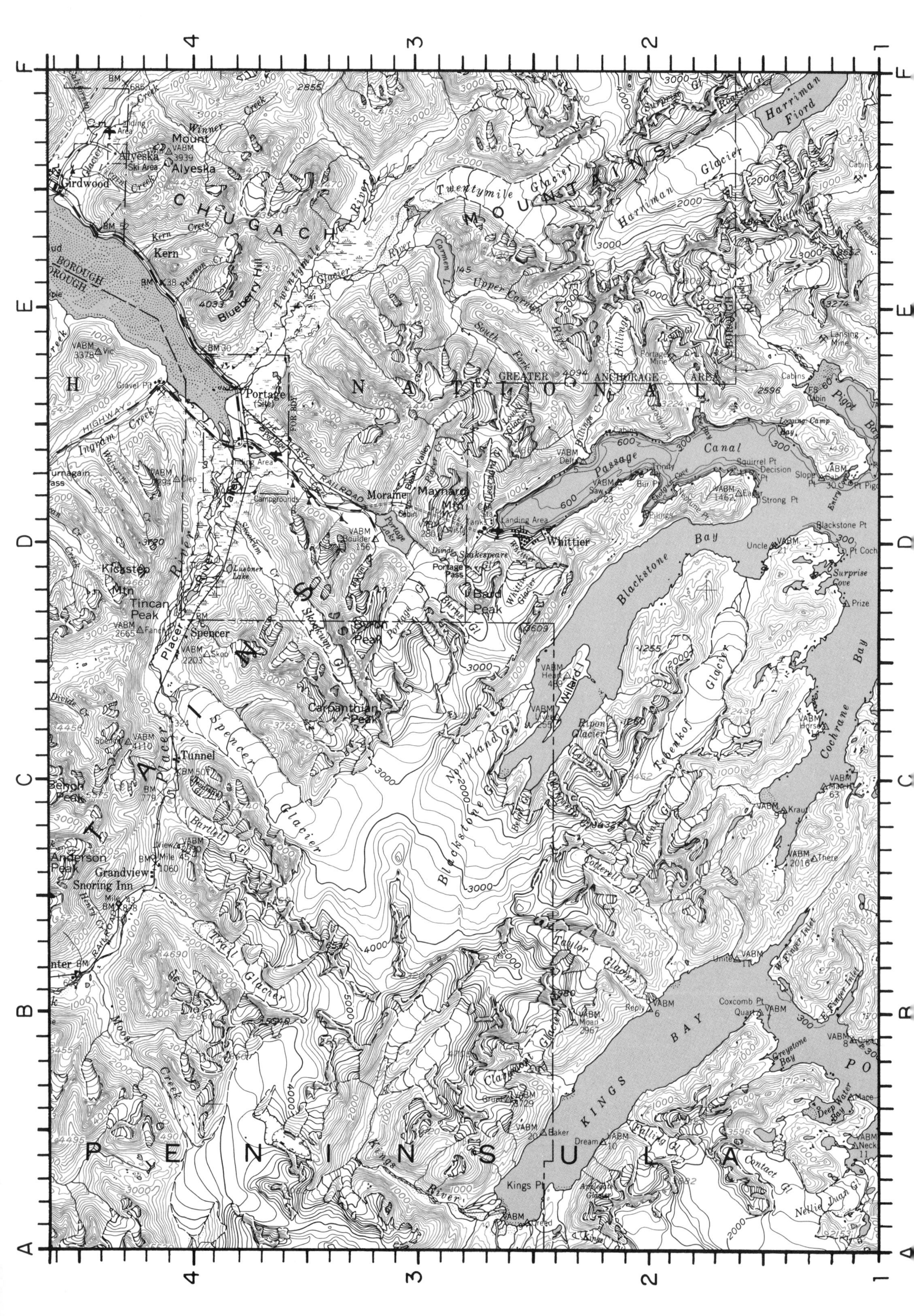

Girdwood
Mount Alyeska
Alyeska Ski Area
Winner Creek
CHUGACH
MOUNTAINS
Kern
Kern Creek
Peterson Cr
Blueberry Hill
Twentymile River
Twentymile Glacier
Harriman Glacier
Harriman Fiord
Surprise Gl
Roaring Gl
Carmen L
Upper Carmen
South Fork
Billings Gl
Portage Mine
Lansing Mine
GREATER ANCHORAGE AREA
BOROUGH
Portage (Site)
HIGHWAY
Ingram Creek
Wolverine
Turnagain Pass
NATIONAL
ALASKA RAILROAD
Landing Area
Campgrounds
Moraine
Maynard Mtn
Portage Lake
Whittier
Portage Pass
Shakespeare Gl
Bard Peak
Whittier Glacier
Passage Canal
Pigot Bay
Logging Camp Bay
Squirrel Pt
Decision Pt
Trinity
Bur Pt
Shotgun Cove
Emerald Cove
Strong Pt
Blackstone Pt
Blackstone Bay
Uncle
Pt Cochrane
Surprise Cove
Prize
Cochrane Bay
Kickstep Mtn
Tincan Peak
Luebner Lake
Shakwak
Placer River
Spencer
Byron Peak
Burns Gl
Willard I
Carpathian Peak
Spencer Glacier
Tunnel
Bench Peak
Bartlett Gl
Blackstone Gl
Northland Gl
Ripon Glacier
Tebenkof Glacier
Anderson Peak
Grandview
Snoring Inn
Taylor Glacier
Trail Glacier
Center
Cotterell Gl
Coxcomb Pt
Reply
KINGS BAY
Greystone Bay
Deep Water Bay
Kings River
Kings Pt
Falling Gl
Contact Gl
Nellie Juan Gl
PENINSULA
Moose Creek
Claremont Gl
Baker
Dream
W Finger Inlet
E Finger Inlet
Kraut
There

QUESTIONS

10.1 Examine Fig. 10.2 which shows a portion of the Seward area of Alaska. Also look at a Google Earth™ satellite image of this area using both the vertical and oblique viewing options. You can obtain an image by typing the following coordinates in the search box: 60° 42′ 19.34″ N, 148° 38′ 31.37″ W. Start viewing from an Eye alt of 30 miles and zoom in as needed.

(a) Identify the following features and give their grid coordinates:

Alpine Valley Glacier________________ Cirque Glacier________________

Ice-free Cirque Basin ________________ Tarn ________________

Aréte________________ Glacial Horn ________________

Glacial Trough ________________ Hanging Valley ________________

Fjord________________ Meltwater Stream ________________

(b) Explain the existence of Carmen Lake (E.2-2.9) in Fig. 10.2. What events led to its development?

You can view the lake on a recent Google Earth™ satellite image by typing the following coordinates in the search box: 60° 54′ 29.95″ N 148° 46′ 07.94″ W.

(c) Compare the topographic map of the Seward area (published in 1953) with the recent Google Earth™ image. Have any of the glaciers increased or decreased in size and by how much? What do you think might have caused the changes that you observe?

Opposite Page: Fig. 10.2 Seward, Alaska (1:250,000, A.0-1.0 in southeast corner).

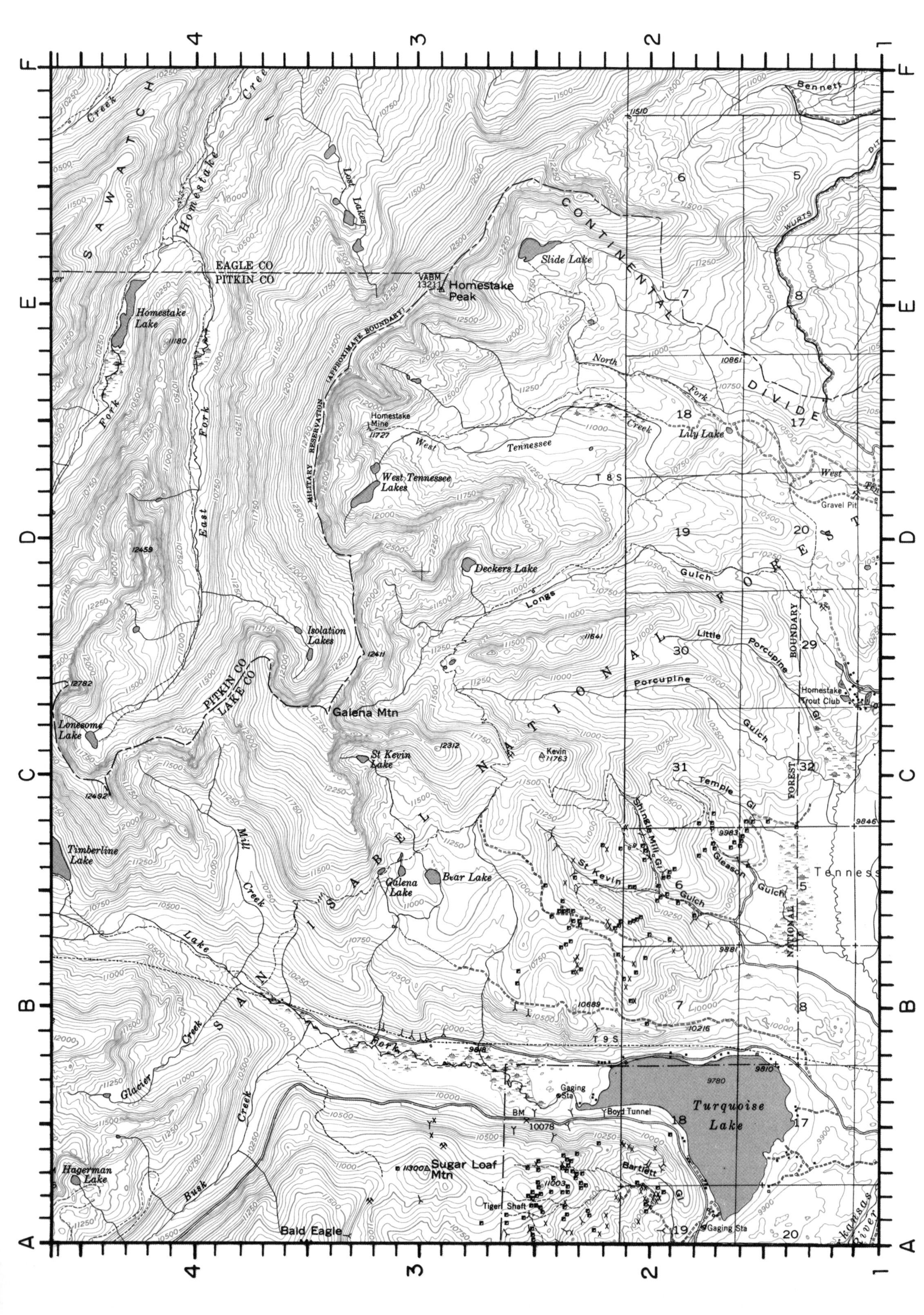

EAGLE CO
PITKIN CO
SAWATCH
Homestake Creek
Lost Lakes
VABM 13211
Homestake Peak
Slide Lake
CONTINENTAL DIVIDE
Homestake Lake
East Fork
MILITARY RESERVATION (APPROXIMATE BOUNDARY)
Homestake Mine 11727
North Fork
West Tennessee Creek
Lily Lake
West Tennessee Lakes
T 8 S
Gravel Pit
Deckers Lake
Longs Gulch
Isolation Lakes
Little Porcupine
Porcupine Gulch
PITKIN CO
LAKE CO
Homestake Trout Club
FOREST BOUNDARY
Lonesome Lake
Galena Mtn
St Kevin Lake
Kevin 11763
Temple Gl
SAN ISABEL NATIONAL FOREST
Timberline Lake
Mill Creek
Shingle Mill Gl
St Kevin Gulch
Gleason Gulch
Tennessee
Galena Lake
Bear Lake
Lake Fork
Glacier Creek
Busk Creek
T 9 S
Gaging Sta
Boyd Tunnel
BM 10078
Turquoise Lake
Sugar Loaf Mtn
Bartlett Gl
Hagerman Lake
Tiger Shaft
Bald Eagle
Arkansas River
Bennett
WURTS DITCH

10.2 The Holy Cross area of Colorado shown in Fig. 10.3 can be viewed using Google Earth™ by typing the following coordinates in the search box: 39° 19′ 29.73″ N, 106° 23′ 29.57″ W. Start viewing from an Eye alt of 20 miles and use both the vertical and oblique viewing options for best understanding. This area has no glaciers today but there is abundant evidence of glaciers in the past. Use Fig. 10.2 and the satellite image to answer the following questions.

(a) Identify the following features and give their grid coordinates:

Terminal Moraine____________________ Cirque ____________________

Paternoster Lakes____________________ Tarn ____________________

Glacial Trough ____________________ Rock Basin ____________________

(b) Do you think the area was glaciated by alpine or by continental glaciers? Explain your answer.

(c) Explain the steep walls and flat floor of Lake Fork Valley (A.8-3.0). What glacial feature is this? How has Turquoise Lake changed since 1949 (published date of the topographic map) when compared to a recent Google Earth™ image. If you see changes, determine if they are natural or if humans played a role?

Opposite Page: Fig. 10.3 Holy Cross, Colorado (1:62,500, A.0-1.0 in southeast corner).

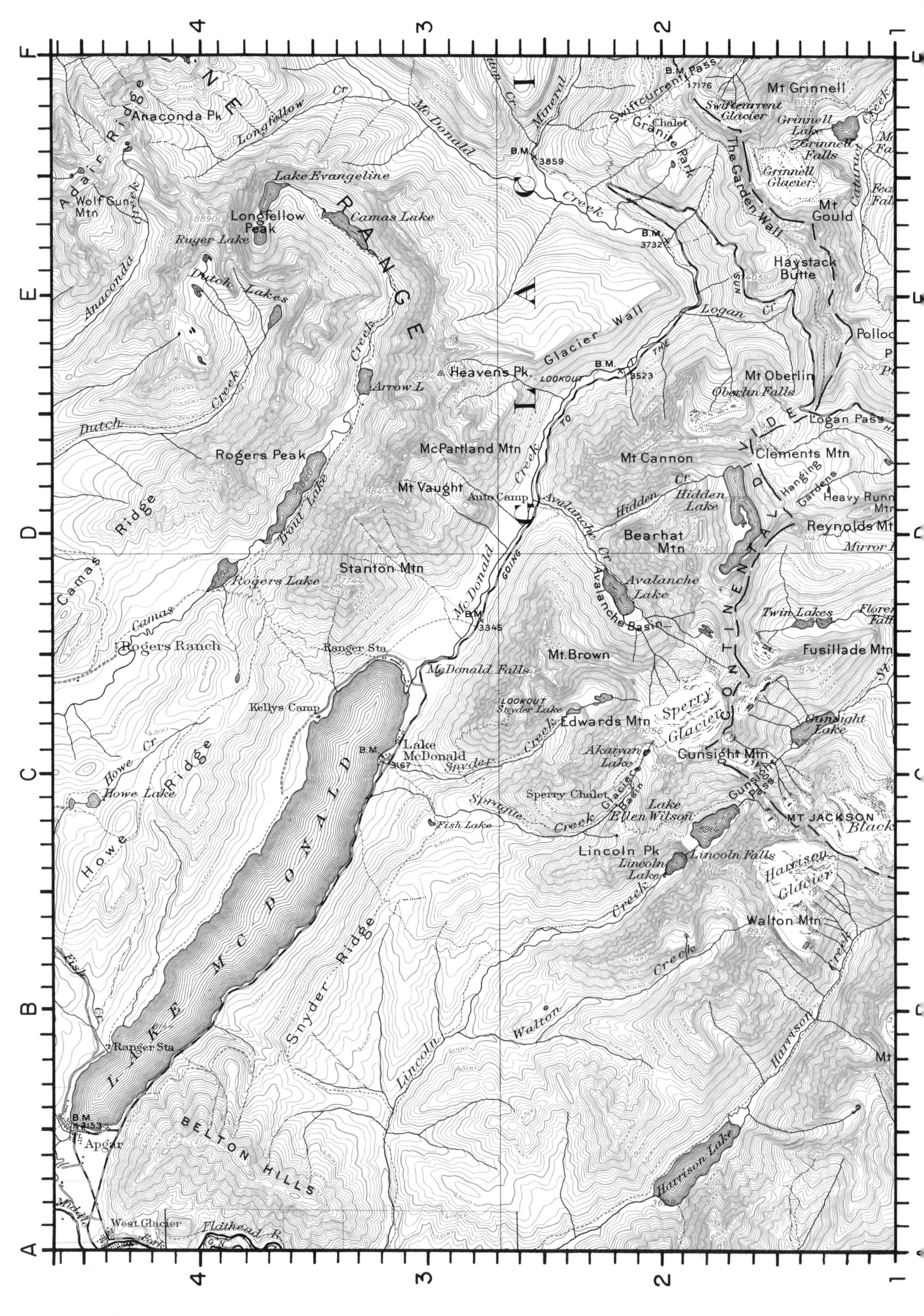

Anaconda Pk
Adair Ridge
Wolf Gun Mtn
Lake Evangeline
Longfellow Peak
Camas Lake
Ruger Lake
Dutch Lakes
Longfellow Cr
McDonald Creek
Mineral Cr
Swiftcurrent Pass
Swiftcurrent Glacier
Mt Grinnell
Grinnell Lake
Grinnell Falls
Grinnell Glacier
Granite Park
Chalet
The Garden Wall
Mt Gould
Haystack Butte
Logan Cr
Glacier Wall
Heavens Pk.
Arrow L
Mt Oberlin
Oberlin Falls
Logan Pass
Clements Mtn
Hanging Gardens
Heavy Runner Mtn
Reynolds Mtn
McPartland Mtn
Mt Cannon
Mt Vaught
Auto Camp
Hidden Cr
Hidden Lake
Rogers Peak
Trout Lake
Dutch Creek
Ridge
Camas Creek
Rogers Lake
Stanton Mtn
Bearhat Mtn
Avalanche Cr
Avalanche Lake
Avalanche Basin
Twin Lakes
Fusillade Mtn
Rogers Ranch
Ranger Sta
Mt. Brown
McDonald Falls
Kellys Camp
Snyder Lake
Edwards Mtn
Sperry Glacier
Gunsight Lake
Gunsight Mtn
Gunsight Pass
Lake McDonald
Akaiyan Lake
Howe Cr
Howe Lake
Howe Ridge
Snyder Creek
Sprague Creek
Sperry Chalet
Glacier Basin
Lake Ellen Wilson
MT JACKSON
Fish Lake
Lincoln Pk
Lincoln Lake
Lincoln Falls
Harrison Glacier
Walton Mtn
LAKE McDONALD
Snyder Ridge
Lincoln Creek
Walton Creek
Harrison Creek
Harrison Lake
Apgar
BELTON HILLS
West Glacier
Flathead R.
GLACIER
LEWIS RANGE
CONTINENTAL DIVIDE
GOING TO THE SUN HIGHWAY
B.M. 3859
B.M. 3732
B.M. 3523
B.M. 3345
B.M. 3153
A B C D E F
1 2 3 4

10.3 There are alpine glaciers in Glacier National Park, Montana, today but there is convincing evidence of much more extensive glaciation in the past. Use Fig. 10.4 and a recent Google Earth™ satellite image to answer the following questions. You can locate an image by typing the following coordinates in the Google Earth™ search box: 48° 36′ 14.14″ N 113° 46′ 06.79″ W. Start viewing from an Eye alt of 20 miles and zoom in and out to see detail.

(a) Explain the shape of Lake McDonald (B.5-3.7) and describe the events that led to its development.

(b) Locate Sperry Glacier on a recent Google Earth™ image and on the topographic map published 1938. How has the glacier changed and why? Do you see any changes in the sizes and shapes of other glaciers in the area? Explain. You can obtain a Google Earth™ image by typing the following coordinates in the search box: 48° 37′ 23.73″ N 113° 45′ 25.41″ W. Start by viewing from an Eye alt of 20,000 feet and use the zoom option to see more detail of specific features. Examine the glacier using both the vertical and oblique options in Google Earth™ as this will give you the best understanding of the landscape.

Opposite Page: Fig. 10.4 Chief Mountain, Montana (1:125,000, A.0-1.0 in southeast corner).

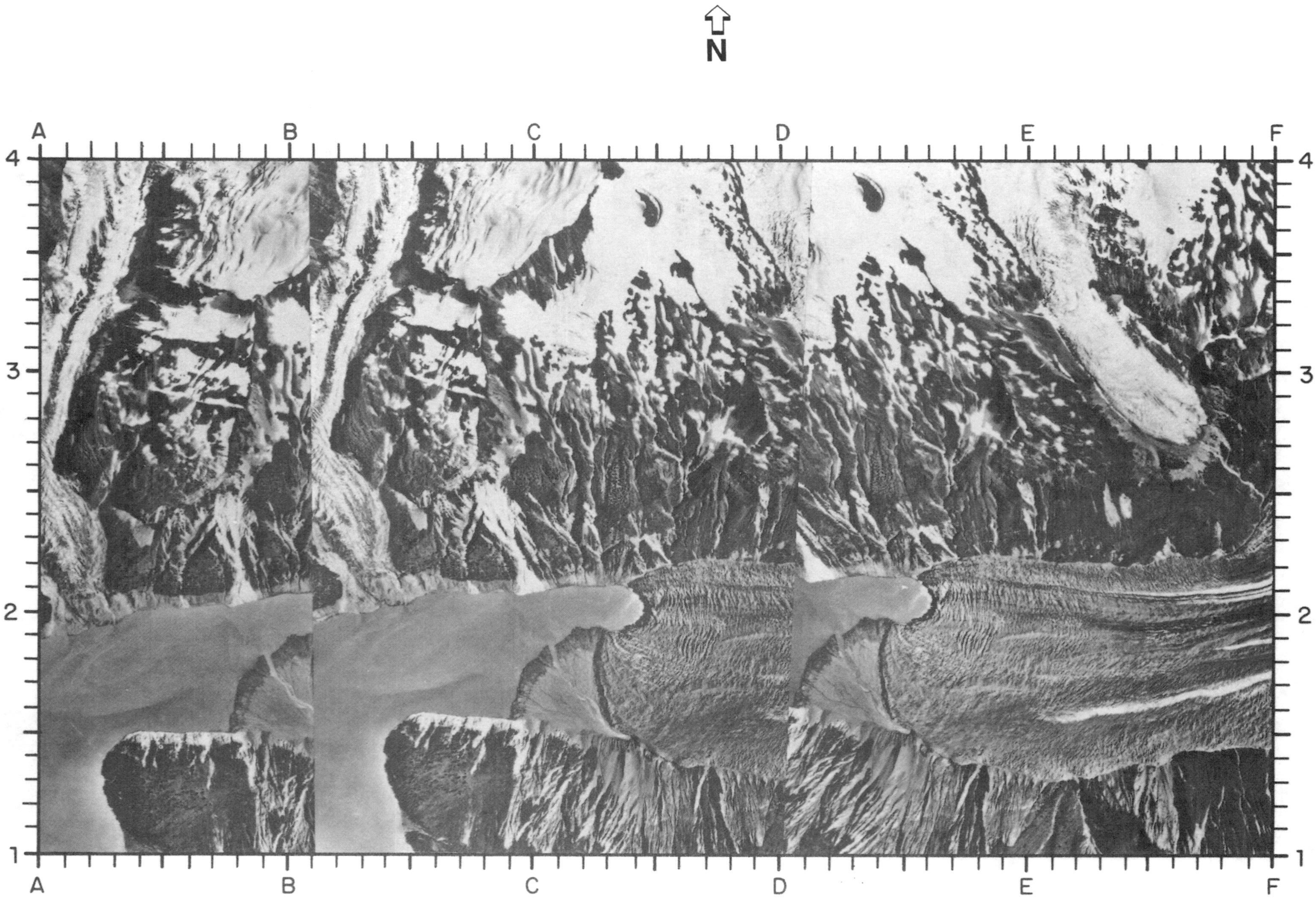

Fig. 10.5 Crillon Glacier, Alaska (1:35,500, A.0-1.0 in southwest corner).

10.4 Fig. 10.5 and 3-D anaglyphs 17 and 18 in Appendix D show Crillon Glacier where it flows into Lituya Bay, one of many Alaskan fjords. Look at these figures and also a recent Google Earth™ satellite image and then answer the questions below. You can obtain a satellite image by typing the following coordinates in the Google Earth™ search box: 58° 39′ 31.74″ N, 137° 28′ 15.11″ W. Start with an Eye alt of 25,000 feet and zoom in and out for the best views. Also, use the oblique viewing option to really get a feel for the characteristics of the glacier.

(a) Identify the following features and give their grid coordinates:

Lateral Moraine____________________ Medial Moraine ____________________

Marginal Crevasse____________________ Transverse Crevasse ____________________

Glacial Snout ____________________ Hanging Valley ____________________

(b) What is the feature at the terminus or snout of the glacier (C.1-1.6) and how was it formed?

(c) Compare the Fig. 10.5 (taken in 1959) and its 3-D anaglyphs, with a recent Google Earth™ satellite image. Have there been any changes in the extent of the Crillon Glacier? For example, has the terminus of the glacier advanced or retreated? Why is the glacier a dark brown color in the **Google Earth**™ image instead of white in the aerial photos?

SECTION 2: Continental Ice Sheets

Continental ice sheets, like valley glaciers, erode and deposit rock and soil. Massive ice sheets can be up to a half mile thick at their edges and act like giant bulldozers as the move across the surface, greatly changing the landscape. The key indicator of how far south continental glaciers advanced in North America and Europe during the last glacial period is the location of terminal moraines. These ridges of glacial till can be several hundred feet high and stretch for hundreds of miles. ***Kame*** and ***kettle topography***, which develops behind terminal moraines, is also typical of areas once covered by ice sheets. ***Kettles*** or ***kettle holes*** are formed when large blocks of the ice are incorporated into ground moraine as the ice sheet melts. The eventual melting of these blocks forms depressions that may fill with water to form ***kettle lakes.*** In contrast, ***kames*** are mounds or glacial drift left after the ice retreats. The drift accumulates in crevasses within the ice and is deposited on the landscape as the ice melts. Glacial drift or till beneath ice may also be molded by the forces of flow. Elliptical, aerodynamic-shaped mounds may be produced called ***drumlins*** that may be preserved after the ice that shaped them melts. These can indicate the direction of glacier flow, which is parallel to the long axis of the drumlin in the direction of its tail. It is common for dozens of drumlins to be found in the same area in what is known as a ***drumlin field.*** Clay,silt, sand and gravel are often carried beyond the terminus of a glacier by ***meltwater streams*** to produce fluvio-glacial features. These include ***outwash plains*** along valleys and ***deltas*** deposited in ***proglacial*** lakes. ***Subglacial meltwater streams*** flow beneath glaciers in ice tunnels produced when the "warm" stream waters melt the ice. These tunnels may eventually fill up with sand and gravel and when the ice retreats, these deposits are left as sinuous ridges called ***eskers*** (see anaglyph 19 in Appendix D).

QUESTIONS

10.5 Fig. 10.6 is a view of Taylor Dry Valley in Antarctica. The ice plateau in the background is the Antarctic Ice Sheet. The upper portion of Taylor Valley is occupied by the snout of Taylor Glacier and beyond the ice is the permanently ice-covered Lake Bonney. Also look at a satellite image of the area and then answer the questions below. You can obtain a satellite image by typing the following coordinates in the Google Earth™ search box: 77° 41′ 37.15″ S, 162° 17′ 01.01″ E. View initially from an Eye alt of 50 miles and use the oblique viewing option for the best scenes.

(a) Identify and label the following features on the photograph.

A Piedmont Glacier

B Outlet Valley Glacier

C Glacial Trough

D Hanging Valley

E Longitudinal Crevasses

(b) Using a Google Earth™ satellite image and the Panoramio pictures attached to the image; explain what a dry valley is and how they may develop. Also, is Taylor Valley near the coast of Antarctica or is it inland?

Fig. 10.6 Taylor Glacier, Taylor dry valley, Victoria Land, Antarctica

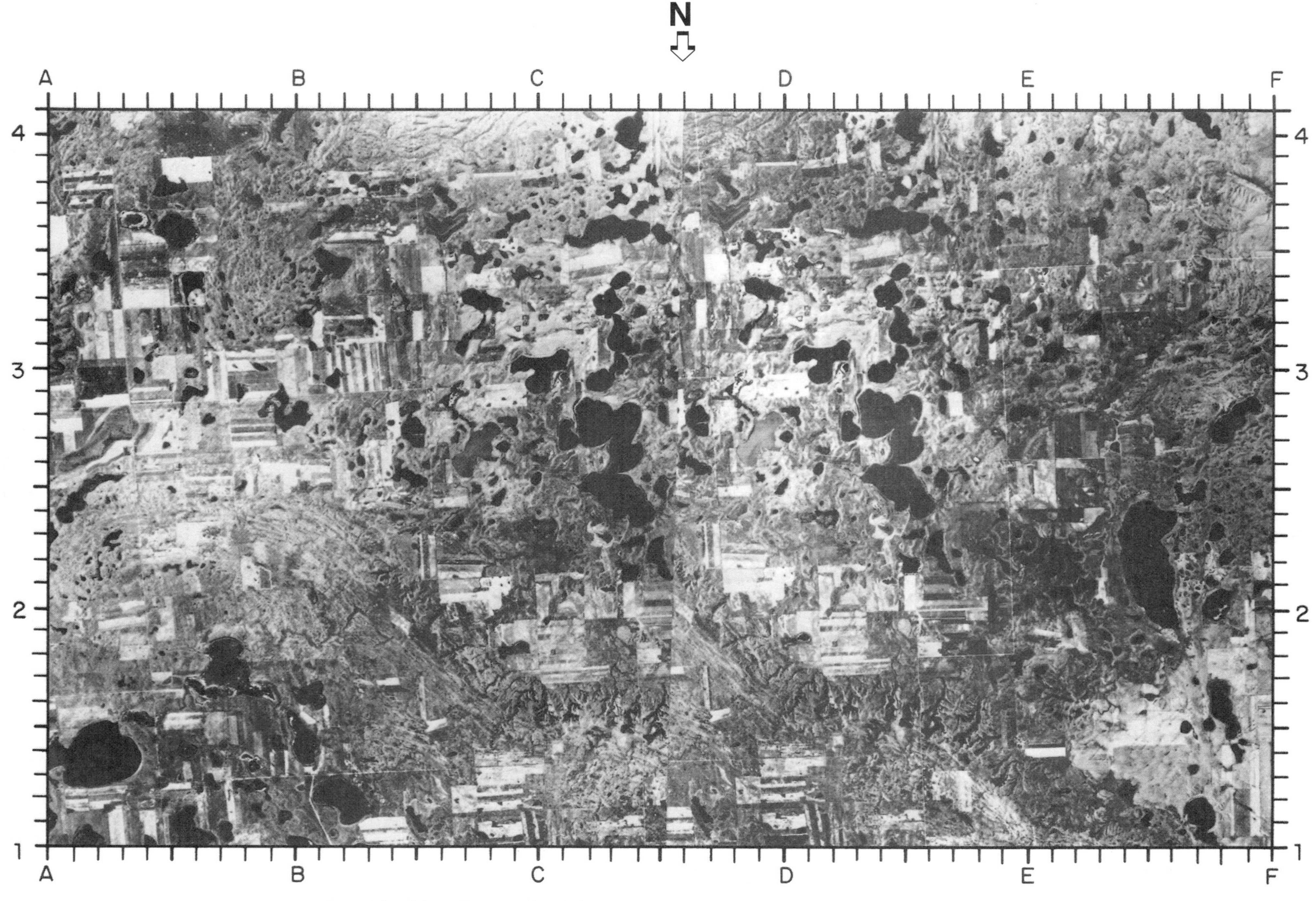

Fig. 10.7 Kidder County, North Dakota (1:80,600, A.0-1.0 in northeast corner).

10.6 Fig. 10.7 and 3-D anaglyph 20 in Appendix D show an area of kame and kettle topography in Kidder County, North Dakota. Examine a satellite image of this area by typing the following coordinates in the Google Earth™ search box: 47° 14′ 35.18″ N, 99° 36′ 03.93″ W. View initially from an Eye alt of 10 miles and zoon in and out to examine the features more closely.

(a) Identify the following features and give their grid coordinates:

Dry Kettle Hole__________________ Kettle lake__________________

Terminal Moraine __________________ Kame __________________

(b) On the Google Earth™ satellite image, zoom out to a higher Eye alt and examine the area. Has this area changed in any way since 1952 (the year the photo in Fig. 10.7 was taken)? Explain your answer.

10.7 Fig. 10.8 and 3-D anaglyphs 21 and 22 in Appendix D show a drumlin field in Fond du Lac County, Wisconsin. Some drumlins are easy to see because of the way the farmers have plowed their fields around them. Look at this on a satellite image by typing the following coordinates in the Google Earth™ search box: 43° 49′ 40.93″N, 88° 16′ 40.70″ W. View initially from an Eye alt of 22,000 feet and zoom in as needed to see more detail. You can obtain outstanding views of the drumlins by viewing them using the Google Earth™ oblique viewing option and experimenting with your direction of view.

(a) Give the grid coordinates of at least two different drumlins visible on Fig. 10.8 and determine which direction the ice was moving when it molded these feature beneath it.

(b) Using a Google Earth™ satellite image, examine nearby areas. Can you see other drumlin fields? Do the long axes of these drumlins confirm the answer you gave to question (a)? What other indications of glacial activity can you see?

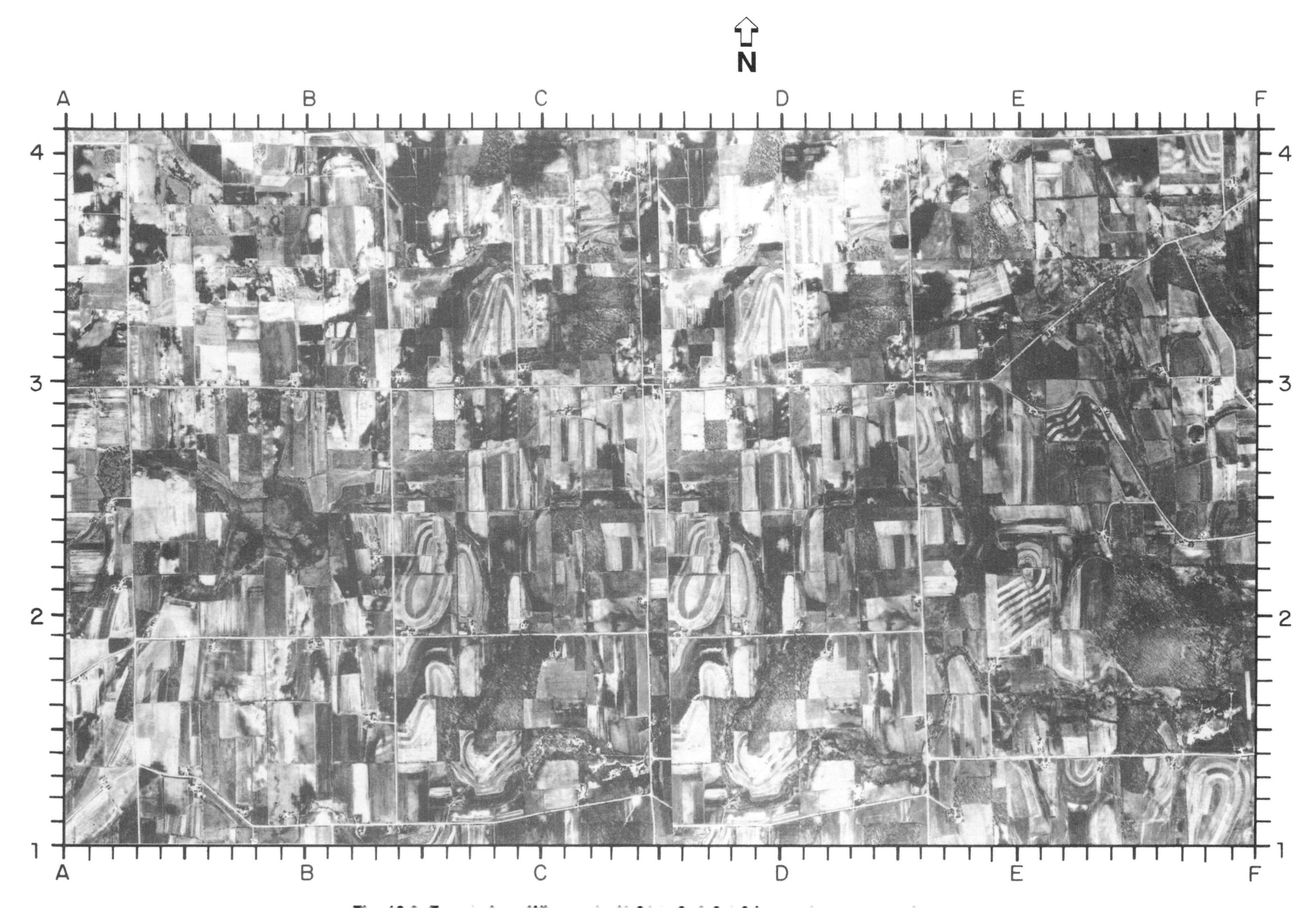

N
A
B
C
D
E
F
4
3
2
1

SECTION #3: Climate Change and Glaciation

The Earth has experienced several periods when temperatures cooled enough to allow the development of large continental ice sheets. The earliest glacial period dates to about 2.3 billion years before present (YBP). The most recent occurred during the Pleistocene Epoch, or "Great Ice Age", and began approximately 1.8 million YBP, and ended approximately 10,000 YBP (Refer to the USGS Geologic Time Scale on the inside back cover). During this time there were several phases of glacier growth, or ***stadials***, when the Earth's average temperature cooled allowing glaciers to expand, and ***interglacial periods*** when the climate warmed to that of the present day or warmer, and the continental ice sheets retreated (Table 10.1). There were also numerous periods that were warmer than stadials but colder than interglacials; these are called ***interstadials***. There are to changes in the amount of sunlight received by the Earth. For a glacial period to begin, the Earth's average temperature of 15°C (59°F) had to drop by 3 to 5°C and stay at this temperature for thousands of years.

Most scientists support the ***astronomical theory of climate change*** proposed by ***Milankovitch***. This theory argues that cyclical changes in the geometrical relationship between the Earth and Sun determine the amount and distribution of solar energy reaching the Earth's surface, and thus its temperature. The principal cycles involve ***eccentricity of the Earth's orbit around the Sun, the obliquity or tilt of the Earth's axis***, and ***axial precession or wobble***. *Eccentricity* is a measure of the shape of the Earth's orbit around the Sun. This orbit varies from being nearly circular (low eccentricity) to being mildly elliptical (high eccentricity) and back to being nearly circular with a periodicity of around 100,000 year. Obliquity is the angle of the Earth's axial tilt with respect to the plane of the Earth's orbit. This varies from 22.1° and 24.5° and back again with a periodicity of approximately 41,000 years. Precession, with a period of roughly 26,000 years, is the trend in the direction of the Earth's axis of rotation relative to the fixed stars. This gyroscopic motion or wobble is due to the tidal forces exerted by the sun and the moon on the solid Earth.

Human activities may also play a role in climate change. Burning of ***fossil fuels***, including coal, oil, and natural gas, releases ***carbon dioxide*** into the atmosphere. Carbon dioxide and methane are ***greenhouse gases*** that reflect the radiation emitted by the Earth, essentially trapping it in the atmosphere. This ***greenhouse effect*** increases the Earth's temperature by trapping heat that otherwise would escape to outer space. Studies of ice cores from both Antarctica and Greenland, and sampling of the atmosphere, have shown an increase in the levels of both of these Greenhouse gases over the past 200 years, compared to the previous 125,000 years.

Table 10.1 Approximate timing of glacial and interglacial phases during the late Pleistocene.

AGE (10^3 YBP)	PHASE NAME
Present - 12	Holocene Interglacial
12 - 75	Wisconsin Glacial
75 - 125	Sangamon Interglacial
125 - 265	Illinoian Glacial
265 - 300	Yarmouth Interglacial
300 - 435	Kansan Glacial
435 - 500	Aftonian Interglacial
>500	Nebraskan Glacial

10.8 The glacial deposits shown in Fig. 10.7 and 10.8 where laid down during various glacial advances. List the glacial period for each of the following dated deposits?

20,000 YBP ____________________ 350,000 YBP ____________________

10.9 The following web site, http://svs.gsfc.nasa.gov developed and maintained by the National Aeronautics and Space Administration (NASA), Goddard Space Flight Center, contains a short video on the effects of current climate change on Antarctic and Arctic ice coverage. Watch this video and answer the following questions. To watch the video, go to the URL above. From the menu on the left-hand side select + Imagery By ID Number. The video you are looking for is #3181, so on this next page click on 3100 to 3199 and then scroll down to 3181. Click on the tile, not the icon, and then scroll down to the picture and menu which reads, VIDEO WITH NARRATION AND NO CAPTIONS and select MPEG-1 199 MB to view the video. If audio is not available then select from the VIDEO WITH MUSIC AND CAPTIONS, MPEG-1 201 MB. You will need Quick Time or some similar software to run the video. It may take a few minutes to download and the video lasts about 7 minutes.

(a) What effect has climate warming had on the ice shelves of Antarctica, particularly the Larsen B Ice Shelf, and what effect has it had on the Greenland Ice Sheet?

(b) How has global warming affected the world's alpine glaciers?

(c) Why is the winter snow cover in the mountains of the western United States important to the region's water resources? How might global warming affect this situation?

(d) What is permafrost? How much of North America has permafrost and what may be happening to it as a result of global warming?

(e) How does ice in polar regions affect temperatures on Earth?

(f) How has global warming affected sea ice around the North Pole? Could the Arctic Ocean become ice-free in the summer during this century?

Student Name________________________________

Exercise 11

PERIGLACIAL LANDSCAPES

MATERIALS

Lens stereoscope (plastic), red/blue 3-D glasses, ruler, magnifying glass (helpful) computer with Google Earth™ software and Internet access.

OBJECTIVES

1. Understand what happens along the margins of continental ice sheets.
2. Recognize and explain the causes of periglacial patterned ground.
3. Understand and explain thermokarst landscapes.
4. Identify and explain the formation of pingos.

INTRODUCTION

In ***periglacial regions*** the freezing and thawing of water in soils and rocks is the dominant geomorphic process in landform development. These conditions exist in polar, sub-polar, and high alpine environments. The short summer thaw in these areas is frequently not sufficient to melt ground frozen during long winter months so that ***permafrost***, or permanently frozen ground, is common. Permafrost varies in thickness from a few feet to more than a thousand feet depending on the mean annual temperature at the surface and the geothermal gradient. The upper surface or limit of the permafrost layer is called the ***permafrost table***. Permafrost is classified as ***continuous*** if it extends beneath all topographic features in an area, ***discontinuous*** if it occurs in patches separated by relatively small areas of unfrozen ground or ***taliks***, and ***sporadic*** if it occurs in small patches separated by broad areas of unfrozen ground.

The layer of soil above the permafrost table is frozen most of the year, but thaws during the summer months. This is the ***active layer*** and it ranges from a few inches to tens of feet in thickness. In the fall season, ***cryostatic*** pressures build in the active layer as the soil refreezes from the surface down. Water trapped in the soil moves towards the ***freezing front*** and freezes as this front migrates unevenly downwards through the active layer. When this water freezes it expands approximately 9%, increasing the volume of the soil in the active layer and causing it to expand upwards in a process called ***frost heaving***. In addition, before the active layer is fully frozen it is not uncommon for ice to develop preferentially beneath stones because they have a higher thermal conductivity than the adjacent soil. This leads to the stones being pushed upwards by the growth of the ice under them resulting in large stones being gradually pushed upwards in the active layer each year. This sorting of the stones is called ***frost sorting*** and it can operate vertically or laterally depending upon the orientation of the freezing front. Many landforms in periglacial environments result from the seasonal freezing and thawing of the active layer and are broadly classified into those produced by the segregation of ice and those produced by thermal contraction. Typical forms include ice wedge polygons, pingos, and patterned ground.

SECTION 1: *Ice Wedge Polygons and Thermokarst*

Polygonal networks of ***thermal contraction cracks***, extending through the active layer into underlying permafrost, can develop when the temperature of ice-rich, frozen soil drops sufficiently for thermal contraction to take place. During the spring these cracks can fill with water that freezes in fall to form ***ice wedges.*** As freezing occurs, the water expands thus exerting pressure on the sediments bounded by the wedges. The wedges continue to grow after each melt season as more water enters the cracks that form in the winter months. As a result, the sediments bounded by the wedges are deformed more each year with the formation of ***ice wedge polygon*** relief. ***Low centered polygons*** are typical of the early stages of deformation as the growth of the ice wedges produces ridges around the margins of the sediment polygons enclosed by the ice wedges. As the centers of the polygons in these systems are lower than the margins they may contain standing water during the summer months (Fig. 11.1). In contrast, ***high centered polygons*** are a later form produced by the continued deformation of the sediment polygons and the expansion of the bounding ridges almost to the centers of the polygons. As a result, the polygon center is elevated and is surrounded by troughs aligned with the ice wedges. These troughs may contain water in summer and this can lead eventually to the degradation of the wedges.

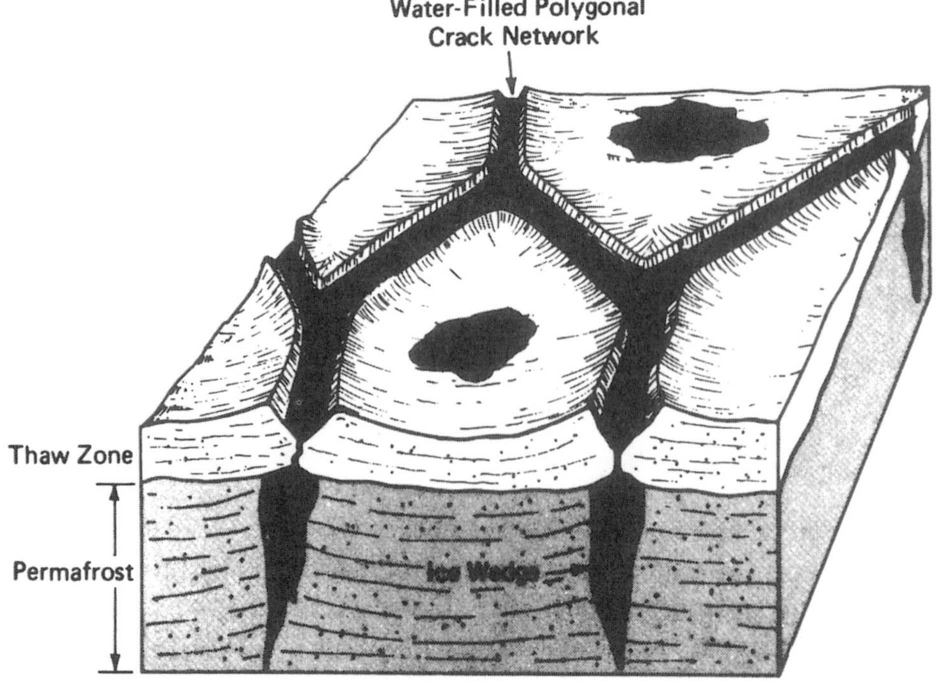

Fig. 11.1 Low centered ice-wedge polygons (from Butzer 1976).

A common landscape type in periglacial regions is ***thermokarst***, which is formed by the spatially uneven melting of ground ice. In some areas this produces an irregular, hummocky terrain as a result of ground subsidence, and ***thaw lakes*** develop in the depressions created. Thermokarst relief can develop due to an increase in depth of the active layer that can result from ground disturbance due to loss of vegetation. However, in the last several decades the rate of development of thermokarst has increased significantly presumably because of an overall warming of climate as a result of global warming.

QUESTIONS

11.1 The aerial photographs of Fig. 11.2 and 3-D anaglyph 23 in Appendix D, taken in the late 1950s, show periglacial forms developed in stratified silt and sand on the Arctic Coastal Plain near Point Barrow, Alaska. The area falls within the zone of continuous permafrost and an area of thermokarst topography. View a Google Earth™ satellite image of the area using the view direction, and vertical and oblique view options to gain a feel for what it is really like. You can locate an image by typing the following coordinates in the search box: 71° 14′ 29.06″ N, 156° 46′ 31.11″ W. View initially from an Eye alt of 16,000 feet and zoon in for greater detail.

(a) On Fig. 11.2, identify the following features and list their grid coordinates below.

Thaw lake __________________ Thaw lake basin (frozen) ____________________

Ice wedge polygons ____________________

(b) Explain why the shorelines of the thaw lakes are serrated. Consider conditions in summer versus winter.

(c) Examine the Google Earth™ satellite image of the Fig. 11.12 area starting with an Eye alt of 55–60 miles. Notice that the long axes of the numerous elongate-shaped thaw lakes in this region are approximately parallel. In which direction (N, S, E, and W) are the lakes oriented, and speculate on what may have caused this. Check the satellite image to see if there have been any changes to the area since the photos were taken in the late 1950s.

Next Page: Fig. 11.2 Point Barrow, Alaska (1:20,000, A.0-1.0 in southwest corner).

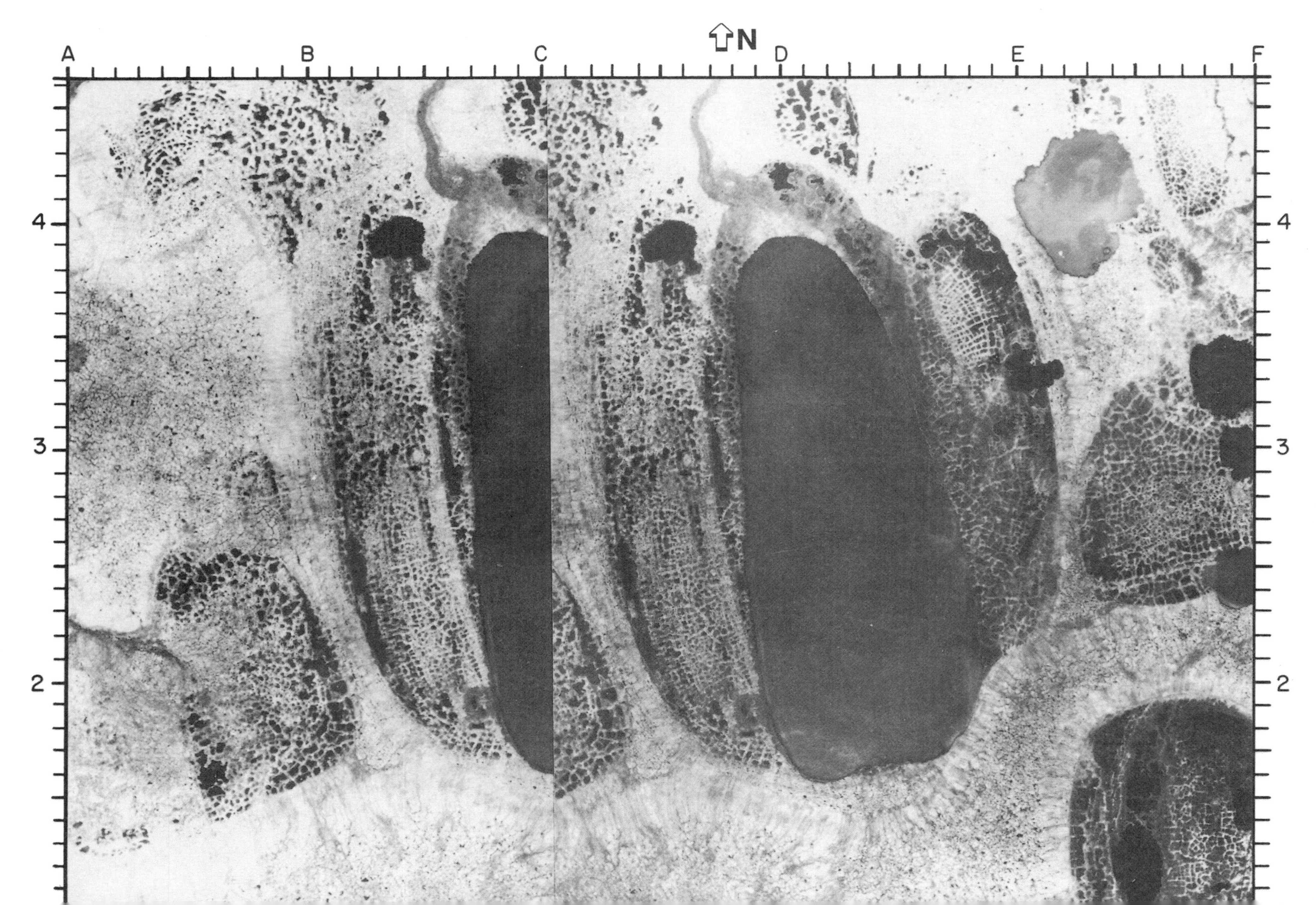
N
A
B
C
D
E
F
4
3
2

SECTION 2: Patterned Ground

Patterned ground is formed by a variety of processes including frost sorting, mechanical sorting, contraction cracking, and downslope movements. The main geometric forms recognized are circles, polygons, stripes, and nets, all of which may be sorted or unsorted. Contraction cracking creates polygonal forms while differential heaving causes circular forms. Stripes reflect the modifying influence of mass wasting processes upon circular and polygonal forms. ***Frost sorting*** of particles occurs because of the repeated freezing and thawing of the ground. When freezing occurs from the surface down, the larger particles move upwards, ***frost heaving***. When freezing occurs from the side, they move laterally, ***frost thrusting***. This lateral movement results in horizontal and vertical layers of different sized particles.

Movement occurs because stones have greater thermal conductivity than damp soil. Ice forms beneath a stone before it forms at the same depth in the nearby soil. Continued growth causes the stone to be moved upward or sideways toward the cooling front. **Mechanical sorting** also occurs where mounds are produced. Coarser particles move under the influence of gravity to form borders of coarser material. ***Stone circles*** develop in this way (Fig. 11.3). When bare rock is subjected to repeated freeze-thaw attack, the surface may become a mass of angular fragments which form a sea of rock or ***felsenmeer***.

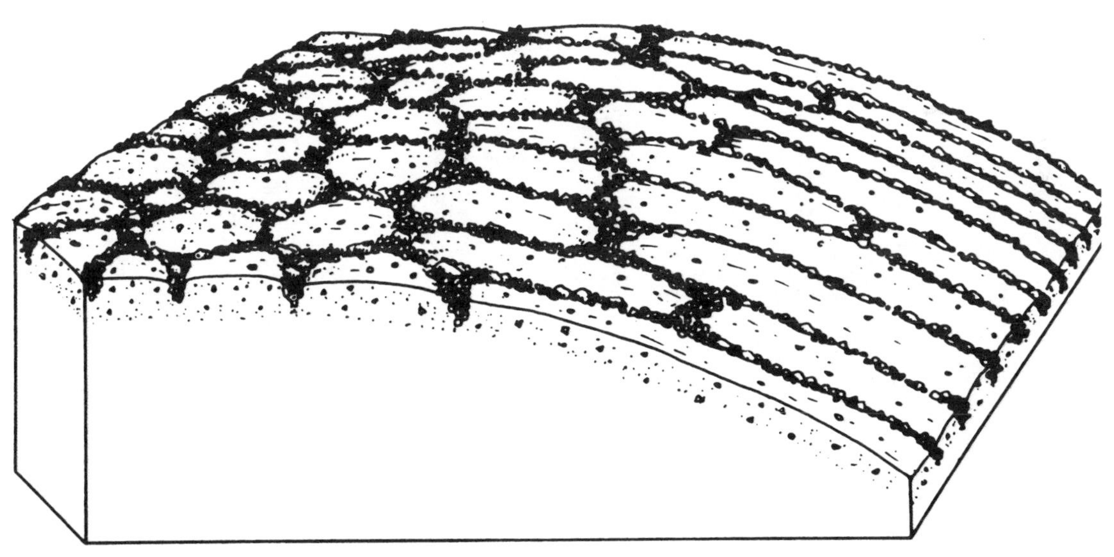

Fig. 11.3 Stone circles, garlands and stripes (from Sharpe 1938).

QUESTIONS

11.2 Remnants of the basaltic plateau to the north of King Hill, ID on the Snake River, as well as the undisturbed upper slopes are characterized by patterned ground phenomena (Fig. 7.3). Examine a Google Earth™ satellite image of this area by typing the following coordinates in the search box: 43° 01′ 44.32″ N, 115° 13′ 04.04″ W. View initially from an Eye alt of 15,000 feet but zoon in and out to gain clarity of the features. Answer the following questions.

(a) On Fig. 7.3 and the satellite image, identify areas of closely packed circular mounds, generally about 50 feet in diameter (around D.3-1.1 on Fig 7.3). To view these on the satellite image, look near 43° 02′ 45.92″ N, 115° 12′ 08.30″ W, from an Eye alt of 6,000 – 7,000 feet. Given that the present climate of this area is not a periglacial one, when could the patterned ground in this region have formed?

11.3 What periglacial features are visible in Fig. 11.4, 11.5, and 11.6?

Fig. 11.4 Periglacial landforms on Plateau Mountain, southern Canadian Rockies.

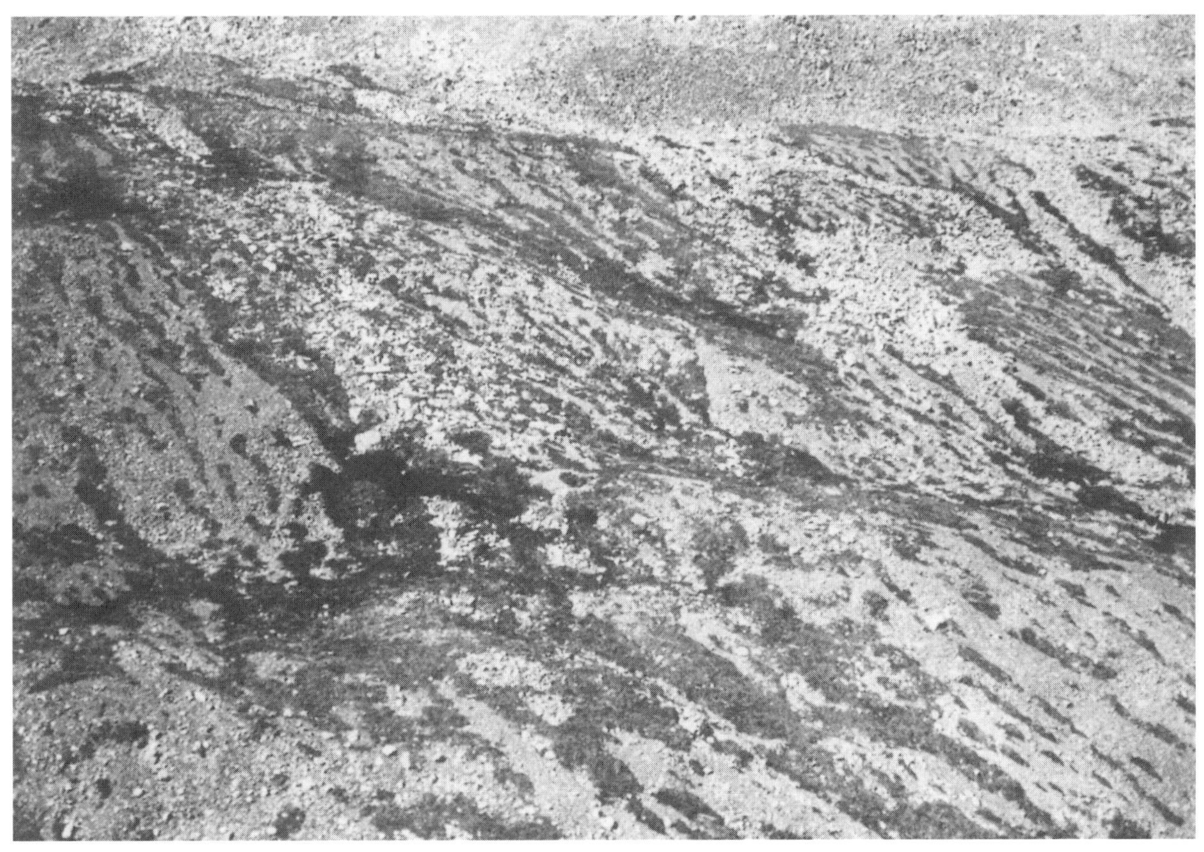

Fig. 11.5 Aerial view of tundra zone in the Mackenzie Mountains of Canada.

Fig. 11.6 Castleguard Meadow, southern Canadian Rockies.

SECTION 3: Pingos

Pingos are ice-cored hills that have formed by the growth of a lens of ice beneath the surface, which has domed upward the surface sediment layers. Pingos can rise more than 200 feet above the surrounding terrain and can survive for a few thousand years. Two basic types are recognized, ***open-system pingos*** and ***closed-system pingos***. Open-system pingos are most common in valley floors. They develop where groundwater in the valley sediments flows upward under hydrostatic pressure from beneath a thin permafrost layer and then freezes below the surface. The ice mass created continues to grow as more water flows towards it, elevating the overlying sediments to form a small dome. In contrast, closed-system pingos develop from small lakes in areas of permafrost when the lakes drain and the surface of the ground, previously kept above freezing by the lake water, freezes over. This freezing at the surface traps water between the frozen surface and the underlying permafrost. The water freezes forming a lens of ice that grows in size as freezing continues. Concentration of the water into an ice-rich lens, coupled with expansion as the water freezes, causes uplift of the ground and the formation of a small dome. Once the initial water trapped by surface freezing becomes part of the ice lens, the lens can grow no further as the system is closed, hence the name "closed system pingo". Closed system pingos are numerous in the Mackenzie River delta of northern Canada and in other arctic regions. Both types of pingo degrade when star-shaped cracks at the crests of the hills expose the buried ice to air, water, vegetation, and ultimately sunshine. This ultimately leads to melting of the ice core and destruction of the pingo.

QUESTIONS

11.4 View a Google Earth™ satellite image centered on coordinates 69° 23′ 59.30″ N, 133° 04′ 45.10″ W at an Eye alt of 5,000 feet. What type of pingo can you see and what other periglacial landforms are visible?

Student Name________________________________

Exercise 12

COASTAL LANDSCAPES

MATERIALS

Lens stereoscope (plastic), red/blue 3-D glasses, ruler, graph paper, calculator computer with Google Earth™ software and Internet access.

OBJECTIVES

1. Understand the forces involved in coastline development.
2. Differentiate between ***depositional*** and ***erosional*** coastal landforms.
3. Classify coastlines by characteristic features and by relative changes in sea level.

INTRODUCTION

Waves in the deep ocean are generated by wind and are produced by the oscillation of water molecules as energy travels through the water column. In fact, there is little or no lateral movement of water in these ***waves of oscillation*** as the energy passes. Waves can be described in terms of their height, wavelength, and period. ***Wave height*** is the vertical distance between the trough of the wave and its crest. It is controlled by ***wind velocity***, ***duration*** and by ***fetch***, which is the open stretch of water across which wind can generate waves. The **wavelength** is the horizontal distance between crests, measured perpendicular to the wave front. ***Wave period*** is the time during which two successive wave crests pass a fixed point. When waves move beyond their region of origin, they are referred to as ***swells***. As waves approach the shore, they begin to be affected by the ocean bottom or "feel bottom", which causes an increase in height and steepness. This can also affect wave length and period. At this point the waves are known as ***waves of translation***. As the wave front continues toward the shore, the wave crest continues to build in height and eventually cannot be supported and it collapses as a ***breaker***. On gently sloping shores such as a sandy beach, a thin sheet of water progresses up the beach after the breaker collapses; this is known as the ***swash***. As this sheet of water returns to the ocean it is known as the ***backwash***.

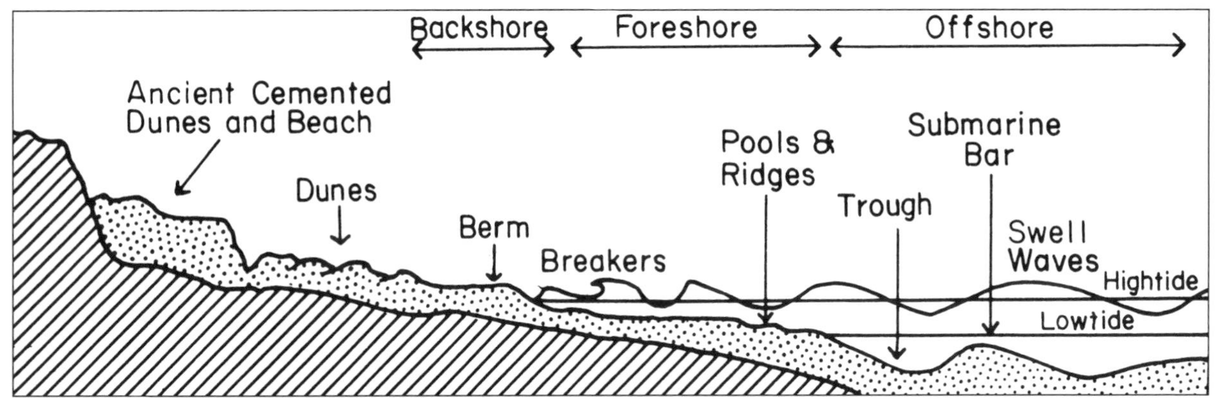

Fig. 12.1 The beach environment.

If the wave front steepens gradually until the crest spills over, a ***spilling breaker*** is formed in the foreshore zone (Fig. 12.1). Spilling breakers produce a weak backwash that does not interfere with the swash of the following breaker. Deposition is the prominent process as sediment is swept up the beach and, over a long period of time, may build a conspicuous ***berm*** as the coarser material is left stranded at the top of the beach in the backshore zone (Fig. 12.1). ***Plunging breakers*** are formed where the sea shallows rapidly, causing the wave front to steepen sharply, and the crest to curl and finally collapse. In plunging breakers, the backwash is strong and interferes with the swash of the following breaker, causing erosion to be the prominent process. This turbulence can create scouring of the sea bottom and form ***pools, ridges, submarine troughs*** and lead to the buildup of ***shallow sandbars*** in the offshore zone. At high tide, plunging breakers can erode the berm.

If the ***offshore zone*** (Fig. 12.1) is of variable depth, the section of wave passing over shallow water will be retarded more than the section in deeper water. As a result, the wave front will be bent, or ***refracted***. ***Wave refraction*** results in an uneven distribution of wave energy along the coast, concentrating it on some areas and minimizing it on others. Shallow water in front of rocky ***headlands*** and deeper water in adjacent ***bays*** causes wave refraction, resulting in wave energy being directed towards the headlands, causing them to erode mor quickly. In contrast, wave energy is deflected away from bays because of deeper water and so these areas are the foci of sand deposition, which is why many bays have extensive beaches.

SECTION I: Depositional Coastlines

Longshore transport of sediment is due to ***longshore*** or ***beach drift***, caused by waves striking the shore obliquely, which creates ***longshore*** or ***littoral currents***. These currents move parallel to the beach, thus moving sand along the beach. Although the direction of drift may vary with wave conditions, there is generally a net movement of sediment in one direction along the coast. The transport and subsequent settling of the sediment creates numerous depositional features on these coastlines (Fig. 12.2). Where drift is along an indented shore, spits and bars are constructed in the direction of transport and parallel to the beach. A ***sand spit*** is a ridge of sediment built across a bay, cove, or other shore opening, but does not span the entire opening. A ***cuspate*** or ***recurved spit*** is one that curves toward the coast. A ***baymouth*** or

barrier bar is a ridge of sediment that extends from one side of a shore opening to the other and often a lake or ***lagoon*** develops in the resulting triangular-shaped depression. Lagoons may also be formed by the development of ***offshore bars*** and ***barrier islands***. The Atlantic and Gulf coasts of the United States are dominated by these features, including Cape Hatteras (North Carolina), St. Simons Island (Georgia), Miami Beach (Florida), and South Padre Island (Texas). A sand bar that forms between the coast and an island is known as a ***tombolo***.

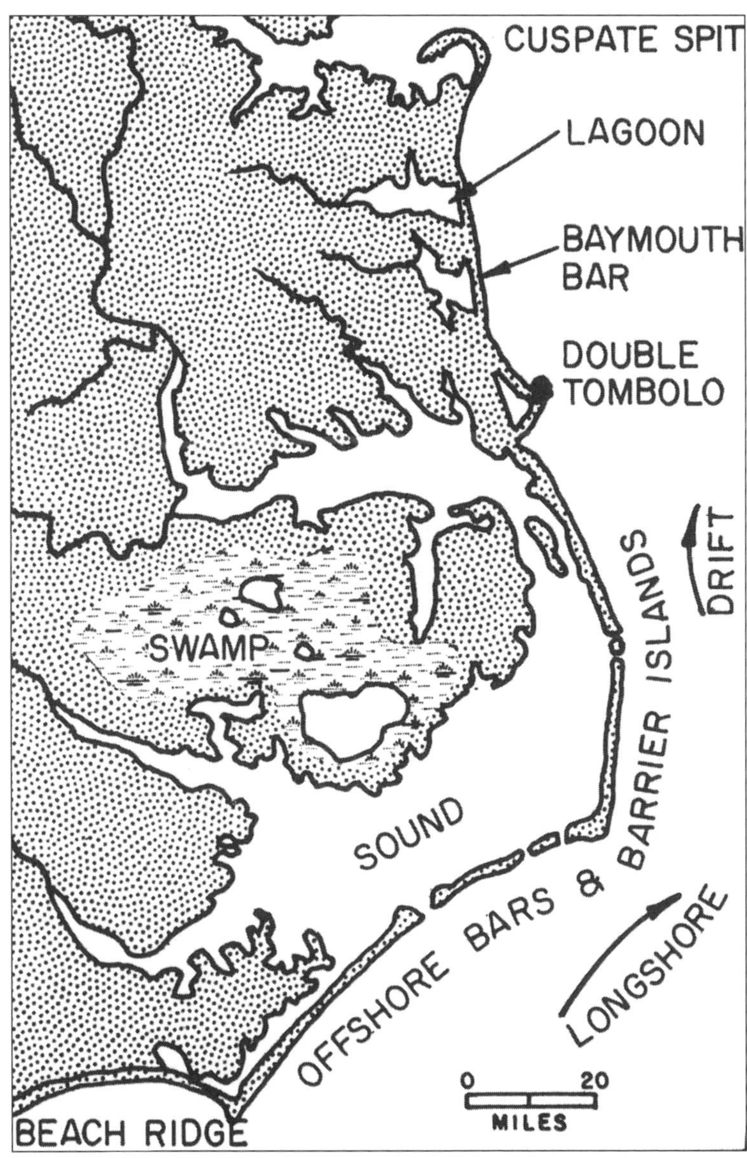

Fig. 12.2 **Landforms produced by the longshore transport of sediment along a submerged coastline.**

QUESTIONS

12.1 Fig. 12.3 shows Little Egg Inlet in Atlantic County, New Jersey. The three photographs were taken in 1940, 1957, and 1963, and show the changes that took place in Island Beach south of the inlet. The tidal channels serve as reference marks in assessing shoreline changes from year to year. Present day conditions in this area can be determined by looking at a recent satellite image. Obtain an image by typing the following coordinates in the Google Earth™ seach box: 39° 28′ 33.70″ N, 74° 19′ 50.85″ W. Start viewing from an Eye alt of 31,000 feet. Use the use the directional and oblique viewing options until you are totally familiar with the landforms in this area. Answer the questions below.

(a) Describe the changes that occurred between 1940 and 1957, between 1957 and 1963, and overall between 1940 and 1963. Was there more erosion or more deposition? Approximately how much change occurred (2X bigger or smaller, 3X etc …) during each time period? Which areas were affected the most?

(b) Examine the orientation of wave crests in the 1940 photograph and deduce the direction of longshore currents and beach drift in this area. How does knowing this help to explain the changes that took place at Little Egg Inlet between 1940 and 1963?

(c) By 1957, a lagoon had developed between the inner and outer spits (B.3-2.0) and this had grown in size by 1963. What evidence is there in the photos to indicate that this lagoon may eventually fill with sediment and become a marsh?

(d) Compare the recent Google Earth™ satellite image with the 3 photographs in Fig. 12.3. How has the area changed since 1963? Has the lagoon filled in? Have most of the changes been from human activities or were they natural? Explain your answers.

A. Little Egg Inlet aerial photograph taken in 1940.

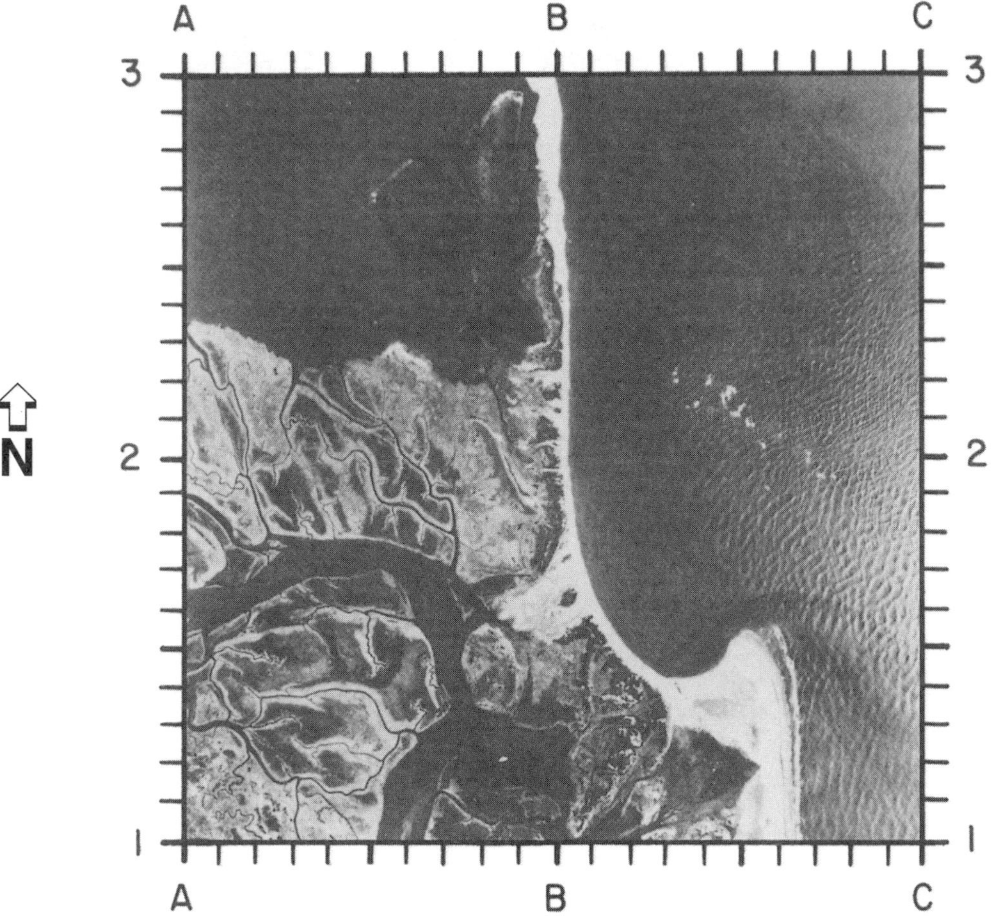

Fig. 12.3 Little Egg Inlet, New Jersey (1:40,500, A.0-1.0 in southwest corner).

B. Little Egg Inlet aerial photograph taken in 1957.

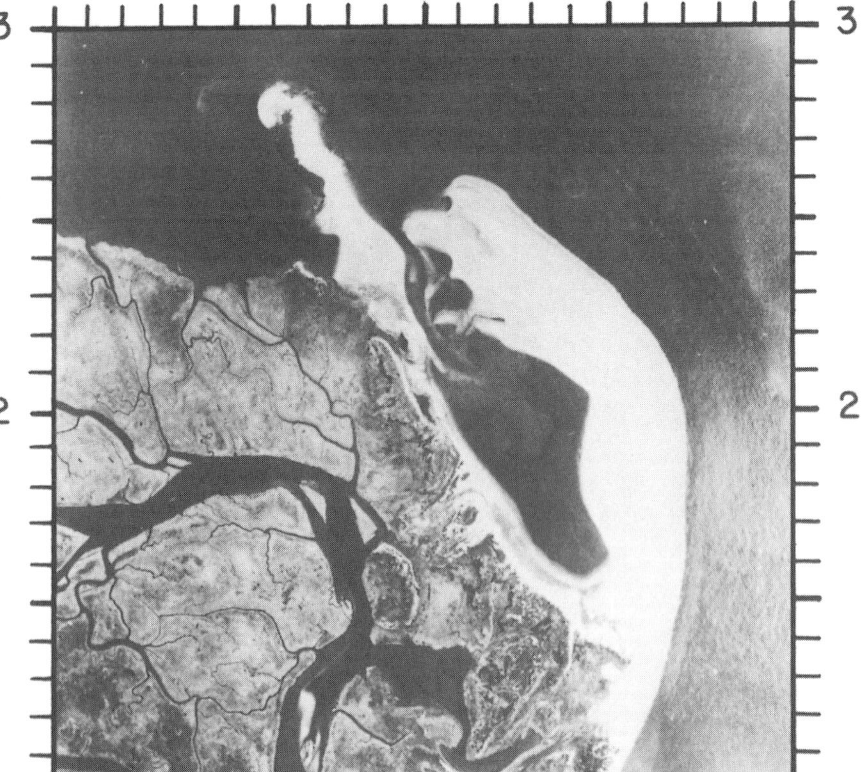

C. Little Egg Inlet aerial photograph taken in 1963.

N

A B C

3 2 1

0 500 1000 1500 2000
Yards

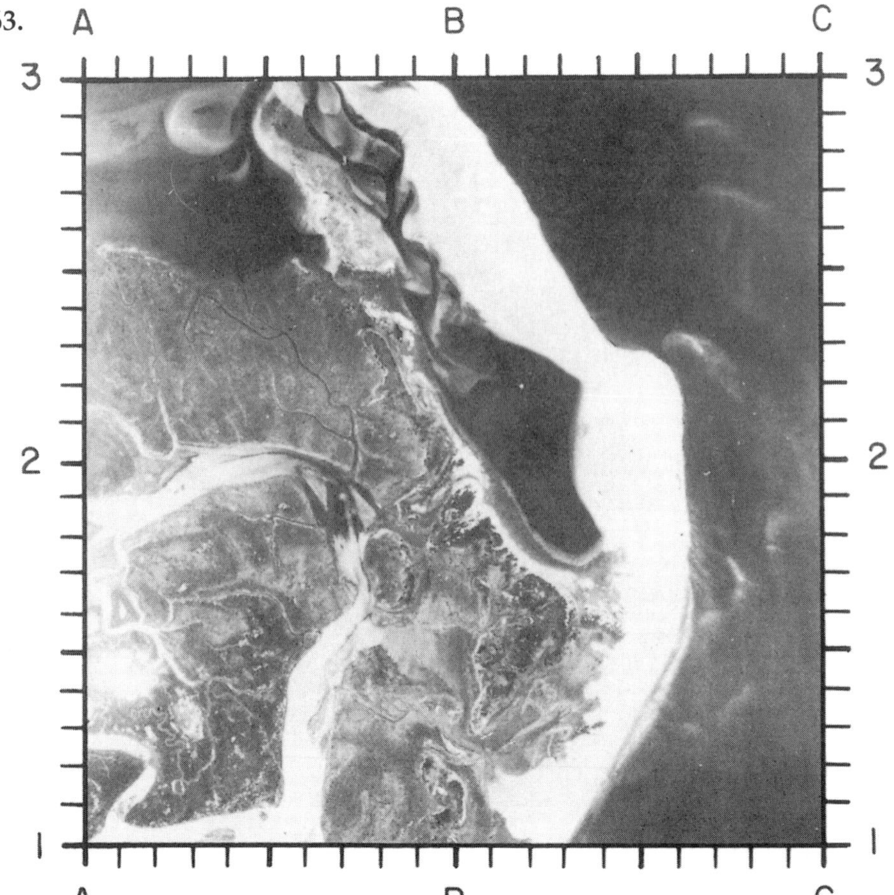

A B C

12.2 Examine Fig. 12.4. and also locate this area of Corpus Christi, TX on a recent satellite image (Google Earth™: 27° 45′ 16.71″ N, 97° 10′ 59.02″ W; Eye alt 38 miles). View both images to answer the following questions.

(a) Identify the following features and give their grid coordinates:

Barrier island ____________________ Sand spit ____________________

Lagoon ____________________ Baymouth bar ____________________

Tidal flat ____________________ Sand dunes ____________________

(b) How did Laguna Larga (A.7-4.3) originate and what relationship is there between it and Oso Bay (C.2-3.4)?

(c) Describe the events that led to the development of Mustang Island (C.5-2.2) and the tidal flats to the west of it.

(d) Why is it necessary to continually dredge a ship channel between the port of Corpus Christi and the sea?

(e) Compare the recent satellite image of the Corpus Christi area with Fig. 12.4. How has the area changed since the map was published in 1956? Can you tell whether the changes are the result of human activities or due to natural processes? Explain your answer.

Next Page: Fig. 12.4 Corpus Christi, Texas (1:250,000, A.0-1.0 in southeast corner).

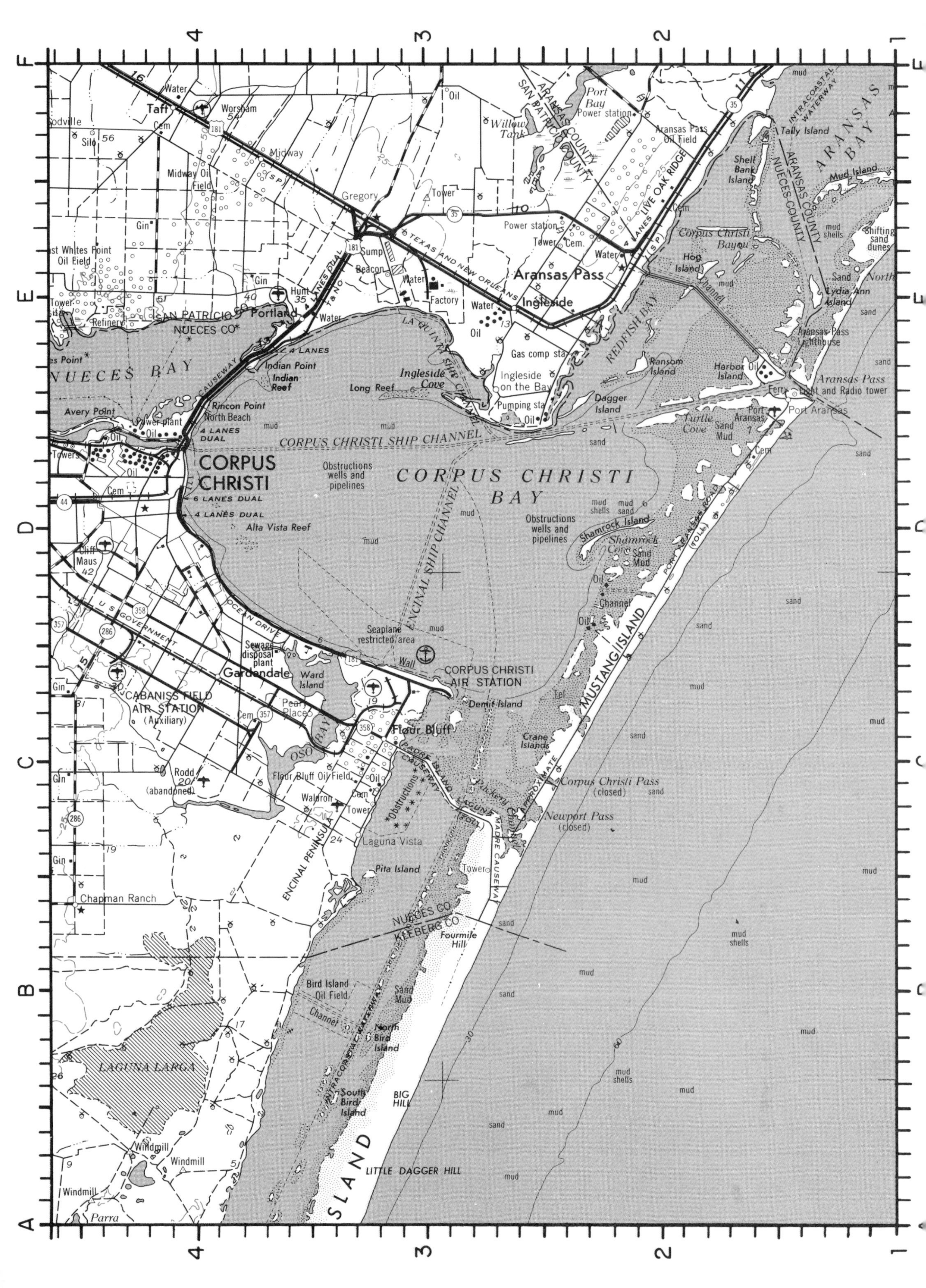

CORPUS CHRISTI
CORPUS CHRISTI BAY
NUECES BAY
ARANSAS BAY
Aransas Pass
Ingleside
Portland
Gregory
Taft
Worsham
Midway
Midway Oil Field
Port Bay
Power station
Aransas Pass Oil Field
LIVE OAK RIDGE
ARANSAS COUNTY
SAN PATRICIO COUNTY
NUECES COUNTY
SAN PATRICIO CO
NUECES CO
TEXAS AND NEW ORLEANS
LA QUINTA SHIP CHANNEL
CORPUS CHRISTI SHIP CHANNEL
ENCINAL SHIP CHANNEL
Ingleside Cove
Ingleside on the Bay
Long Reef
Indian Point
Indian Reef
Rincon Point
North Beach
Avery Point
REDFISH BAY
Ransom Island
Harbor Island
Dagger Island
Turtle Cove
Port Aransas
Aransas Pass Light and Radio tower
Aransas Pass Lighthouse
Lydia Ann Island
Mud Island
Tally Island
Shell Bank Island
Hog Island
Corpus Christi Bayou
INTRACOASTAL WATERWAY
Shifting sand dunes
Obstructions wells and pipelines
Alta Vista Reef
Shamrock Island
Shamrock Cove
MUSTANG ISLAND
PORT ARANSAS ROAD (TOLL)
Seaplane restricted area
CORPUS CHRISTI AIR STATION
Demit Island
Crane Islands
Corpus Christi Pass (closed)
Newport Pass (closed)
Packery Channel
APPROXIMATE
OCEAN DRIVE
U S GOVERNMENT
Sewage disposal plant
Ward Island
Gardendale
CABANISS FIELD AIR STATION (Auxiliary)
Pearl Place
OSO BAY
Flour Bluff
Flour Bluff Oil Field
Waldron
Laguna Vista
ENCINAL PENINSULA
PADRE ISLAND CAUSEWAY
LAGUNA MADRE CAUSEWAY
Pita Island
NUECES CO
KLEBERG CO
Fourmile Hill
Bird Island Oil Field
North Bird Island
South Bird Island
BIG HILL
LITTLE DAGGER HILL
ISLAND
LAGUNA LARGA
Chapman Ranch
Rodd (abandoned)
Cliff Maus
Whites Point Oil Field
Refinery
Windmill
Parra

12.3 Fig. 12.5 and 3-D anaglyph 24 in Appendix D show the Provincetown MA portion of the Cape Cod sand spit that was deposited by longshore drift from the east. The western end of the cape, shown here, has been eroded with the formation of the spit to the south of Provincetown. Submerged sandbars are visible offshore which trend roughly at right angles to the beach. Also look at a recent satellite image of the area (Google Earth™: 42° 02′ 46.76″ N 70° 09′ 46.24″ W; Eye alt 22,000 feet) and answer the following questions.

(a) Identify the following features and give their grid coordinates.

Recurved spit ____________________ Sand dunes ____________________

Tidal flat ____________________ Marsh area ____________________

(b) Describe the processes that led to the development of Long Point (B.0-2.3).

(c) North of Provincetown is an area of numerous small ponds. Explain the relationship between this area and the sand strip on which Provincetown is built.

(d) What evidence is there on the map to indicate that the Pilgrims landed here before landing at Plymouth Rock on the mainland? Why is Provincetown and the Pilgrims' resting site located on the south side of the Cape Cod Spit? (Note the larger setting shown on the inset map.)

(e) Compare the recent satellite image with Fig. 12.5. How has the area changed since the map was published in 1941 and to what extent are the changes due to human activities as opposed to natural events? Explain your answer.

Next Page: Fig. 12.5 Provincetown, Massachusetts (1:24,000, A.0-1.0 in southeast corner).

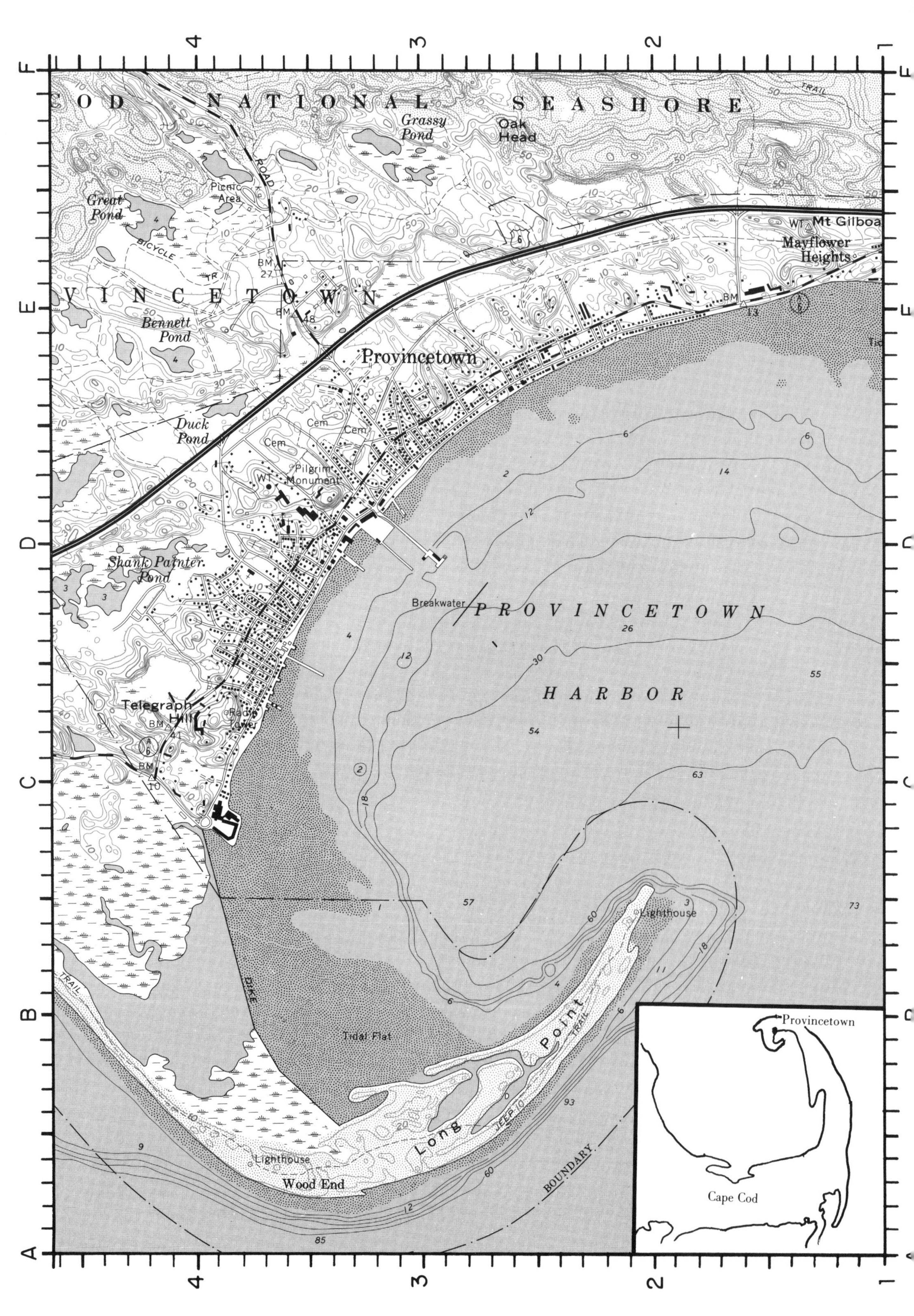

COD NATIONAL SEASHORE
Grassy Pond
Oak Head
Great Pond
Picnic Area
ROAD
BICYCLE TR
VINCETOWN
Bennett Pond
Duck Pond
Provincetown
Cem
Pilgrim Monument
Shank Painter Pond
Telegraph Hill
Radio Tower
Mt Gilboa
Mayflower Heights
Breakwater
PROVINCETOWN
HARBOR
DIKE
Tidal Flat
Lighthouse
Long Point
JEEP TRAIL
BOUNDARY
Wood End
Provincetown
Cape Cod

SECTION 2: Coastlines of Erosion

The destructive impact of breakers is considerable and is concentrated within a narrow vertical range of 10-20 feet. As waves attack rocky coastlines, ***sea cliffs*** and ***wave-cut notches*** originate where the waves undercut coastal rocks and sediments (Fig. 12.6). At the bases of these cliffs, the land is gradually eroded to form broad, gently sloping ***wave-cut platforms,*** often partially exposed at low tide. ***Sea caves*** may also be formed at the bases of cliffs, especially along faults and joints. Occasionally the hydraulic power of wave erosion may create a vertical connection or tube between a sea cave at the base of a cliff and the top of the cliff; this is called a ***blowhole***. The erosive power of waves is particularly effective on ***headlands*** or other protrusions along a rocky coast. Projecting sections along cliffs can be isolated from the main cliff by wave erosion along fault and joint weaknesses that parallel the main trend of the cliff. The resulting feature is a ***sea stack***. Erosion on opposite sides of a headland or sea stack may create a tunnel from one side to the other producing a ***sea arch***.

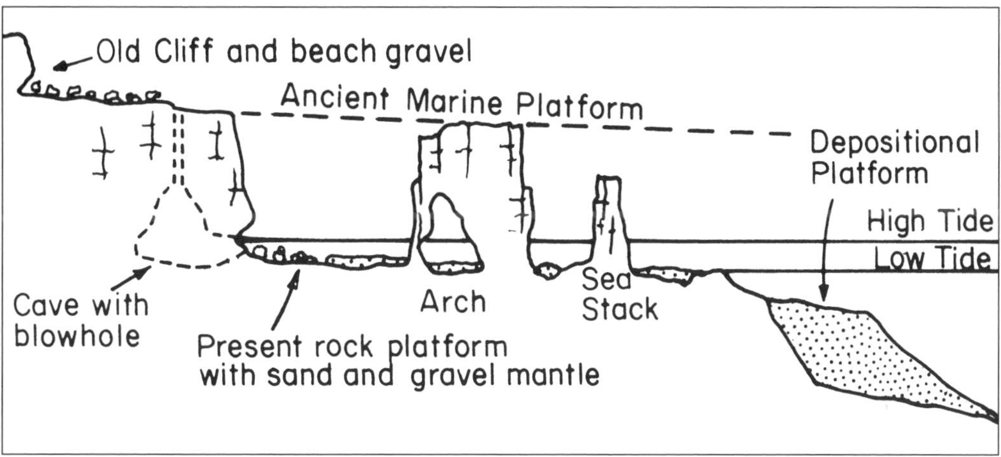

Fig. 12.6 Landforms of rocky coastlines.

QUESTIONS

12.4 Fig. 12.7 and 3-D anaglyph 25 in Appendix D) show the southwest portion of San Clemente Island in Los Angeles County, California. The island is 21 miles long, 4 miles wide, and rises more than 2,000 feet above sea level; it is formed of a series of gently dipping Miocene volcanic rocks. Look at a recent Google Earth™ satellite image of the island by typing the following coordinates in the search box: 32° 55′ 07.98″ N, 118° 32′ 32.12″ W. View initially from an Eye alt of 20,000 feet and zoon in and out as needed to get the best scenes. Also take advantage of the vertical and oblique viewing options to look at the coast fromdifferent angles. Answer the following questions.

(a) Identify the following features and give their grid coordinates:

Rocky headland ____________________ Bay ____________________

Sea cliff above sea level ________________ Sea cliff at sea level ________________

Wave-cut platform ____________________ Sea stack ____________________

(b) Examine the bay on the photograph that is immediately east of the headland and identify the wave crests (wave crests are also visible on the satellite image). Why have the waves been refracted in this way?

(c) Outline the processes that formed the San Clemente Island wave-cut platforms, which are now above sea level. These are clearly visible on both the photographs and the Google Earth™ satellite image.

(d) Compare the recent Google Earth™ satellite image with Fig. 12.7 (taken in 1954). How has the area changed since 1954? Can you tell whether the changes are due to human activity or to natural processes? This area has not changed as much as the Little Egg Inlet, NJ area (Fig 12.3) or Corpus Christi, TX (Fig. 12.4). Why is this?

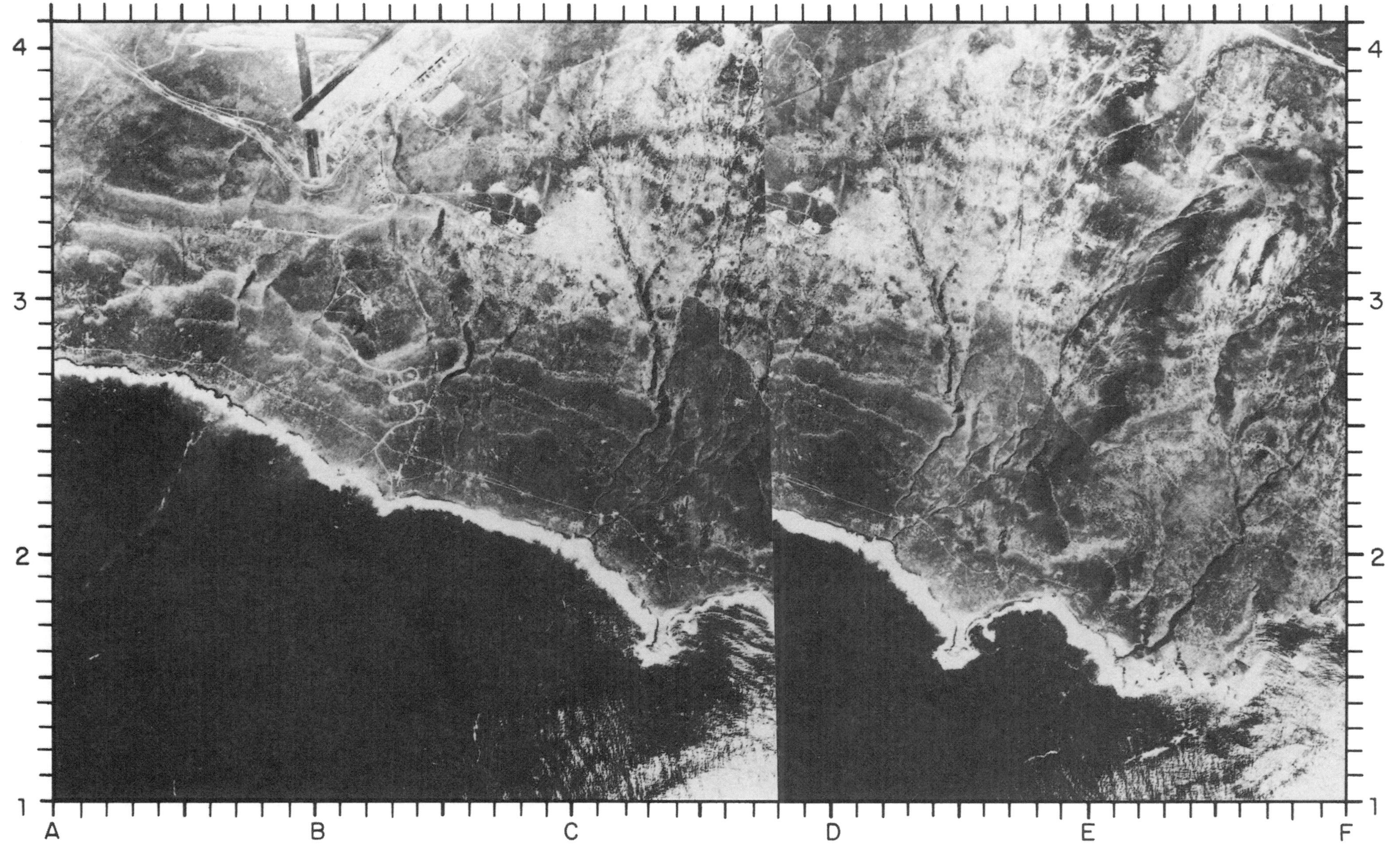

Fig. 12.7 **Eel Point, San Clemente Island, California (1:26,300, A.0-1.0 in west corner).**

12.5 Fig. 12.8 is a photograph of Marsden Rock on the northeast coast of England between the towns of South Shields and Whitburn. Examine a satellite image of this area by typing the following coordinates in the Google Earth™ search box: 54° 58′ 38.77″ N, 01° 22′ 31.01″ W. View initially from an Eye alt of 3,000 feet and use the oblique and directional viewing options to look at the coastal landforms from different angles. When you have looked in detail at this spectacular coast answer the following questions.

(a) What is Marsden Rock? What other coastal features can you see on the Google Earth™ satellite image?

(b) Explain how the pattern of wave refraction in this area has shaped the coastal landforms.

Fig. 12.8 Marsden Rock, England

SECTION 3: Submergent, Emergent and Living Coastlines

There are two broad categories of coastline ***submergent coastlines*** that are dominated by depositional landforms and ***emergent coastlines*** where erosional landforms are more common (Fig. 12.9). Nearly all coastlines have been affected by relative movements between land and sea. Uplift or depression of land can result from glacial ***isostasy***, tectonic deformation, and ***sedimentoisostasy***. Emergent coastlines occur in areas where the land has been raised relative to sea level. Typical coastal landforms include wave-cut platforms, sea cliffs, sea stacks, and caves that may be at present sea level or high above it. Common depositional features that may also be high above sea level today include coastal dunes and beach sand, gravel and cobble deposits. Emergent coastlines are typical of tectonically active areas, such as the west coast of North America, where the land is literally "emerging from the sea". Submergent coastlines are found in areas that are sinking or are being "submerged by the sea". During the Pleistocene Epoch, a great volume of water was locked in huge ice sheets on continents. This caused a world-wide or ***eustatic*** lowering of sea level by over 400 feet. The rise in sea level that followed the melting of these ice sheets submerged many of the world's coastal regions. As a result, submergent coastlines are often characterized by bays, estuaries, and fjords. In many areas, such as the Atlantic and Gulf coasts of the United States, coastal submergence continues today aided by the weight of sediment being deposited offshore.

An important category of coastline is the ***living coastline***, where waves break not on solid rock or sand but on living organisms or their remains. ***Coral reef, mangrove,*** and ***salt marsh coastlines are examples of living coastlines***. Coral reefs are found in tropical areas and are composed of living coral and the hard, calcium carbonate exoskeletons the animals form to support and protect themselves. The largest known coral reef is the Great Barrier Reef off the northeast coast of Australia, which is more than 1200 miles long. The three principal types of coral reef are fringing, barrier and atoll, all of which help protect inland areas by absorbing wave energy, especially during storms. Mangroves colonize the coastlines of tropical and subtropical areas where ocean water is seasonally made brackish by input of fresh river water during the wet season. The load of silt carried by the rivers is trapped by the mangroves and serves to fertilize and stabilize them. Mangroves can tolerate saline conditions in the dry season but require the brackish water of the wet season for their long-term survival. Mangrove swamps and mangrove forests along coastlines are unique ecosystems that also protect the coastline from the erosive power of waves. In contrast to trees and shrubs of mangroves, salt marshes are dominated by grasses and are found in mid- to high-latitude coastal areas. They also protect the shore from erosion by absorbing wave energy, and like mangroves are important sediment traps.

QUESTIONS

12.6 Examine the coastal regions shown in this manual in the following figures and also use Google Earth™ to look at recent satellite images of these areas. Are the coastlines you see emergent, submergent, or living coastlines.

Fig. 10.2 ____________________ Fig. 12.3 ____________________

Fig 12.7 ____________________ Fig. 12.8 ____________________

19° 30′ 06.36″ N, 154° 50′ 16.84″ W ____________________

17° 38′ 43.10″ S, 146° 29′ 19.30″ E ____________________

31° 11′ 44.18″ N, 81° 21′ 53.55″ W ____________________

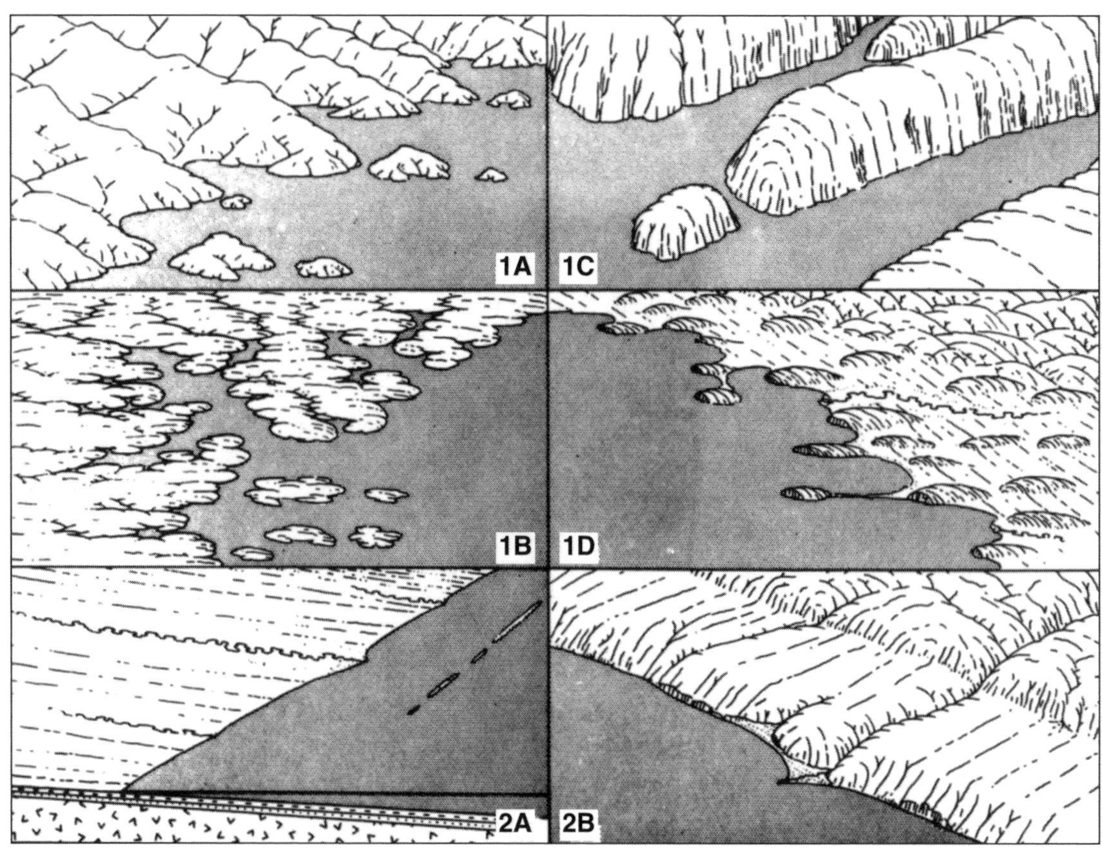

Fig. 12.9 Submergent and emergent coastlines. 1A = submerged mountainous coast, 1B = submerged coastal plain, 1C = fjord coast, 1D = submerged drumlin field, 2A = emergent coastal plain, 2B = emergent steeply sloping coastal region (after Strahler 1975)

Student Name________________________________

Exercise 13

ARID AND SEMIARID LANDSCAPES

MATERIALS

Lens stereoscope (plastic), red/blue 3-D glasses, ruler, graph paper, calculator, computer with Google Earth™ software and Internet access.

OBJECTIVES

1. Describe the landforms of dry-land areas and differentiate those of erosional and depositional origin.
2. Understand how structure and rock type influence erosional landforms in arid areas.
3. Recognize different desert landforms on topographic maps, aerial photos, and satellite images.
4. Estimate the vertical dimensions of desert landforms using aerial photos.

INTRODUCTION

Arid and semiarid environments cover about one third of the Earth's land surface. Arid regions are those receiving an average of less than 10 inches of precipitation per year, while semiarid regions receive 10-20 inches per year. Both climate zones may experience long periods of drought and some extreme arid areas may receive no precipitation at all in some years. Rainfall is often sporadic and of great intensity, and so has significant impact on the environment. As a result of the climatic conditions, arid and semiarid landscapes are dominated by ***aeolian (wind)*** processes during dry intervals and by short-lived but significant ***fluvial processes*** after rains. The lack of rain limits vegetation resulting in extensive areas of bare ground that can be eroded by wind and water. Arid and semiarid environments have a higher incidence of incoming solar radiation or ***insolation*** and higher rates of ***potential evapotranspiration*** compared to other environments, mainly because of the lack of cloud. As a result, they are susceptible to ***mechanical weathering*** processes such as ***thermoclastis*** and ***salt weathering***, which yield piles of debris or talus at the bases of many mountains. In contrast, due to lack of water, chemical weathering is much less important than in better-watered areas.

SECTION I: Erosional Landforms of Arid Areas

Erosion by both aeolian and fluvial processes is a prominent factor in the development of arid landscapes. The lack of vegetation in these areas increases the impact of wind and water on bare soil and exposed rock. Wind removes dry, loose deposits from deserts leaving broad areas called ***desert pavement or reg*** that are covered by larger pebbles and stones. These protect, or armor, the underlying soil from further erosion. Where loose sediments are deep, erosion can produce depressions or ***deflation hollows***. Silt-sized particles picked up by wind may be carried aloft in ***suspension*** to heights of several hundred or even thousands of feet. Large suspension events of this type are ***dust storms*** and may carry material hundreds or thousands of miles from their point of origin. Heavier, sand-sized particles carried by the wind bounce across the surface, reaching heights less than about 10 feet, in a process called ***saltation***. Large saltation events are classified as ***sand storms***. Armed with sand grains near the surface, the wind is a powerful agent of ***abrasion***. Softer rocks are more susceptible to abrasion and are scoured more rapidly, leaving the harder layers to form positive relief features including ***pedestal rocks*** and ***yardangs***.

Fluvial erosion is triggered by irregular storms and so is sporadic. However, when rain does fall it can be extremely destructive, particularly when the water is channeled along the major valleys, or ***wadis***, that are normally dry. ***Gullies, canyons and dry stream beds*** are all typical of arid regions, and many of these forms originated when the climate was wetter than it is today. ***Badlands*** are found in many arid areas and are testament to the effectiveness of erosion by streams generated by infrequent rain. Dissection of upland ***plateaus*** by streams results in a landscape similar to Monument Valley in Arizona, which is characterized by steep-sided ***mesas, buttes***, and ***pinnacles***, all specific forms of the ***monadnock*** (Fig. 13.1).

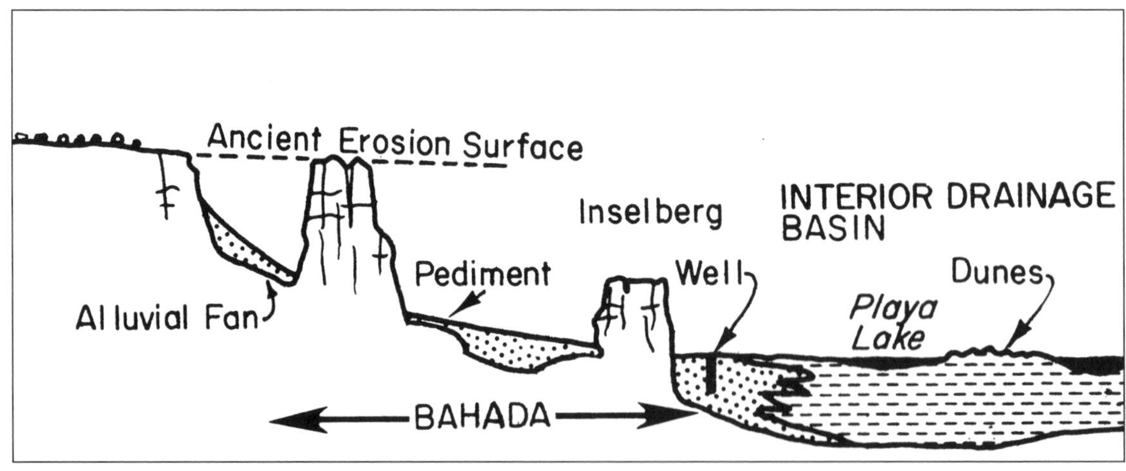

Fig. 13.1 Model of desert landscape in a block faulted terrain.

Next Page: Fig. 13.2 Douglas, Arizona (1:250,000, A.0-1.0 in southwest corner).

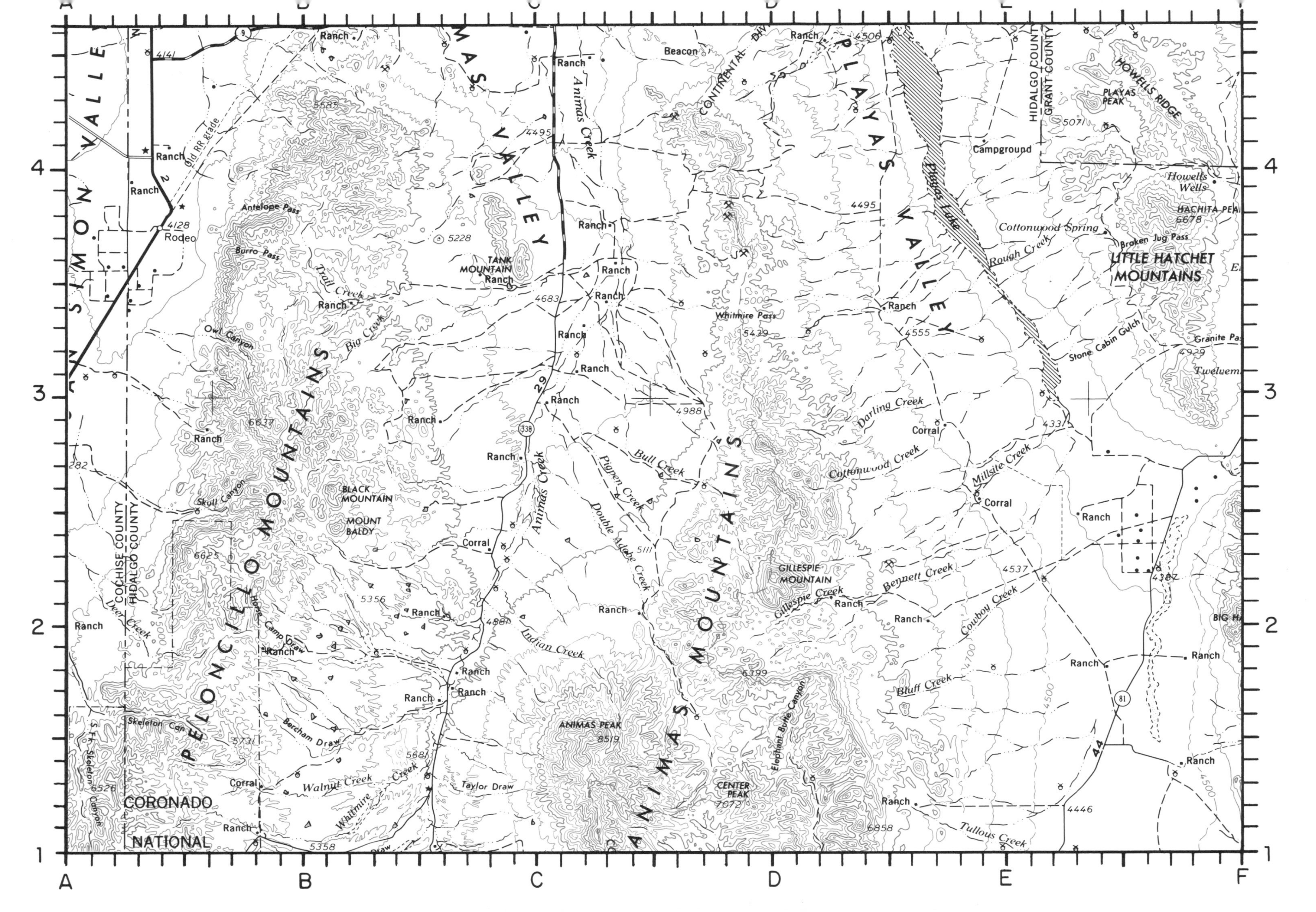

PLAYAS VALLEY
ANIMAS MOUNTAINS
PELONCILLO MOUNTAINS
LITTLE HATCHET MOUNTAINS
HOWELLS RIDGE
PLAYAS PEAK
HACHITA PEAK
6678
Howells Wells
Broken Jug Pass
Cottonwood Spring
Rough Creek
Playas Lake
Campground
HIDALGO COUNTY
GRANT COUNTY
Stone Cabin Gulch
Granite Pass
4929
Twelvemile
5071
4506
Beacon
CONTINENTAL DIV
4495
Ranch
4555
Whitmire Pass
5439
Animas Creek
Rodeo
4128
4141
Old RR grade
Antelope Pass
Burro Pass
Trail Creek
Big Creek
Owl Canyon
5585
TANK MOUNTAIN
5228
4683
4988
Darling Creek
Corral
Cottonwood Creek
Millsite Creek
Bull Creek
Pigpen Creek
Double Adobe Creek
5111
GILLESPIE MOUNTAIN
Gillespie Creek
Bennett Creek
Cowboy Creek
Bluff Creek
4537
4387
4331
BLACK MOUNTAIN
MOUNT BALDY
6637
6625
Skull Canyon
Horse Camp Draw
5356
4880
Indian Creek
ANIMAS PEAK
8519
6399
Elephant Butte Canyon
CENTER PEAK
7072
6858
Tullous Creek
4446
4500
4700
5000
6000
7000
Taylor Draw
Walnut Creek
Whitmire Creek
5681
Bercham Draw
5731
Skeleton Canyon
S. Fk. Skeleton Canyon
6526
CORONADO
NATIONAL
5358
282
COCHISE COUNTY
Deer Creek
SIMON VALLEY
BIG HATCHET
A B C D E F
1 2 3 4

QUESTIONS

13.1 Fig. 13.2 shows a portion of the Douglas, Arizona region just north of the U.S.-Mexico border. The area lies within the Basin and Range Province of the western U.S., where relief is dominated by a series of horst block mountains separated by interior basins developed in graben structures. To familiarize yourself with the area obtain a Google Earth™ satellite image by typing the following coordinates in the search box: 31° 47′ 22.62″ N, 108° 41′ 12.43″ W. View initially from an Eye alt of 34 miles and use both the vertical and oblique viewing options. The oblique views should be very helpful in giving you a real feel for what the area is like. When you have familiarized yourself with the area answer the following questions.

(a) What evidence is there on the Google Earth™ satellite image to suggest that this region has an arid climate? Can you detect changes to the area since the map was published in 1959? Explain.

(b) Identify the following features and give their grid coordinates. Find these on the satellite image before looking at the map.

Horst Block Mountain ____________________ Playa Lake____________________

Basin or Graben____________________ Alluvial Fan ____________________

Dry Stream Bed ____________________ Canyon ____________________

(c) Construct an east to west topographic profile from Antelope Pass (A.9-3.8) to Cottonwood Spring (E.4-3.7). Use a horizontal scale of 1:250,000 and a vertical scale of 1 inch equals 1,000 feet. The contour interval of the map is 100 feet.

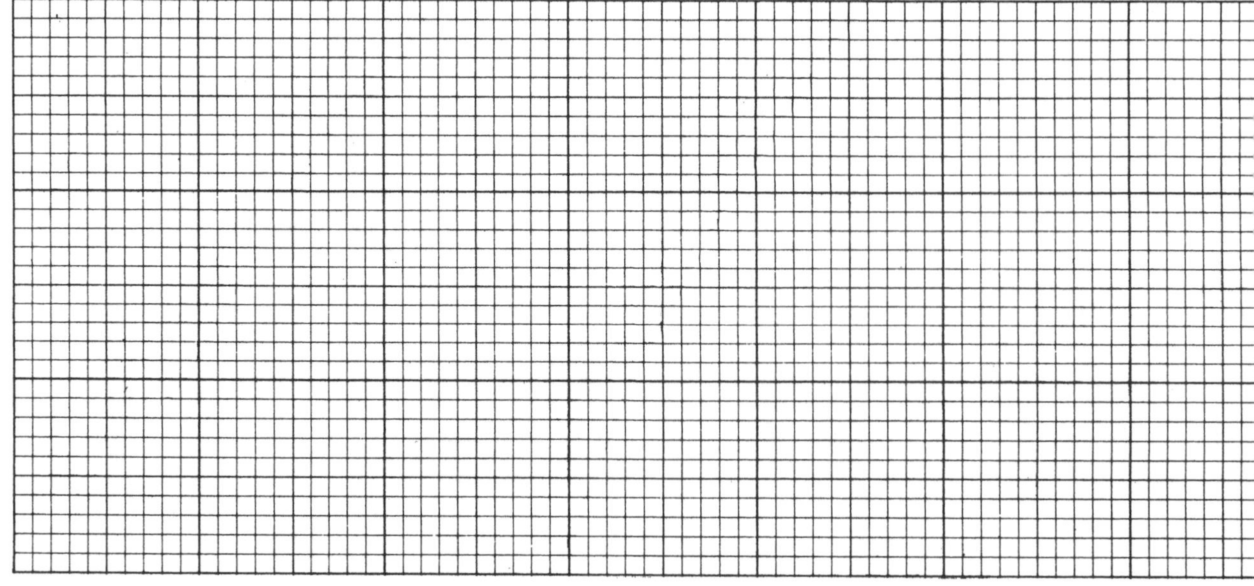

(d) Examine place names to determine the rock type forming the Little Hatchet Mountains.

13.2 Fig. 13.3 and 3-D anaglyph 26 in Appendix D show a part of the northwest side of the Sacaton Mountains in Arizona. The region is dominated by a dense network of dry stream channels outlined by desert shrubs. Also view a Google Earth™ satellite image of this area by typing the following coordinates in the search box: 33° 00′ 18.58″ N, 111° 52′ 15.16″ W. Start viewing from an Eye alt of 20,000 ft and use both the vertical and oblique viewing options. The oblique option will be very helpful in giving you excellent views of the mountains from different directions.

(a) Identify the following features and give their grid coordinates:

Braided Stream ____________________ Inselberg ____________________

Parallel Drainage ____________________

(b) Compare the aerial photo taken in 1957 with the Google Earth™ satellite image. What natural and human-induced changes can you see?

13.3 Type the following coordinates in the Google Earth™ search box: 19° 01′ 02″ N, 18° 57′ 48.51″ E. The area you will see is located in north-central Chad within the Sahara Desert. Start viewing from an Eye alt of 20 miles and zoom in to 10 miles. Use the oblique and directional viewing options to look at these landforms in detail. What are the aeolian abrasion landforms visible on the image? These landforms cover a large area just south of the Tibesti Massif in Chad. Based on the alignment of these surface features, what is the prevailing wind direction in this region?

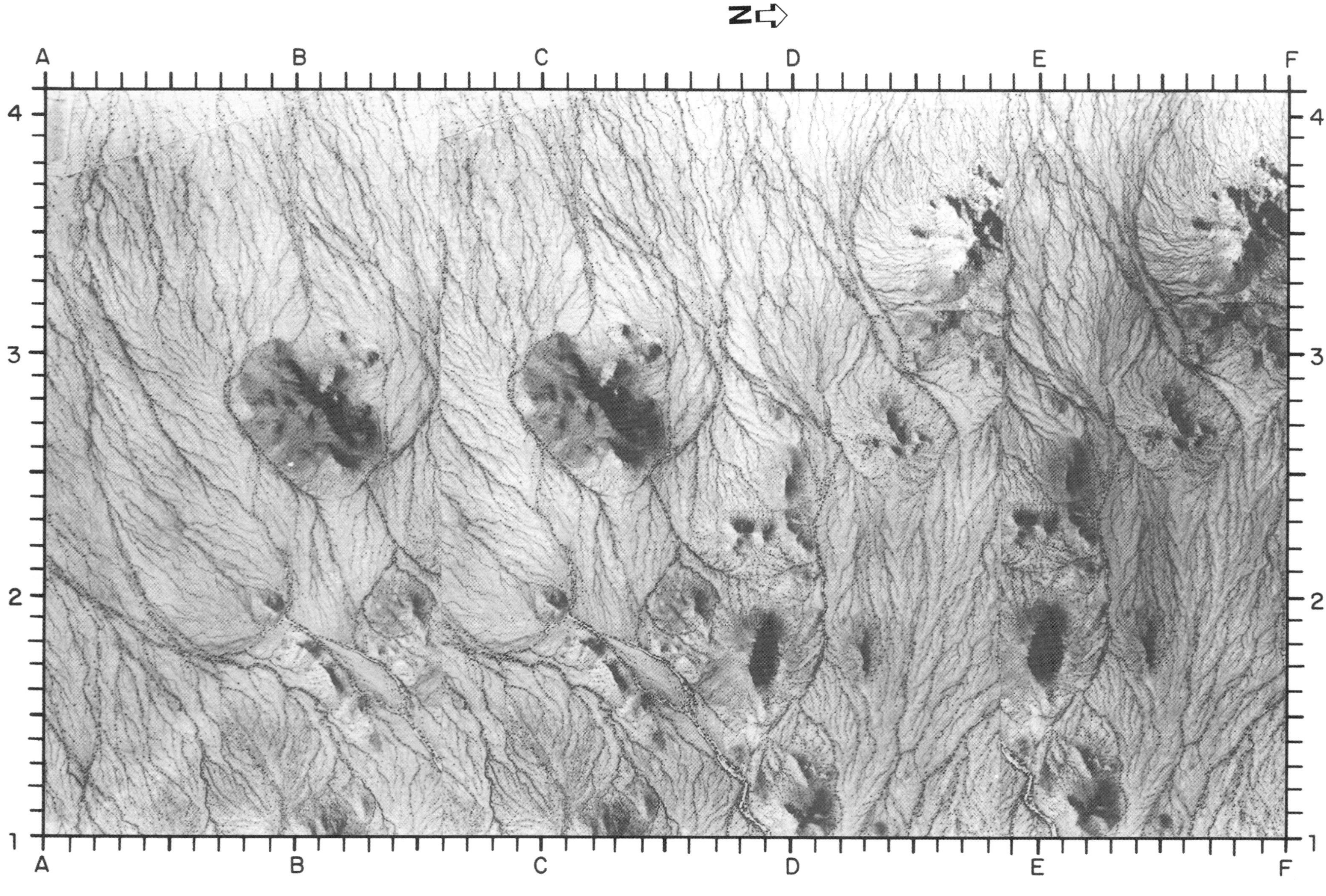

Fig. 13.3 Sacaton Mountains piedmont, Arizona (1:26,800, A.0-1.0 in southeast corner).

13.4 Fig. 13.4 shows the Twenty-nine Palms area of the Mojave Desert in southern California. What is the aeolian feature in the foreground of the photo? What aeolian process creates features of this kind?

Fig. 13.4 Twenty-nine Palms area of the Mojave Desert, southern California.

SECTION 2: Depositional Landforms in Arid Areas

Aeolian dunes may occur singly or in fields. ***Free dunes*** migrate across the landscape while ***tied dunes*** are stabilized by vegetation, rocks or major topographic obstructions. There are three broad categories of dune based on the wind patterns that produce them (Fig 13.5). ***Crescentric dunes*** are formed by ***unidirectional winds*** and include ***parabolic***, ***barchan***, and ***transverse*** dunes. Parabolic dunes often form downwind of a deflation hollow and have the horns of their crescent pointing upwind. Barchan dunes form with the horns of the crescent facing in the downwind direction, while transverse dunes form perpendicular to the prevailing wind pattern. A typical barchan dune has a long, relatively gentle ***windward slope*** rising to a ***crest,*** and a much steeper ***leeward slope*** or ***slipface.*** Sand blown over the crest falls into a wind shadow and comes to rest at its natural angle of repose, which for dry sand is 30° - 35°. ***Linear dunes*** are formed by ***bi-directional winds*** and include ***longitudinal*** and ***seif*** dunes. Both are long, sinuous ridges that are elongated in the direction of the resultant wind, often with slipfaces on both sides of the ridge. ***Star dunes*** are pin-wheel-shaped mounds formed by a ***complex and changing wind pattern.*** They can be hundreds of feet high and are usually quite stable. ***Loess*** is an aeolian deposit of silt-size material that can be several hundred feet deep. This dust often originates in deserts and can be blown hundreds of miles from its source. The loess deposits of northern China are over 1,000 feet thick in some areas, while thinner loess deposits are common in Europe, North America, and South America. Some loess originates from the margins of continental glaciers, particularly from glacial outwash deposits. Katabatic winds blowing off the ice transport "glacial flour" (fine silt produced by glacial abrasion) from the outwash to areas beyond the ice where it is often trapped in vegetated river valleys. This is what happened with the loess deposits of the northern Mississippi valley in the U.S., and with other such deposits in Europe.

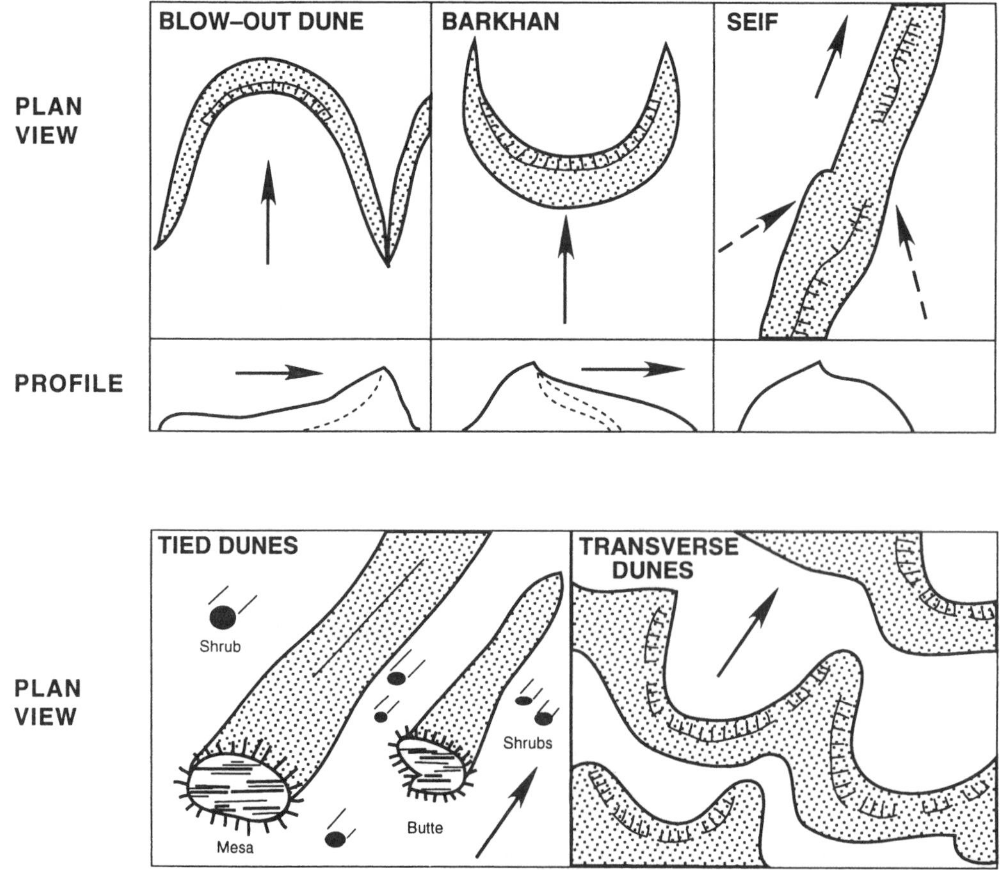

Fig. 13.5 Sand dune types. Arrows indicate the effective wind direction (after Butzer, 1976).

QUESTIONS

13.5 Fig. 13.6 and 3-D anaglyph 27 in Appendix D show the Comb Ridge region in the Monument Valley NP area of northern Arizona. Comb Ridge (D.1-1.0) is a north-facing cliff capped by Navajo Sandstone that dips gently to the southeast. In the north, Little Capitan Valley (D.0-2.4) separates the ridge from the dip slope on the De Chelly Sandstone (D.5-4.0). You will get a better appreciation for the landforms in this area by looking at them using both the vertical and oblique viewing options in Google Earth™. Using the oblique option and viewing the landscape from different directions and from different altitudes will give you spectacular views of natural rock arches, mesas, buttes, and rock pinnacles. You can obtain a Google Earth™ satellite image by typing the following coordinates in the search box: 36° 50′ 55.23″ N, 110° 00′ 42.81″ W. View initially from an Eye alt of 24,000 ft. When you have thoroughly scanned the area answer the following questions.

(a) Identify the following features and give their grid coordinates. You may find it easier to locate some of the features on the satellite image before locating them on the map.

Transverse Dune ____________________ Mesa ____________________

Barchan Dune ____________________ Butte ____________________

Tied Dune ____________________ Ephemeral Lake __________________

Longitudinal Dune ____________________

(b) What is the direction of the prevailing wind and what is the source of the sand in this area?

(c) A series of washes drains into Little Capitan Valley from the north. How have the sand dunes affected these drainage routes? Describe and explain any differences you observe between the recent Google Earth™ satellite image and the 1951 aerial photos in Fig. 13.6.

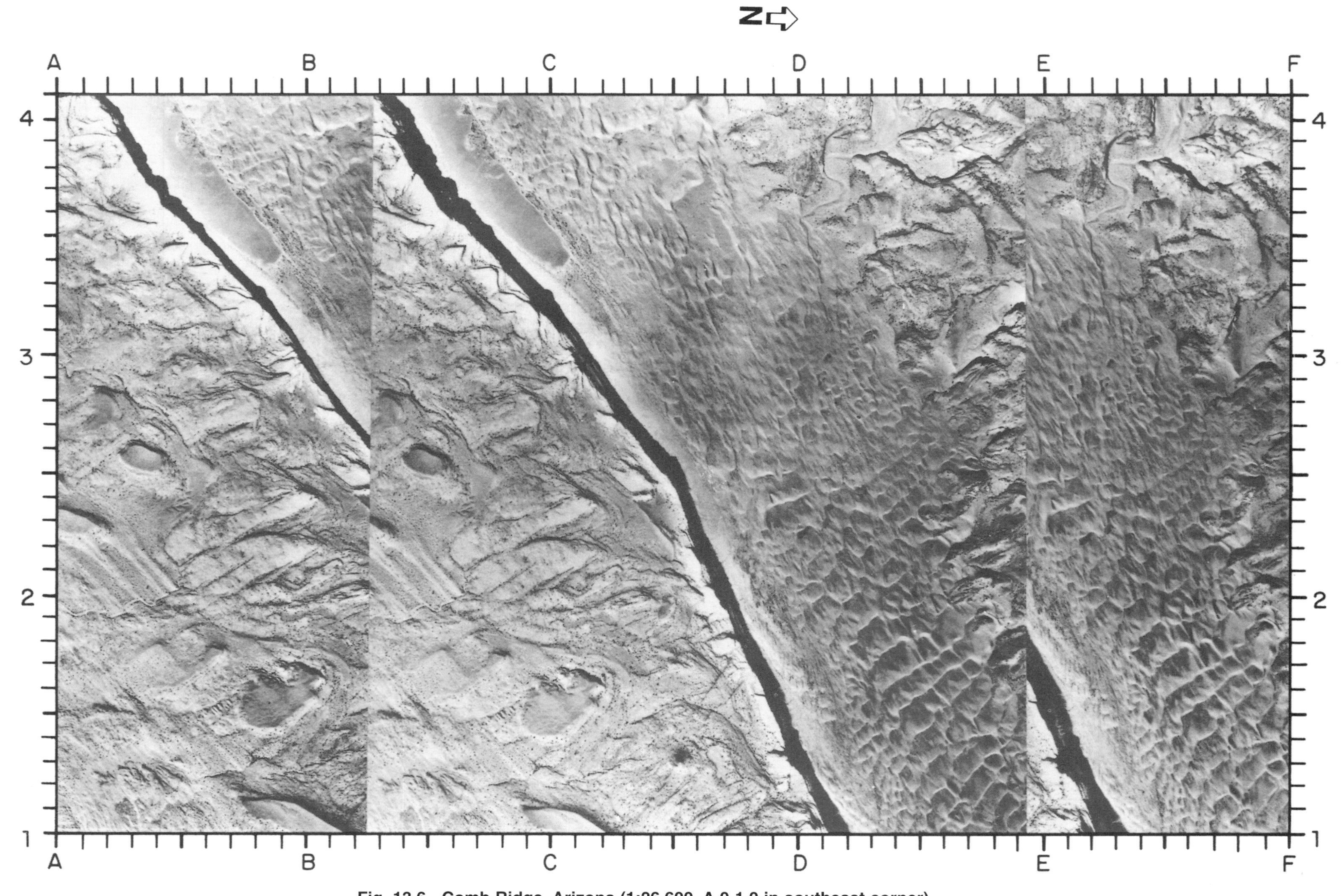

Fig. 13.6 Comb Ridge, Arizona (1:26,600, A.0-1.0 in southeast corner).

13.6 Fig. 13.7 and 3-D anaglyph 28 in Appendix D show the sand dunes of the Khārān Kalāt region of western Pakistan. View a Google Earth™ satellite image of this area by typing the following coordinates in the search box: 28° 00′ 40.92″ N, 65° 17′ 26.58″ E. View the area initially from an Eye alt of 20 miles and zoom into the landscape in the oblique view option to take a close look at the dunes from different directions. You will notice that the crests of the major dunes run northwest to southeast. Small white patches of salt indicate that ponds sometimes form at the bases of some of the dunes (e.g. B.5-1.5).

(a) What dune type dominates this area and what is the spacing between crests? What is the dominant, sand-transporting wind direction?

(b) Compare the 1953 photos in Fig. 13.7 with the recent Google Earth™ satellite image. Are the salt pans visible in the photos evident in the satellite image? Are there any ephemeral lakes? Explain your answers.

(c) Calculate the relative height of one of the dunes near the center (principal point) of one of the photographs. To do this, sketch a profile of a dune and assume that the angle of rest of sand grains on the slip-face is 35°. Then use the tangent tables found in Appendix B.

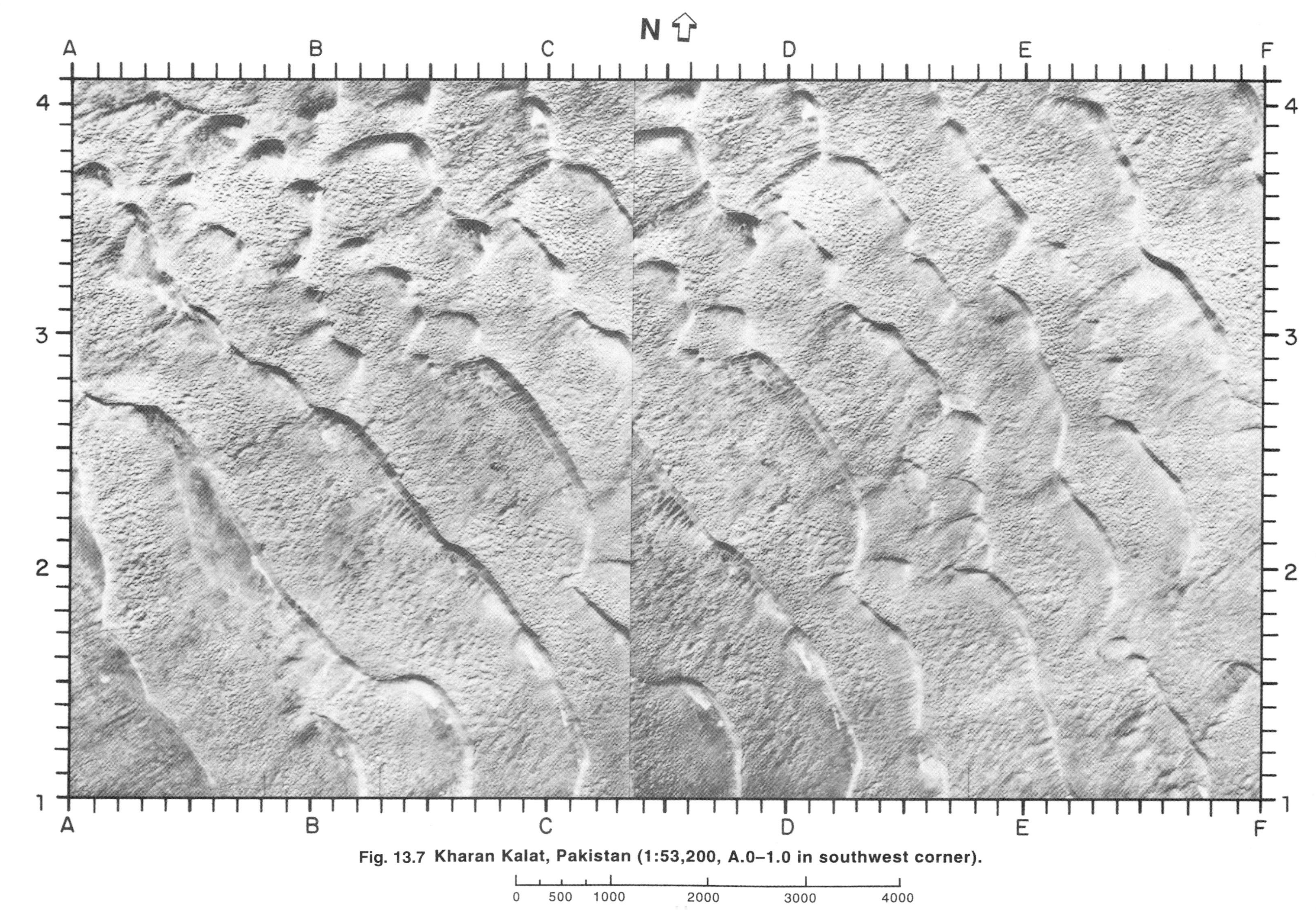

Fig. 13.7 Kharan Kalat, Pakistan (1:53,200, A.0–1.0 in southwest corner).

Student Name ____________________

Exercise 14

LANDSCAPE INTERPRETATION

MATERIALS

Lens stereoscope (plastic), red/blue 3-D glasses, computer with Google Earth™ software and Internet access.

OBJECTIVES

This exercise is designed as a self-test. It is the culmination of what you have learned in Exercises 1-13. To maximize its benefits, work through the questions before consulting the answers that are provided.

INTRODUCTION

Individual landforms can develop quite quickly and may be produced by a single process, such as the annual freezing and thawing of the ground, or solution, or a landslide triggered by an earthquake. However, whole landscapes take a very long time to develop and are shaped by a wide variety of processes. Landscape morphology is strongly influenced by rock structure and lithology, by its stage in the geomorphic cycle of erosion, and by the dominant operative geomorphic processes. Marked differences between, for example, glacial and arid landscapes emphasize that geomorphic processes and the landforms they produce vary considerably from one climatic region to another.

Paleomagnetic and other evidence has conclusively demonstrated that in the 200-250 million years that have elapsed since the fragmentation of Pangaea into the continents we see today, land masses have experienced multiple changes in base level as a result of tectonic activity. During the same period continents have drifted across climate zones with each helping to shape their surfaces. Therefore, it is important to understand that today's landscapes have complex geologic and geomorphic histories including multiple episodes of tectonic deformation, base level change, and climatic change. Sorting out the impact of these various processes on landscapes is a fascinating challenge akin to a detective trying to solve a murder mystery.

Since the Earth's formation around 4.5 billion years ago, the planet has been subjected to numerous episodes of glaciation, flooding, sea-level change, and volcanic, seismic, and tectonic activity. Within the last 2 million years alone, during the Pleistocene Epoch, environmental conditions have varied dramatically. High- and mid-latitude regions were alternately glaciated and then ice free, while lower latitude areas experienced marked variations in both temperature and precipitation. Glacially-induced sea level changes of up to 400 feet affected fluvial and coastal erosion and deposition patterns. There can be no doubt that many of the landforms making up today's landscapes are inherited from much earlier periods when conditions were very different from those existing at the present time. But at the same time, these landscapes continue to undergo change as these same geomorphic processes continue to operate.

Previous exercises in this manual have concentrated attention on specific geomorphic and geologic processes, and upon particular geologic and climatic landscape types. This exercise is different as it focuses on the complete interpretation of five complex landscapes in the United States and upon one hypothetical terrain. The various landscapes are depicted either in geological sections, maps, aerial photographs, or satellite images. Answers are given in Appendix E and should be consulted only after each question in the exercise has been completed. View these exercises as a challenge and they are your opportunity to show how much you have learned about landforms and landscapes. Remember that what you learn here will be carried with you for the rest of your life. Every time you drive or fly somewhere you will see new landscapes and you will be surprised to find that you already know something about them because of what you have learned by working through the exercises in this manual. After reading the interpretation given in Appendix E, you should then refer to the original materials and familiarize yourself with the evidence quoted in the answer provided to verify its accuracy.

QUESTIONS

14.1 (a) Fig. 14.1 is a hypothetical geological cross section. From youngest to oldest, identify the seven events that are depicted (labeled A thru G). Place these in the correct order in the table below and briefly explain how each event can be dated relative to the other events.

AGE	EVENT (letter on the diagram)	DESCRIPTION
Youngest 7		
6		
5		
4		
3		
2		
Oldest 1		

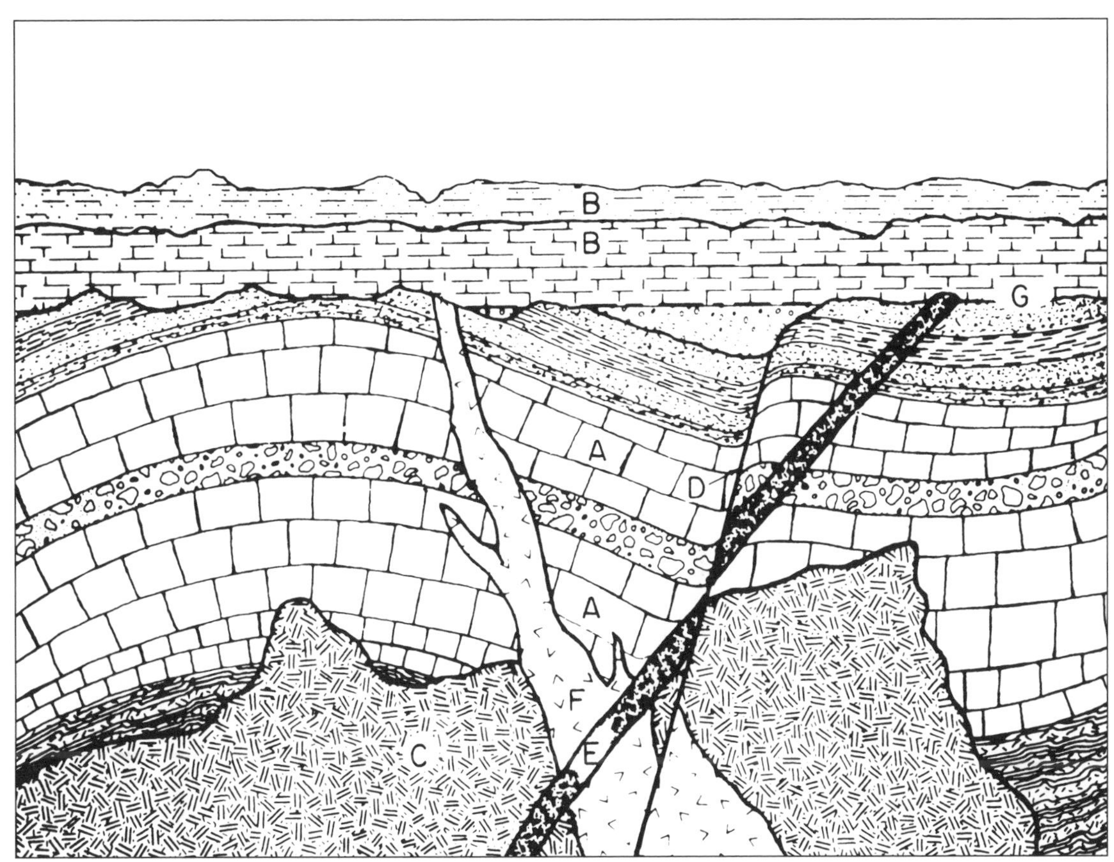

Fig. 14.1 Hypothetical geologic section (after Scovel et al. 1965).

(b) What kind of fault is depicted at site D?

14.2 Fig. 14.2 is a stereo model of an area 15 miles south of Salt Lake City, Utah. To the east are the Wasatch Mountains, dissected by the Little Cottonwood Canyon (E.1-1.0) in the north and Bells Canyon (C.2-1.0) in the south. At the mouth of each canyon is a gravelly deltaic deposit laid down in Lake Bonneville, a pluvial lake that occupied a portion of the Great Basin to the west during Pleistocene glacial periods. The climate of this region was much colder and wetter at that time and the Great Salt Lake is all that remains of pluvial Lake Bonneville. Before answering the questions below, examine Fig. 14.2 and 3-D anaglyphs 29 and 30 in Appendix D. Also, obtain a Google Earth™ satellite image of the area by typing the following coordinates in the search box: 40° 33′ 54.49″ N 111° 47′ 44.32″ W in the search box. View initially from an Eye alt of 25,000 ft and look at the area using both the vertical and oblique options, in the latter case from several directions. When you are familiar with the area answer the following questions.

(a) Identify the following features and give their grid coordinates:

Horst ____________________ Graben ____________________

Fault Scarp ____________________ Glacial Trough ____________________

Alpine Terminal Moraine ____________________

Parallel mountain drainage ____________________

(b) Briefly summarize the geomorphic processes that were important in shaping this area.

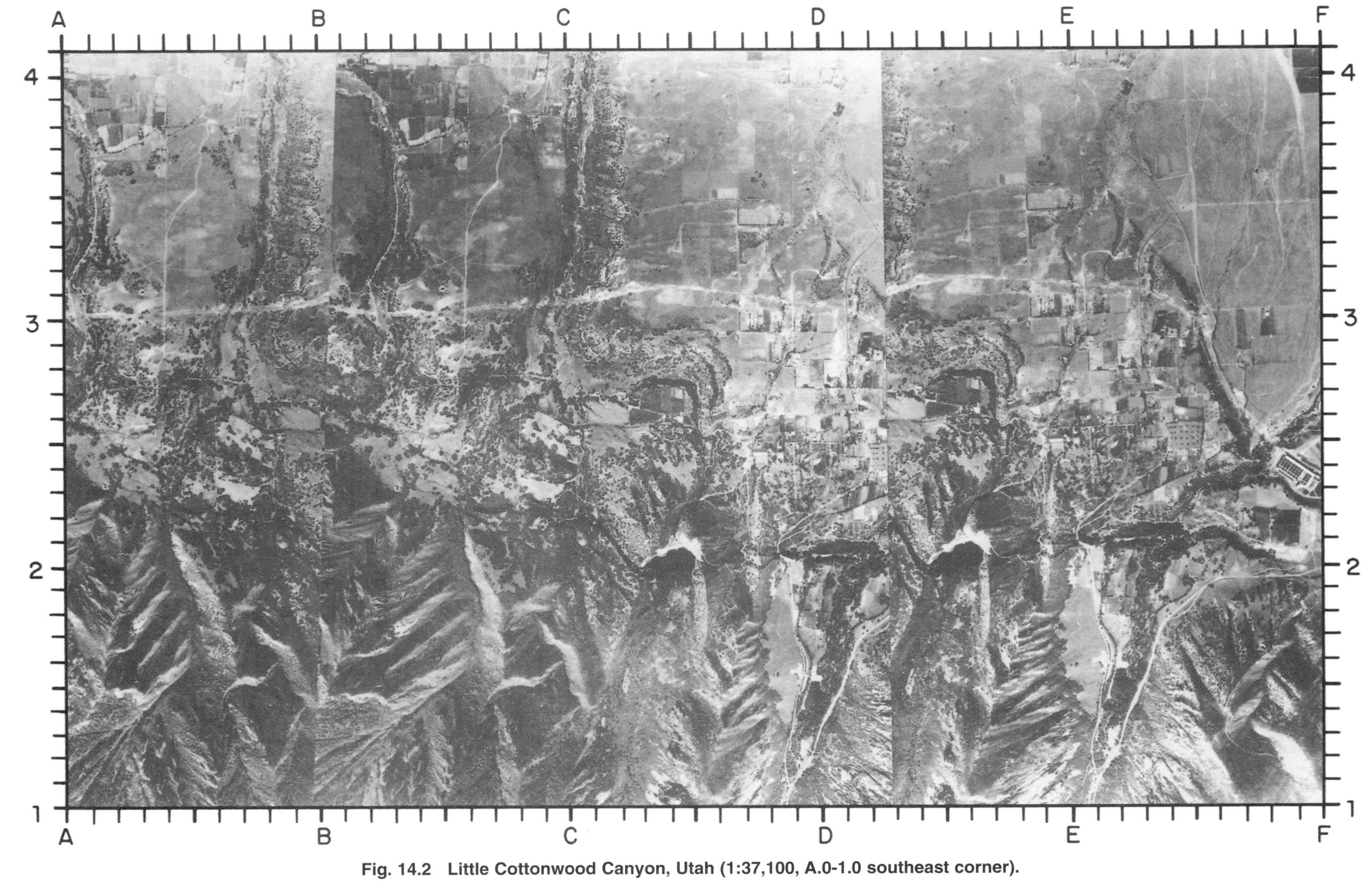

Fig. 14.2 Little Cottonwood Canyon, Utah (1:37,100, A.0-1.0 southeast corner).

14.3 The photographs in Fig. 14.3a and Fig. 14.3b, and 3-D anaglyphs 31 and 32 in Appendix D, show Deep Lake in the floor of Little Rock Creek Canyon, Wyoming. Deep Lake is located at the south end of the Beartooth Mountains and was carved out of the granite gneiss underlying the area. Examine Fig. 14.3 and a satellite image of this area. To obtain a satellite image type the following coordinates in the Google Earth™ search box: 44° 53′ 37.34″ N 109° 23′ 43.99″ W. View the area initially from an Eye alt of 50,000 feet and use both the vertical and oblique options. You will find the oblique views particularly informative. When you have familiarized yourself with the area answer the following questions.

(a) Identify the following features and give their grid coordinates:

Fault Scarp ____________________ Alluvial Fan ____________________

Alpine Terminal Moraine ________________ Glacial Trough ________________

Cirque ____________________ Hanging Valley ____________________

Landslide evidence ____________________

(b) Briefly summarize the geomorphic processes that were important in shaping this area.

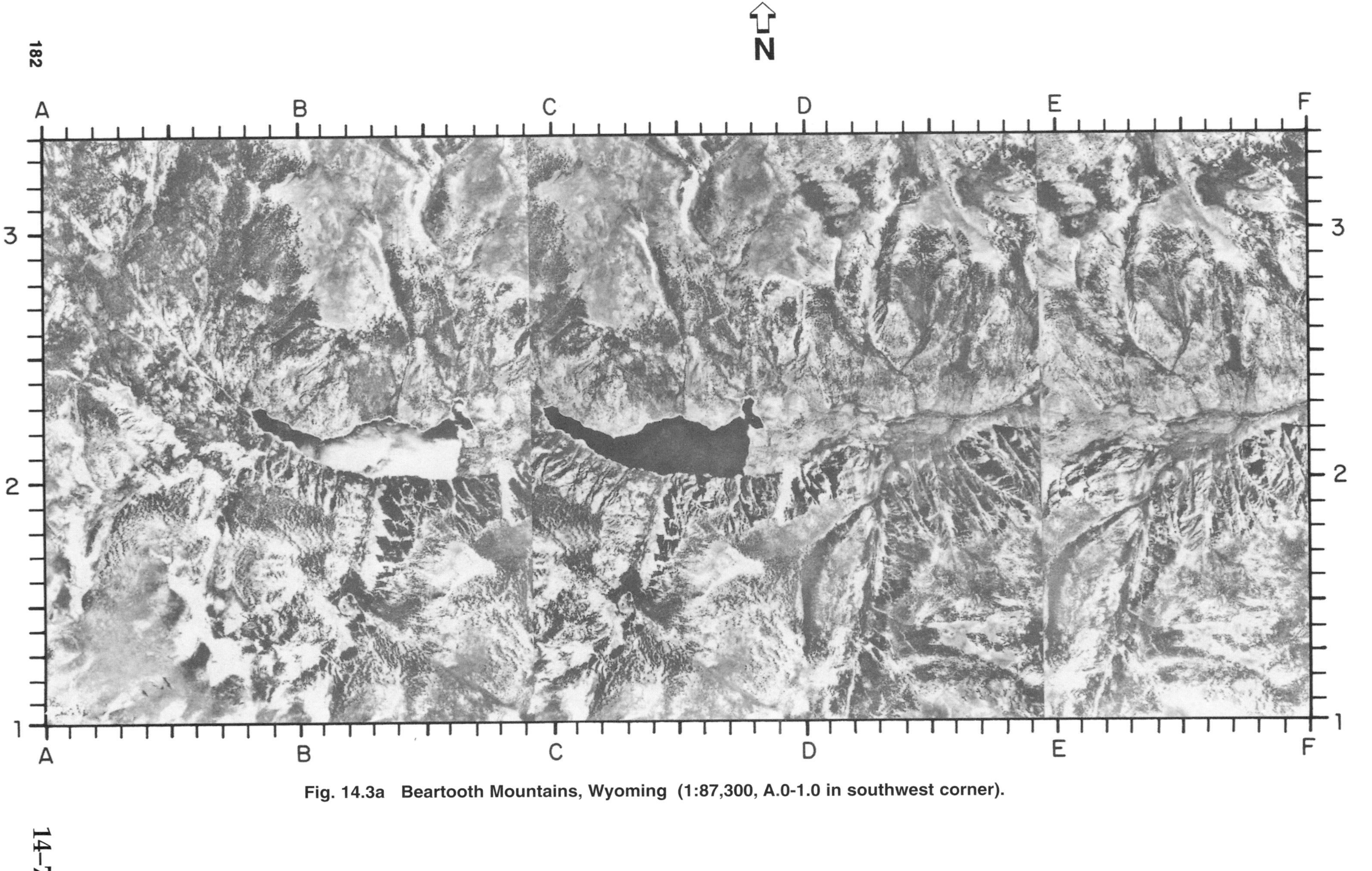

Fig. 14.3a Beartooth Mountains, Wyoming (1:87,300, A.0-1.0 in southwest corner).

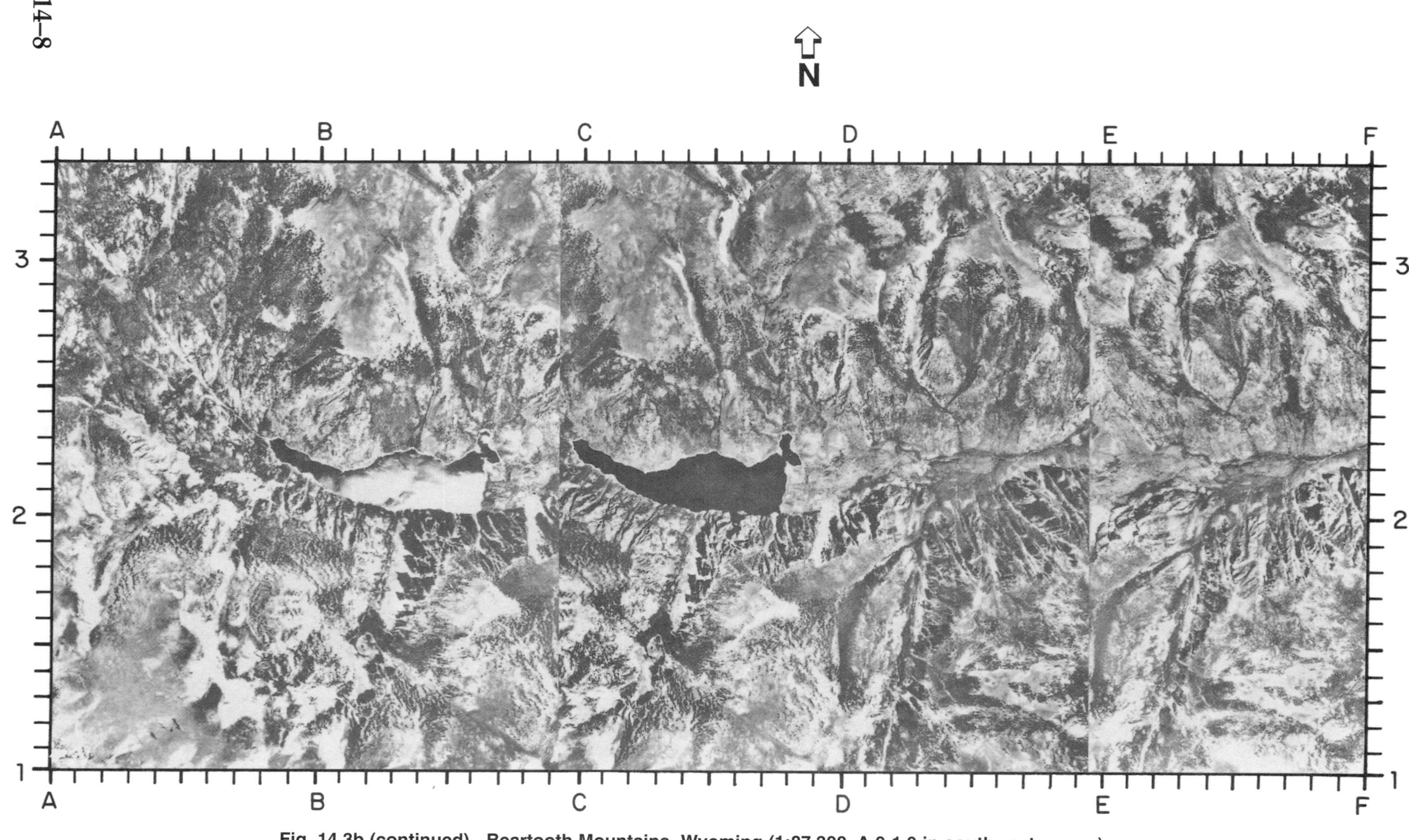

Fig. 14.3b (continued) Beartooth Mountains, Wyoming (1:87,300, A.0-1.0 in southwest corner).

14.4 (a) Figures 14.4 and 14.5 show the Kapoho-Cape Kumukahi region of the big island of Hawaii in 1954 and 1961, respectively. Sugar cane fields and forest dominate the 1954 photographs and the town of Kapoho (D.2-2.7) is clearly visible. Examine both sets of photographs and describe any changes you can detect in this area between 1954 and 1961. Bearing in mind that the Hawaiian Islands are of volcanic origin, postulate on the changes that might have brought about these changes. The 3-D anaglyphs for Fig. 14.4 and 14.5 may help in your interpretation; these are 33 and 34 in Appendix D.

(b) Compare Figures 14.4 and 14.5 with a recent satellite image (Google Earth™: 19° 30′ 06.36″ N 154° 50′ 16.84″W; Eye alt 25,000 ft) and describe changes in the area since 1954. How have the volcanic vents and surrounding areas changed since 1961?

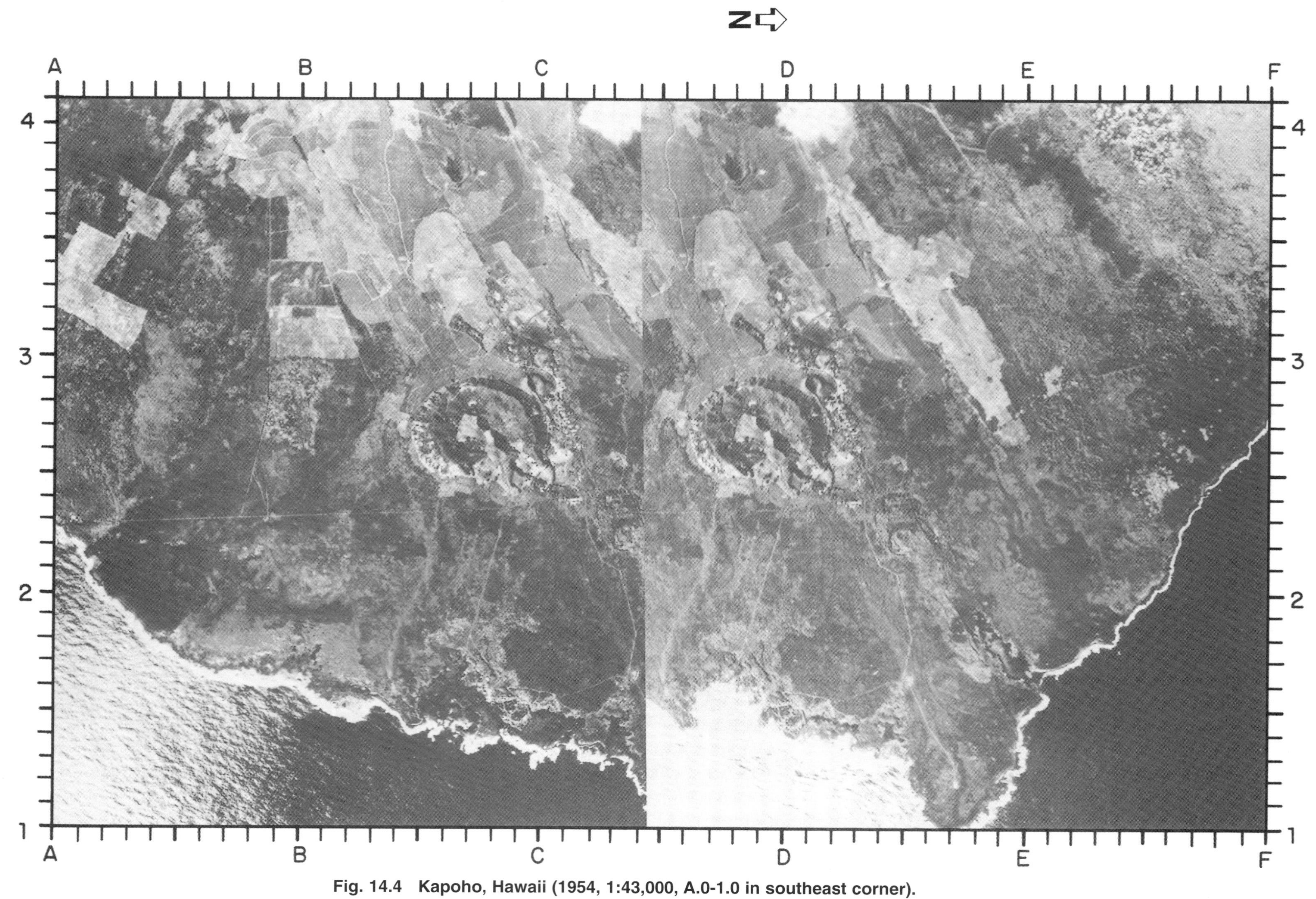

Fig. 14.4 Kapoho, Hawaii (1954, 1:43,000, A.0-1.0 in southeast corner).

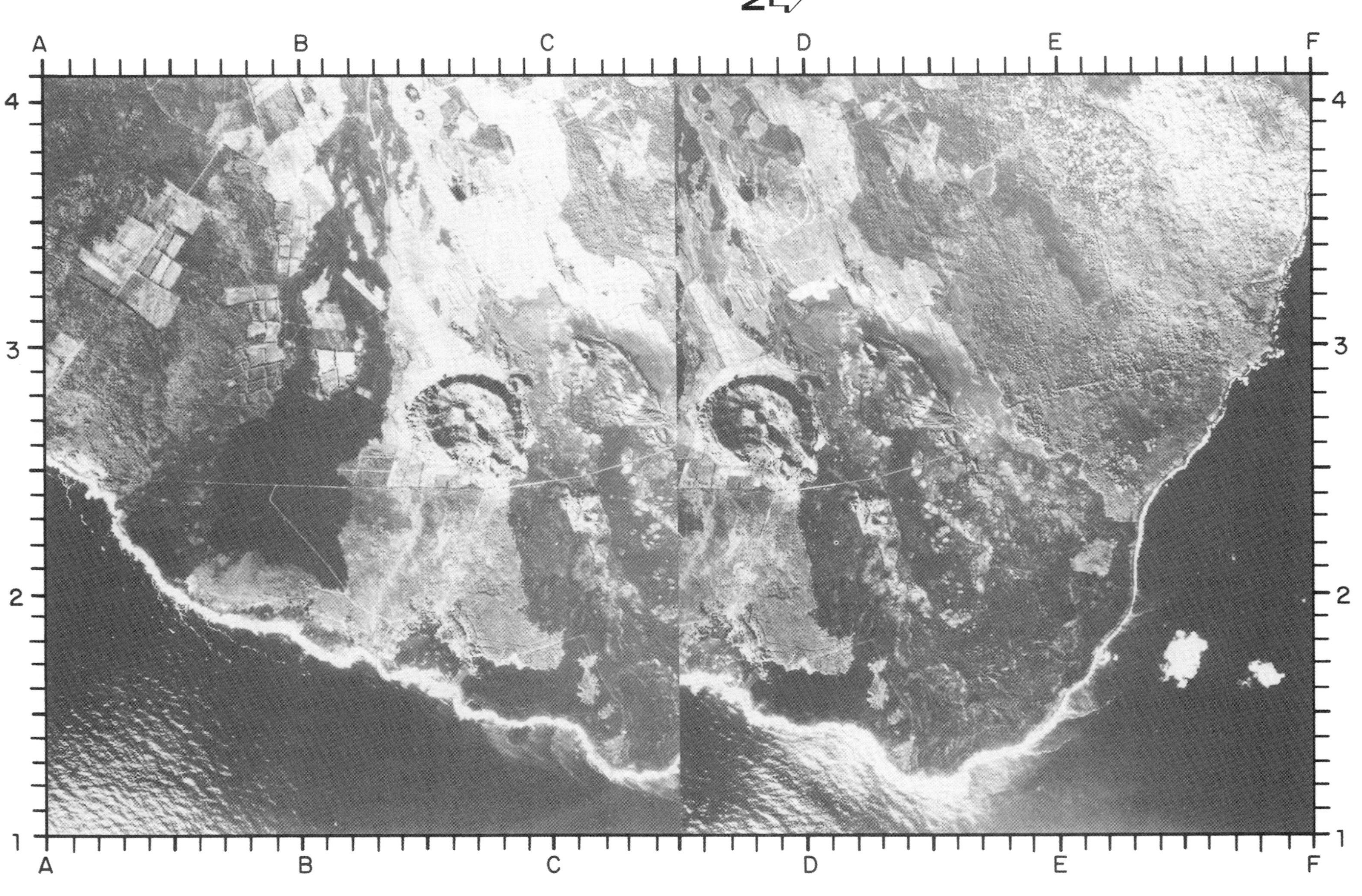

Fig. 14.5 Kapoho, Hawaii (1961, 1:53.400, A.0-1.0 in southeast corner).

14.5 Fig. 14.6 was taken with the Skylab 4 Earth Terrain camera on January 26, 1974, at approximately 7:45 pm Pacific time. The image shows parts of the Coachella Valley, the Salton Sea (lower right), the Chuckawalla Mountains, and the town of Indio (to the west of the Salton Sea) in southern California. The area is located in the Basin and Range province and the Mojave Desert. Examine the photograph and a recent satellite image (Google Earth™: 33° 42′ 33.21″ N 116° 07′ 53.51″ W; Eye alt 70 miles) and describe the landforms and drainage patterns that are visible. You may need to zoom in on the landscape to better identify individual landforms.

Fig. 14.6 Skylab 4 earth terrain camera image of the Salton Sea region of southern California.

14.6 Fig. 14.7 was taken from Skylab 3 by the Earth Terrain camera on August 12, 1973 at approximately 2:45 pm Mountain time. The image covers the Zuni Mountain region of New Mexico, USA. This area is located on the southeast edge of the Colorado Plateau and is quite arid climatically. Examine the photograph and a recent satellite image (Google Earth™: 34° 58′ 46.53″ N 108° 10′ 52.87″ W; Eye alt 90 miles) and describe the landforms and drainage patterns that are visible. You may need to zoom in on the landscape to better identify individual landforms.

N

Fig. 14.7 Skylab 3 earth terrain camera image of the Zuni Mountain region of New Mexico.

14.7 Examine a Google Earth™ satellite image of each of the locations listed below. Give verbal details of the location and then with reference to the information in the table below say if the landforms of the area are volcanic, structural, fluvial, karst, glacial, periglacial, coastal, or aeolian. You may choose more than one category if you have examples of different landforms in the area. After you have done this examine the list of landforms in the category/ies you have selected and choose those that you can see on the satellite image. Scroll around the image and move beyond it a little to see what landforms are nearby. In some cases your final answer might be as brief as the example below; in other cases it may include multiple landform categories and several specific landforms.

Location: Mt. Rainier, Washington, USA
Landform Category: Volcanic
Specific Landform: Composite volcanic cone

(a) 23° 19′ N 106° 17′ E (Eye alt 10 miles)
Location: ______________________________
Landform Category: ______________________________
Specific Landform: ______________________________

(b) 44° 58′ 14.96″ N 29° 22′ 26.27″ E (Eye alt 48 km)
Location: ______________________________
Landform Category: ______________________________
Specific Landform: ______________________________

(c) 16° 41′ 27.66″ S 71° 51′ 04.76″ W (Eye alt 20,000 feet
Location: ______________________________
Landform Category: ______________________________
Specific Landform: ______________________________

(d) 69° 57′ N 130° 29′ W (Eye alt 70 miles)
Location: ______________________________
Landform Category: ______________________________
Specific Landform: ______________________________

(e) 32° 49′ S, 17° 51′ E (Eye alt 10 miles)
Location: ______________________________
Landform Category: ______________________________
Specific Landform: ______________________________

(f) 50° 49′ N 160° 22′ E (Eye alt 50 miles)
Location: ______________________________
Landform Category: ______________________________
Specific Landform: ______________________________

(g) 69° 32′ N 19° 57′ E (Eye alt 200 miles)
Location: ______________________________
Landform Category: ______________________________
Specific Landform: ______________________________

(h) 27° 35′ N 53° 00′ E (Eye alt 50 miles)
Location: ______________________________
Landform Category: ______________________________
Specific Landform: ______________________________

(i) 25° 36′ 43.11″ N 28° 48′ 53.38″ E (Eye alt 7 km)
Location: ______________________________
Landform Category: ______________________________
Specific Landform: ______________________________

(k) 18° 28′ 31.43″ S 21° 19′ 31.85″ E (Eye alt 35 km)
Location: ______________________________
Landform Category: ______________________________
Specific Landform: ______________________________

(l) 21° 49′ 31.84″ S 15° 11′ 13.90″ E (Eye alt 11 km)
Location: ______________________________
Landform Category: ______________________________
Specific Landform: ______________________________

(m) 23° 52′ 25.69″ S 14° 55′ 02.43″ E (Eye alt 30 km)
Location: ______________________________
Landform Category: ______________________________
Specific Landform: ______________________________

(n) 50° 28′ 34.38″ S, 73° 03′ 26.79″ W (Eye alt 4.75 km)
Location: ______________________________
Landform Category: ______________________________
Specific Landform: ______________________________

(o) 50° 29′ 8.25″ S, 73° 00′ 54.78″ W (Eye alt 4.75 km)
Location: ______________________________
Landform Category: ______________________________
Specific Landform: ______________________________

(p) 19° 17′ 57.65″ S, 22° 47′ 17.23″ E (Eye alt 300 km)
Location: ______________________________
Landform Category: ______________________________
Specific Landform: ______________________________

(q) 22° 35′ 43.68″ S, 14° 31′ 09.36″ E (Eye alt 6 km)
Location: ______________________________
Landform Category: ______________________________
Specific Landform: ______________________________

(r) 44° 08′ 4.67″ N, 15° 18′ 56.25″ E (Eye alt 75 km)
Location: ______________________________
Landform Category: ______________________________
Specific Landform: ______________________________

(s) 25° 10′ 05.41″ N, 110° 11′ 43.86″ E (Eye alt 7 km)
Location:______________________________________
Landform Category:_________________________________
Specific Landform:_________________________________

(t) 24° 19′ 35.77″ N, 109° 34′ 20.29″ E (Eye alt 5 km)
Location:______________________________________
Landform Category:_________________________________
Specific Landform:_________________________________

(u) 23° 37′ 03.58″ N, 106° 53′ 45.00″ E (Eye alt 5 km)
Location:______________________________________
Landform Category:_________________________________
Specific Landform:_________________________________

(v) 44° 15′ 38.80″ N, 28° 36′ 14.34″ E (Eye alt 48 km)
Location:______________________________________
Landform Category:_________________________________
Specific Landform:_________________________________

The following locations can be examined using Google Earth™ Mars images.

(w) 13° 26′ 19″ N 90° 54′ 05″ W (Eye alt 100 miles)
Location:______________________________________
Landform Category:_________________________________
Specific Landform:_________________________________

(x) 10° 11′ 09″ N 157° 38′ 06″ E (Eye alt 10 miles)
Location:______________________________________
Landform Category:_________________________________
Specific Landform:_________________________________

(y) 7° 49′ 52″ N 154° 51′ 32″ E (Eye alt 15 miles)
Location:______________________________________
Landform Category:_________________________________
Specific Landform:_________________________________

(z) 42° 41′ 27″ S 161° 44′ 57″ W (Eye alt 15 miles)
Location:______________________________________
Landform Category:_________________________________
Specific Landform:_________________________________

Landform categories and specific landforms for question 14.7.

A. Volcanic Landforms

1. cinder cone
2. shield cone
3. composite cone
4. caldera
5. batholith
6. dike
7. volcanic neck

B. Structural Landforms

1. anticline
2. syncline
3. hogback
4. cuesta
5. dome
6. basin
7. horst
8. graben
9. joints in bedrock

C. Fluvial Landforms

1. meander
2. oxbow lake
3. youthful stream
4. mature stream
5. old age stream
6. delta
7. floodplain

D. Karst Landforms

1. dolines
2. cockpits
3. disappearing stream
4. polje
5. cone & tower karst
6. uvala

E. Glacial Landforms

1. hanging valley
2. ice-scoured bedrock
3. striations
4. U-shaped valley
5. horn
6. cirque
7. arête
8. tarn
9. fjord
10. valley glacier
11. ice dammed lake
12. radial crevasses

F. Periglacial Landforms

1. patterned ground
2. ice wedge polygon
3. thaw lake
4. thermokarst

G. Coastal Landforms

1. spit
2. barrier island
3. baymouth bar
4. beach ridges
5. lagoon
6. sand dunes
7. sea cliff
8. sea cave
9. sea stack
10. sea arch
11. wave-cut platform
12. emergent coastline
13. submergent coastline

H. Aeolian Landforms

1. yardang
2. desert pavement
3. butte
4. mesa
5. arroyo/wadi
6. alluvial fan
7. ephemeral lake/playa
8. barchan dune
9. relict linear dune
10. active linear dune
11. star dune

APPENDIX A

SELECTED BAR SCALES

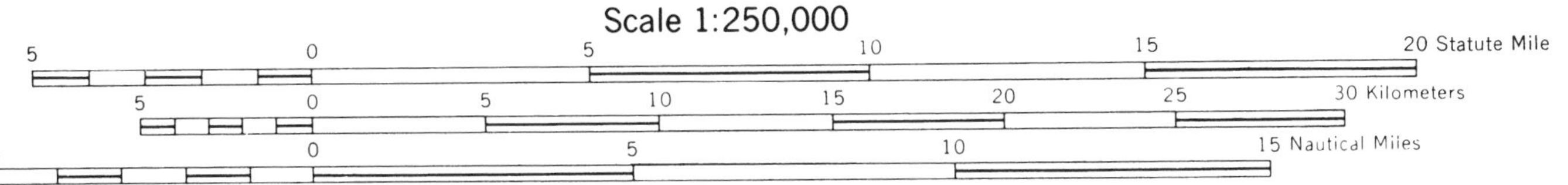

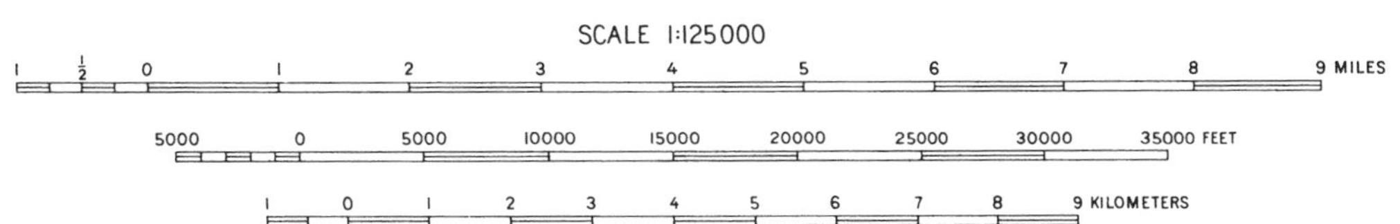

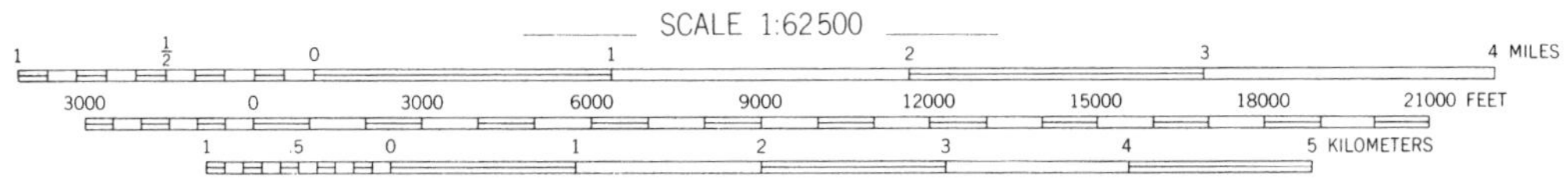

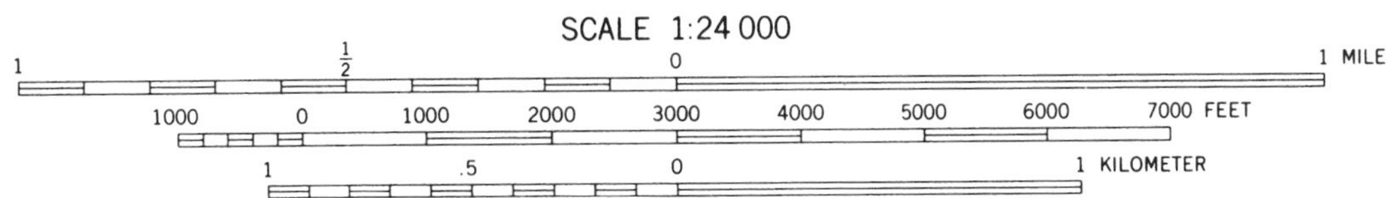

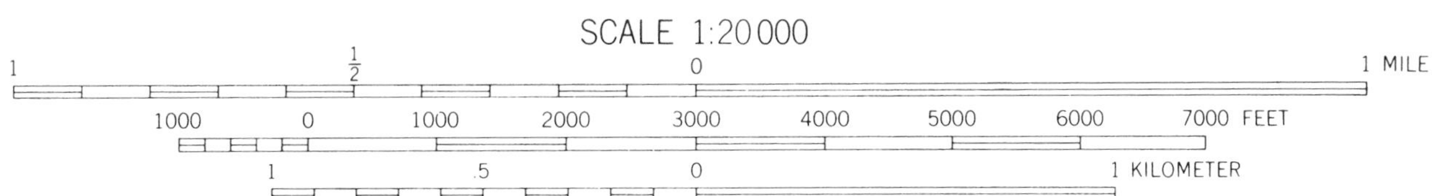

APPENDIX B

TANGENT TABLES

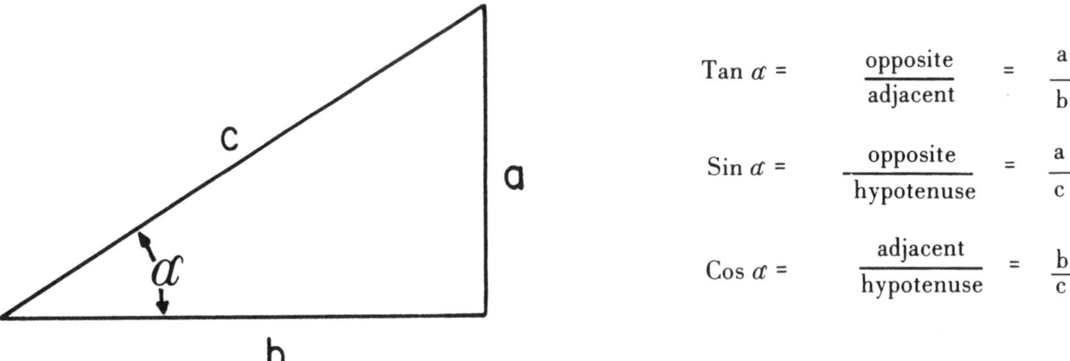

NATURAL TANGENTS

Degrees	0′ 0°·0	6′ 0°·1	12′ 0°·2	18′ 0°·3	24′ 0°·4	30′ 0°·5	36′ 0°·6	42′ 0°·7	48′ 0°·8	54′ 0°·9	Mean Differences 1	2	3	4	5
0	·0000	0017	0035	0052	0070	0087	0105	0122	0140	0157	3	6	9	12	15
1	·0175	0192	0209	0227	0244	0262	0279	0297	0314	0332	3	6	9	12	15
2	·0349	0367	0384	0402	0419	0437	0454	0472	0489	0507	3	6	9	12	15
3	·0524	0542	0559	0577	0594	0612	0629	0647	0664	0682	3	6	9	12	15
4	·0699	0717	0734	0752	0769	0787	0805	0822	0840	0857	3	6	9	12	15
5	·0875	0892	0910	0928	0945	0963	0981	0998	1016	1033	3	6	9	12	15
6	·1051	1069	1086	1104	1122	1139	1157	1175	1192	1210	3	6	9	12	15
7	·1228	1246	1263	1281	1299	1317	1334	1352	1370	1388	3	6	9	12	15
8	·1405	1423	1441	1459	1477	1495	1512	1530	1548	1566	3	6	9	12	15
9	·1584	1602	1620	1638	1655	1673	1691	1709	1727	1745	3	6	9	12	15
10	·1763	1781	1799	1817	1835	1853	1871	1890	1908	1926	3	6	9	12	15
11	·1944	1962	1980	1998	2016	2035	2053	2071	2089	2107	3	6	9	12	15
12	·2126	2144	2162	2180	2199	2217	2235	2254	2272	2290	3	6	9	12	15
13	·2309	2327	2345	2364	2382	2401	2419	2438	2456	2475	3	6	9	12	15
14	·2493	2512	2530	2549	2568	2586	2605	2623	2642	2661	3	6	9	12	16
15	·2679	2698	2717	2736	2754	2773	2792	2811	2830	2849	3	6	9	13	16
16	·2867	2886	2905	2924	2943	2962	2981	3000	3019	3038	3	6	9	13	16
17	·3057	3076	3096	3115	3134	3153	3172	3191	3211	3230	3	6	10	13	16
18	·3249	3269	3288	3307	3327	3346	3365	3385	3404	3424	3	6	10	13	16
19	·3443	3463	3482	3502	3522	3541	3561	3581	3600	3620	3	7	10	13	16
20	·3640	3659	3679	3699	3719	3739	3759	3779	3799	3819	3	7	10	13	17
21	·3839	3859	3879	3899	3919	3939	3959	3979	4000	4020	3	7	10	13	17
22	·4040	4061	4081	4101	4122	4142	4163	4183	4204	4224	3	7	10	14	17
23	·4245	4265	4286	4307	4327	4348	4369	4390	4411	4431	3	7	10	14	17
24	·4452	4473	4494	4515	4536	4557	4578	4599	4621	4642	4	7	11	14	18
25	·4663	4684	4706	4727	4748	4770	4791	4813	4834	4856	4	7	11	14	18
26	·4877	4899	4921	4942	4964	4986	5008	5029	5051	·5073	4	7	11	15	18
27	·5095	5117	5139	5161	5184	5206	5228	5250	5272	5295	4	7	11	15	18
28	·5317	5340	5362	5384	5407	5430	5452	5475	5498	5520	4	8	11	15	19
29	·5543	5566	5589	5612	5635	5658	5681	5704	5727	5750	4	8	12	15	19
30	·5774	5797	5820	5844	5867	5890	5914	5938	5961	5985	4	8	12	16	20
31	·6009	6032	6056	6080	6104	6128	6152	6176	6200	6224	4	8	12	16	20
32	·6249	6273	6297	6322	6346	6371	6395	6420	6445	6469	4	8	12	16	20
33	·6494	6519	6544	6569	6594	6619	6644	6669	6694	6720	4	8	13	17	21
34	·6745	6771	6796	6822	6847	6873	6899	6924	6950	6976	4	9	13	17	21
35	·7002	7028	7054	7080	7107	7133	7159	7186	7212	7239	4	9	13	18	22
36	·7265	7292	7319	7346	7373	7400	7427	7454	7481	7508	5	9	14	18	23
37	·7536	7563	7590	7618	7646	7673	7701	7729	7757	7785	5	9	14	18	23
38	·7813	7841	7869	7898	7926	7954	7983	8012	8040	8069	5	9	14	19	24
39	·8098	8127	8156	8185	8214	8243	8273	8302	8332	8361	5	10	15	20	24
40	·8391	8421	8451	8481	8511	8541	8571	8601	8632	8662	5	10	15	20	25
41	·8693	8724	8754	8785	8816	8847	8878	8910	8941	8972	5	10	16	21	26
42	·9004	9036	9067	9099	9131	9163	9195	9228	9260	9293	5	11	16	21	27
43	·9325	9358	9391	9424	9457	9490	9523	9556	9590	9623	6	11	17	22	28
44	·9657	9691	9725	9759	9793	9827	9861	9896	9930	9965	6	11	17	23	29

NATURAL TANGENTS

Degrees	0′ 0°·0	6′ 0°·1	12′ 0°·2	18′ 0°·3	24′ 0°·4	30′ 0°·5	36′ 0°·6	42′ 0°·7	48′ 0°·8	54′ 0°·9	Mean Differences 1	2	3	4	5
45	1·0000	0035	0070	0105	0141	0176	0212	0247	0283	0319	6	12	18	24	30
46	1·0355	0392	0428	0464	0501	0538	0575	0612	0649	0686	6	12	18	25	31
47	1·0724	0761	0799	0837	0875	0913	0951	0990	1028	1067	6	13	19	25	32
48	1·1106	1145	1184	1224	1263	1303	1343	1383	1423	1463	7	13	20	27	33
49	1·1504	1544	1585	1626	1667	1708	1750	1792	1833	1875	7	14	21	28	34
50	1·1918	1960	2002	2045	2088	2131	2174	2218	2261	2305	7	14	22	29	36
51	1·2349	2393	2437	2482	2527	2572	2617	2662	2708	2753	8	15	23	30	38
52	1·2799	2846	2892	2938	2985	3032	3079	3127	3175	3222	8	16	24	31	39
53	1·3270	3319	3367	3416	3465	3514	3564	3613	3663	3713	8	16	25	33	41
54	1·3764	3814	3865	3916	3968	4019	4071	4124	4176	4229	9	17	26	34	43
55	1·4281	4335	4388	4442	4496	4550	4605	4659	4715	4770	9	18	27	36	45
56	1·4826	4882	4938	4994	5051	5108	5166	5224	5282	5340	10	19	29	38	48
57	1·5399	5458	5517	5577	5637	5697	5757	5818	5880	5941	10	20	30	40	50
58	1·6003	6066	6128	6191	6255	6319	6383	6447	6512	6577	11	21	32	43	53
59	1·6643	6709	6775	6842	6909	6977	7045	7113	7182	7251	11	23	34	45	56
60	1·7321	7391	7461	7532	7603	7675	7747	7820	7893	7966	12	24	36	48	60
61	1·8040	8115	8190	8265	8341	8418	8495	8572	8650	8728	13	26	38	51	64
62	1·8807	8887	8967	9047	9128	9210	9292	9375	9458	9542	14	27	41	55	68
63	1·9626	9711	9797	9883	9970	2·0057	2·0145	2·0233	2·0323	2·0413	15	29	44	58	73
64	2·0503	0594	0686	0778	0872	0965	1060	1155	1251	1348	16	31	47	63	78
65	2·1445	1543	1642	1742	1842	1943	2045	2148	2251	2355	17	34	51	68	85
66	2·2460	2566	2673	2781	2889	2998	3109	3220	3332	3445	18	37	55	73	92
67	2·3559	3673	3789	3906	4023	4142	4262	4383	4504	4627	20	40	60	79	99
68	2·4751	4876	5002	5129	5257	5386	5517	5649	5782	5916	22	43	65	87	108
69	2·6051	6187	6325	6464	6605	6746	6889	7034	7179	7326	24	47	71	95	119
70	2·7475	7625	7776	7929	8083	8239	8397	8556	8716	8878	26	52	78	104	131
71	2·9042	9208	9375	9544	9714	9887	3·0061	3·0237	3·0415	3·0595	29	58	87	116	145
72	3·0777	0961	1146	1334	1524	1716	1910	2106	2305	2506	32	64	96	129	161
73	3·2709	2914	3122	3332	3544	3759	3977	4197	4420	4646	36	72	108	144	180
74	3·4874	5105	5339	5576	5816	6059	6305	6554	6806	7062	41	81	122	163	204
75	3·7321	7583	7848	8118	8391	8667	8947	9232	9520	9812	46	93	139	186	232
76	4·0108	0408	0713	1022	1335	1653	1976	2303	2635	2972	53	107	160	213	267
77	4·3315	3662	4015	4374	4737	5107	5483	5864	6252	6646					
78	4·7046	7453	7867	8288	8716	9152	9594	5·0045	5·0504	5·0970					
79	5·1446	1929	2422	2924	3435	3955	4486	5026	5578	6140					
80	5·6713	7297	7894	8502	9124	9758	6·0405	6·1066	6·1742	6·2432					
81	6·3138	3859	4596	5350	6122	6912	7720	8548	9395	7·0264					
82	7·1154	2066	3002	3962	4947	5958	6996	8062	9158	8·0285					
83	8·1443	2636	3863	5126	6427	7769	9152	9·0579	9·2052	9·3572					
84	9·5144	9·677	9·845	10·02	10·20	10·39	10·58	10·78	10·99	11·20					
85	11·43	11·66	11·91	12·16	12·43	12·71	13·00	13·30	13·62	13·95					
86	14·30	14·67	15·06	15·46	15·89	16·35	16·83	17·34	17·89	18·46					
87	19·08	19·74	20·45	21·20	22·02	22·90	23·86	24·90	26·03	27·27					
88	28·64	30·14	31·82	33·69	35·80	38·19	40·92	44·07	47·74	52·08					
89	57·29	63·66	71·62	81·85	95·49	114·6	143·2	191·0	286·5	573·0					
90	∞														

Mean differences cease to be sufficiently accurate.

APPENDIX C

CONVERSION TABLES

Metric Units

Length

100 centimeters = 1 meter

1,000 meters = 1 kilometer

Area

1 square kilometer = 100 hectares

1 square meter = 10,000 square centimeters

Volume

1 liter = 0.001 cubic meter
or 1 cubic decimeter

1 cubic meter = 1,000,000 cubic centimeters (milliliters)

Weight

1 kilogram = 1,000 grams

1 metric ton = 1,000 kilograms

Energy

1 calorie = amount of heat required to raise 1 gram of water 1C°, with water at a temperature of 4°C.

English Units

1 square mile = 640 acres

1 acre = 43,560 square feet

1 barrel = 42 gallons

Metric Prefixes

mega	= 10^6	(1,000,000)
kilo	= 10^3	(1,000)
hecto	= 10^2	(100)
deci	= 10^{-1}	(0.1)
centi	= 10^{-2}	(0.01)
milli	= 10^{-3}	(0.001)

Boiling temperature =	212°F =	100°C
Freezing temperature =	32°F =	0°C
Difference:	180°	100°
Ratio:	9:5	

English-Metric Conversions

1 inch = 2.54 centimeters

1 foot = 0.3048 meter

1 yard = 0.9144 meter

1 mile = 1.609 kilometers

1 square mile = 2.590 square kilometers

1 acre = 0.4047 hectare

1 cubic foot = 0.0283 cubic meter

1 gallon = 3.784 liters

1 pound = 0.4536 kilogram

1 Fahrenheit degree = 0.56 Celcius degree

Metric-English Conversions

1 centimeter = 0.394 inch

1 meter = 3.281 feet or 1.094 yards

1 kilometer = 0.6214 mile

1 square meter = 1.196 square yards

1 hectare = 2.471 acres

1 square kilometer = 0.386 square mile

1 cubic meter = 1.308 cubic yards

1 liter = 1.057 quarts

1 kilogram = 2.205 pounds

1 Celsius degree = 1.8 Fahrenheit degrees

Formulas

Area of circle = $\pi r^2 = 0.785\ d^2$

circumference of circle = $\pi d = 2\pi r$

surface of sphere = $4\pi r^2$

volume of sphere = $\frac{4}{3}\pi r^3 = \frac{1}{6}\pi d^3 = 4.19 r^3$

$\pi = 3.1416$

APPENDIX D

3-D ANAGLYPHS

Anaglyph #	Corresponding Figure (Page#)	Name
1	n/a	Kilaua Crater, Hawai'i, USA
2	n/a	Kilaua Crater, Hawai'i, USA
3	Fig. 5.3 (p. 5-6)	Menan Buttes, Idaho, USA
4	Fig. 5.3 (p. 5-6)	Menan Buttes, Idaho, USA
5	Fig. 5.4 (p. 5-8)	Asama Volcano, Japan
6	Fig. 5.5 (p. 5-11)	Spanish Peaks, Colorado, USA
7	Fig. 6.8a (p. 6-11)	Pine Mountain, Oklahoma, USA
8	Fig. 6.8b (p. 6-12)	Pine Mountain, Oklahoma, USA
9	Fig. 6.9 (p. 6-14)	Circle Ridge, Wyoming, USA
10	Fig. 6.9 (p. 6-14)	Circle Ridge, Wyoming, USA
11	Fig. 6.12 (p. 6-19)	Santa Ana Mesa, New Mexico, USA
12	Fig. 6.12 (p. 6-19)	Santa Ana Mesa, New Mexico, USA
13	Fig. 7.3 (p. 7-5)	King Hill, Idaho, USA
14	Fig. 7.4 (p. 7-7)	Slumgullion, Colorado, USA
15	Fig. 9.3 (p. 9-5)	Park City, Kentucky, USA
16	Fig. 9.6 (p. 9-12)	Manati, Puerto Rico
17	Fig. 10.5 (p. 10-10)	Crillon Glacier, Alaska, USA
18	Fig. 10.5 (p. 10-10)	Crillon Glacier, Alaska, USA
19	n/a	Sunkhaze Stream, Maine, USA
20	Fig. 10.7 (p. 10-14)	Kidder County, North Dakota, USA
21	Fig. 10.8 (p. 10-16)	Fond du Lac, Wisconsin, USA
22	Fig. 10.8 (p. 10-16)	Fond du Lac, Wisconsin, USA
23	Fig. 11.2 (p. 11-4)	Point Barrow, Alaska, USA
24	Fig. 12.5 (p. 12-10)	Provincetown, Massachusetts, USA
25	Fig. 12.7 (p. 12-13)	Eel Point, San Clemente Island, California, USA
26	Fig. 13.3 (p. 13-6)	Sacaton Mountains, Arizona, USA
27	Fig. 13.6 (p. 13-10)	Comb Ridge, Arizona, USA
28	Fig. 13.7 (p. 13-12)	Khārān Kalāt, Pakistan
29	Fig. 14.2 (p. 14-5)	Little Cottonwood Canyon, Utah, USA
30	Fig. 14.2 (p. 14-5)	Little Cottonwood Canyon, Utah, USA
31	Fig. 14.3a (p. 14-7)	Beartooth Mountains, Wyoming, USA
32	Fig. 14.3b (p. 14-8)	Beartooth Mountains, Wyoming, USA
33	Fig. 14.4 (p. 14-10)	Kapoho, Hawai'i, USA (1954)
34	Fig. 14.5 (p. 14-11)	Kapoho, Hawai'i, USA (1961)

#1 Kilaua Crater, Hawai'i, USA

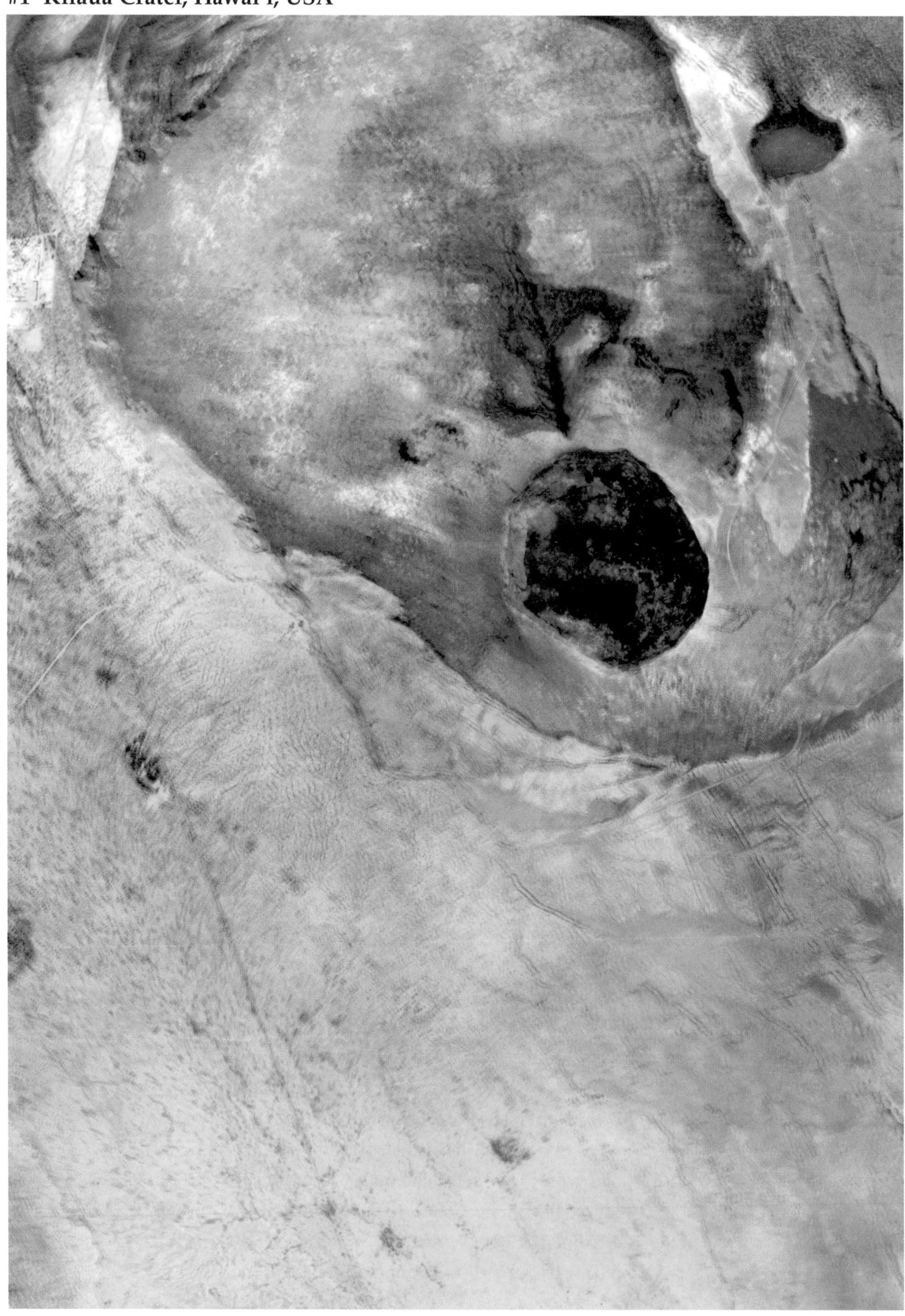

#2 Kilaua Crater, Hawai'i, USA

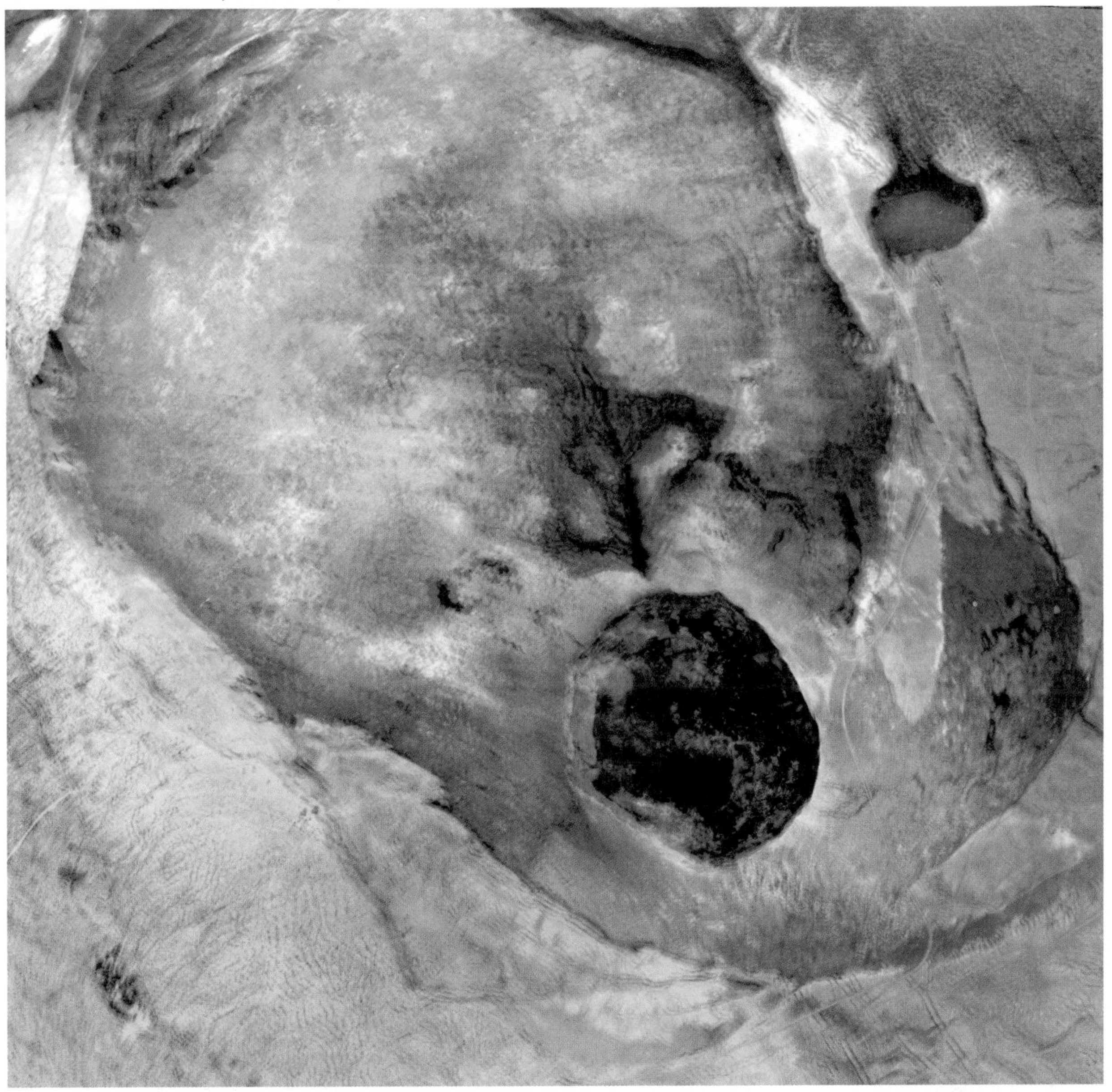

#3 Menan Buttes, Idaho, USA

#4 Menan Buttes, Idaho, USA

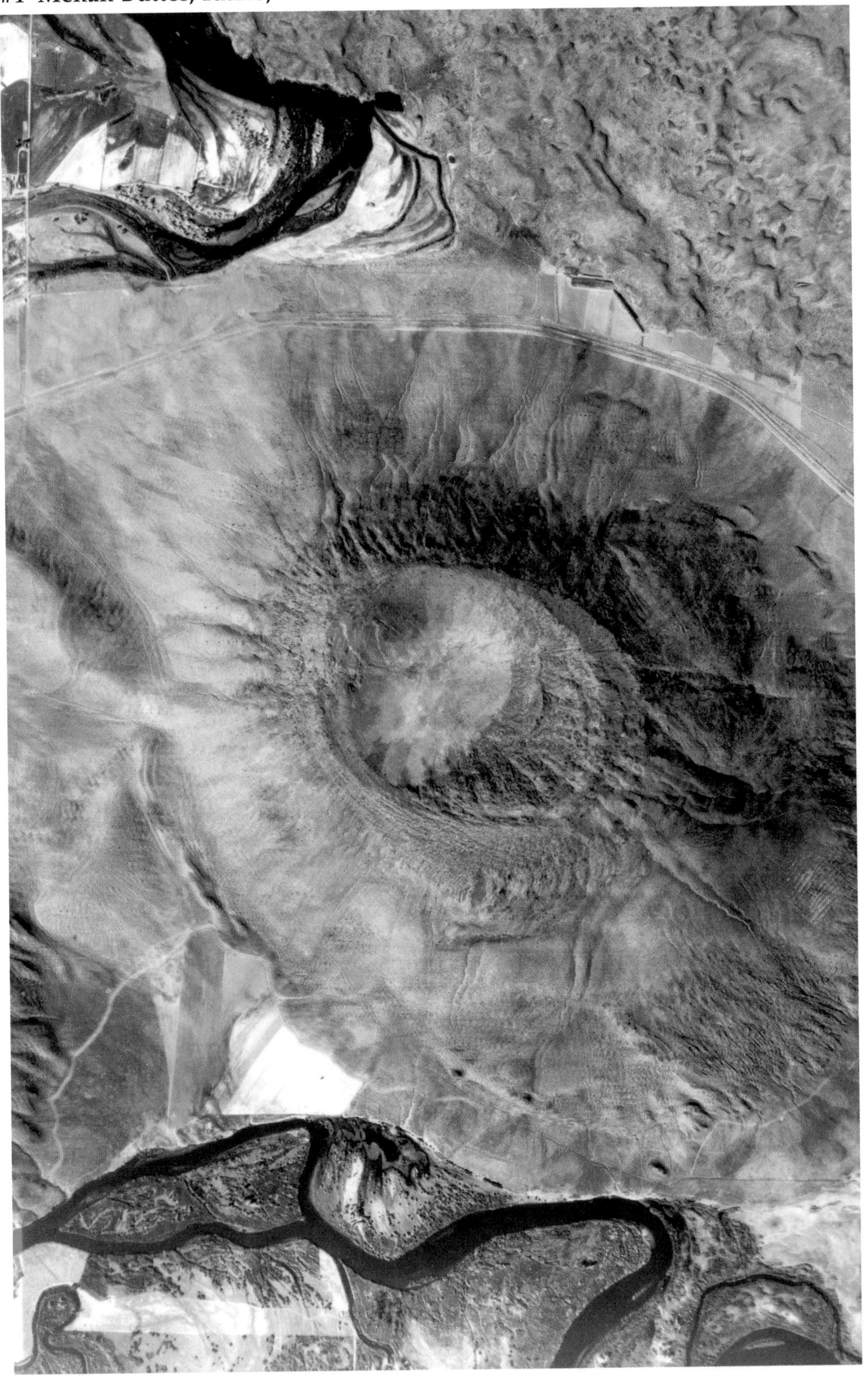

#5 Asama Volcano, Japan

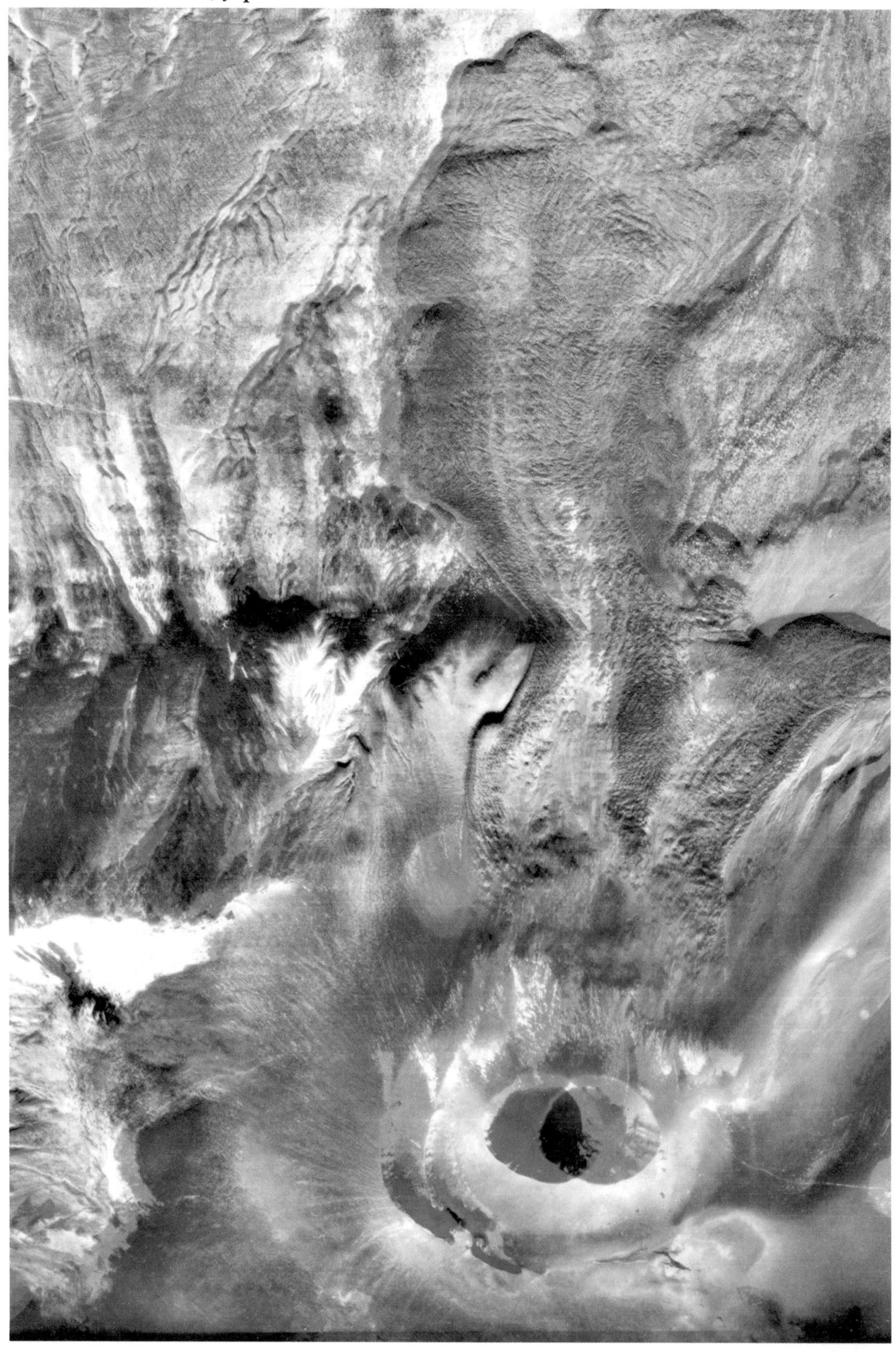

#6 Spanish Peaks, Colorado, USA

#7 Pine Mountain, Oklahoma, USA

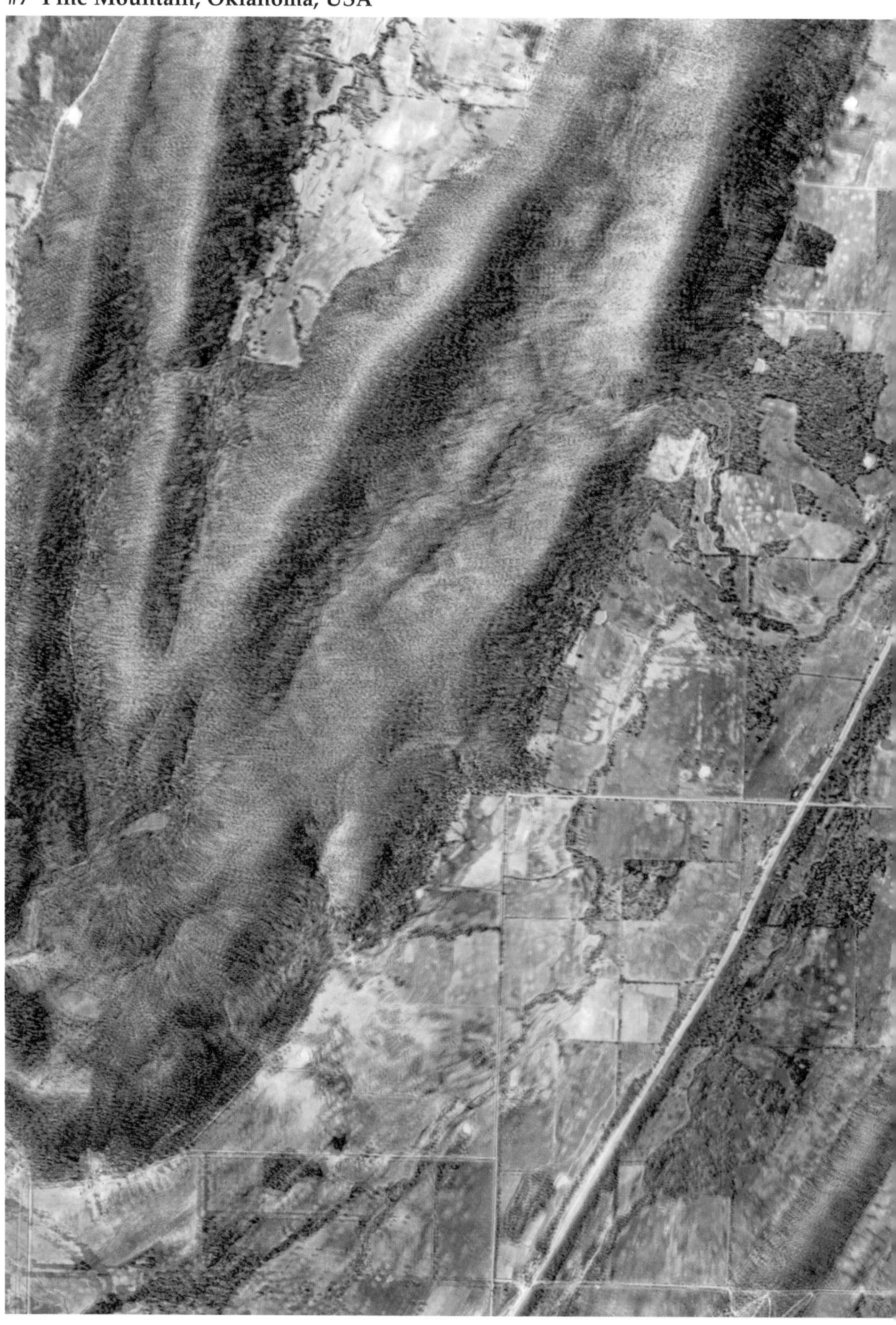

#8 Pine Mountain, Oklahoma, USA

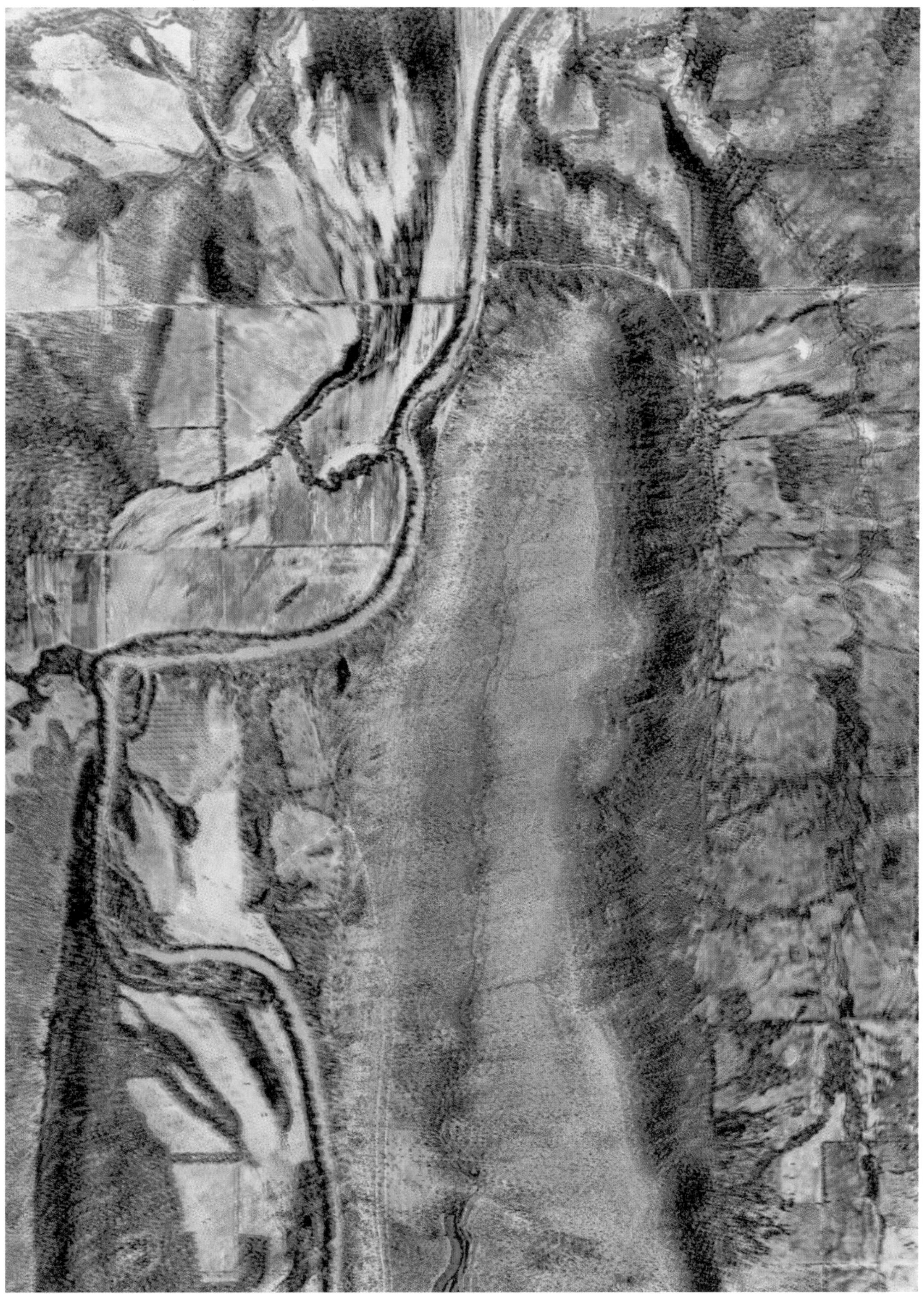

#9 Circle Ridge, Wyoming, USA

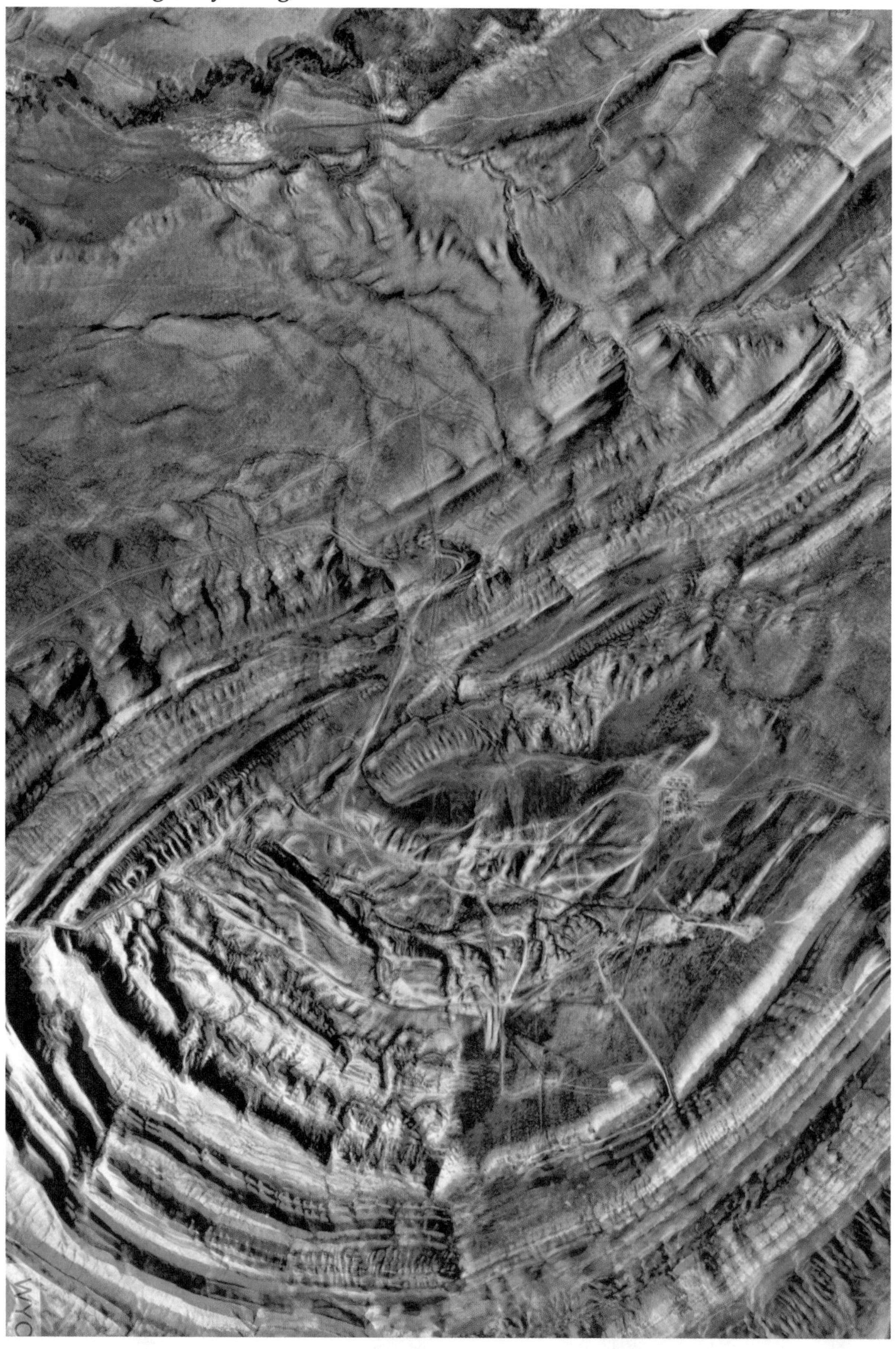

#10 Circle Ridge, Wyoming, USA

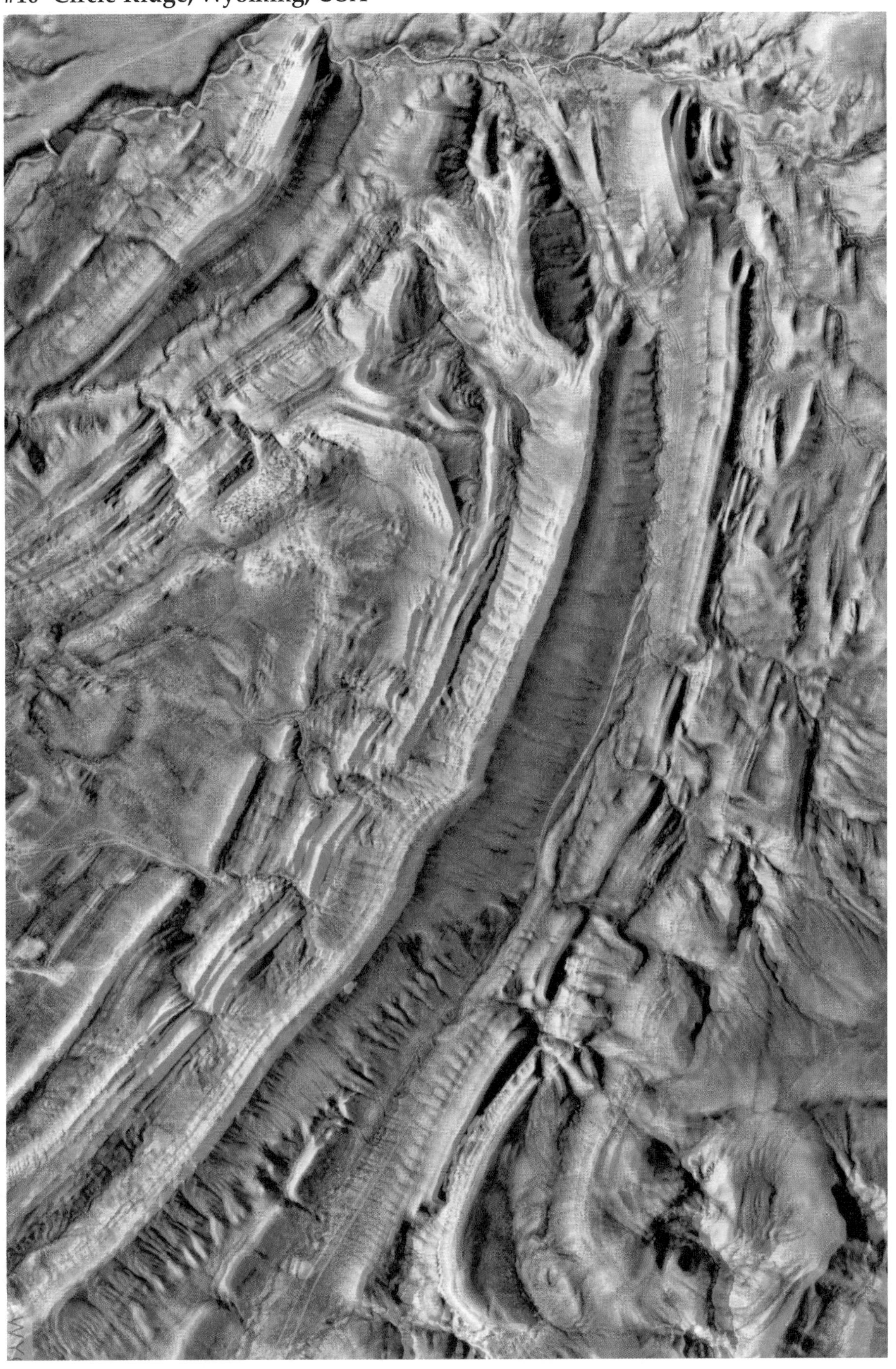

#11 Santa Ana Mesa, New Mexico, USA

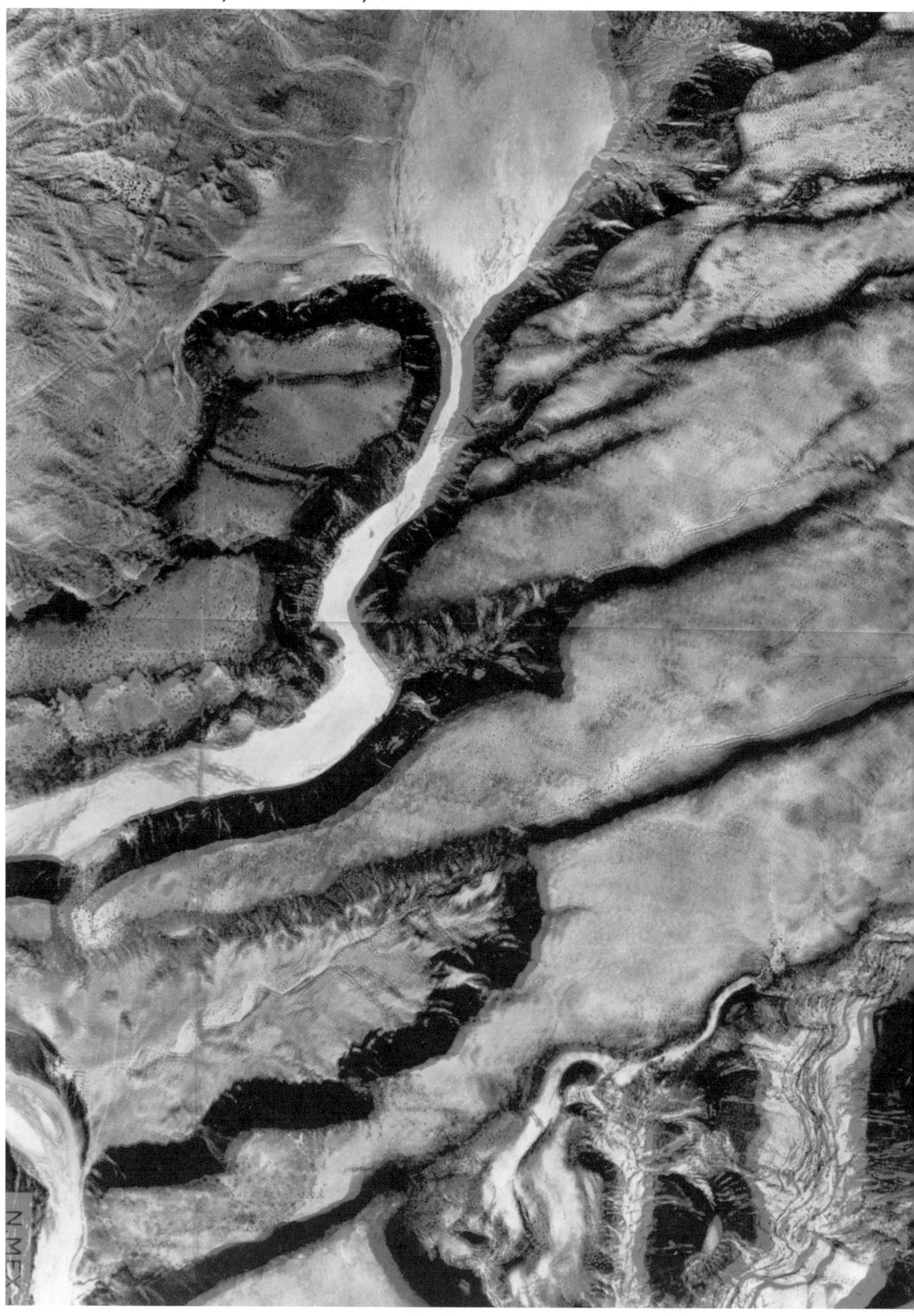

#12 Santa Ana Mesa, New Mexico, USA

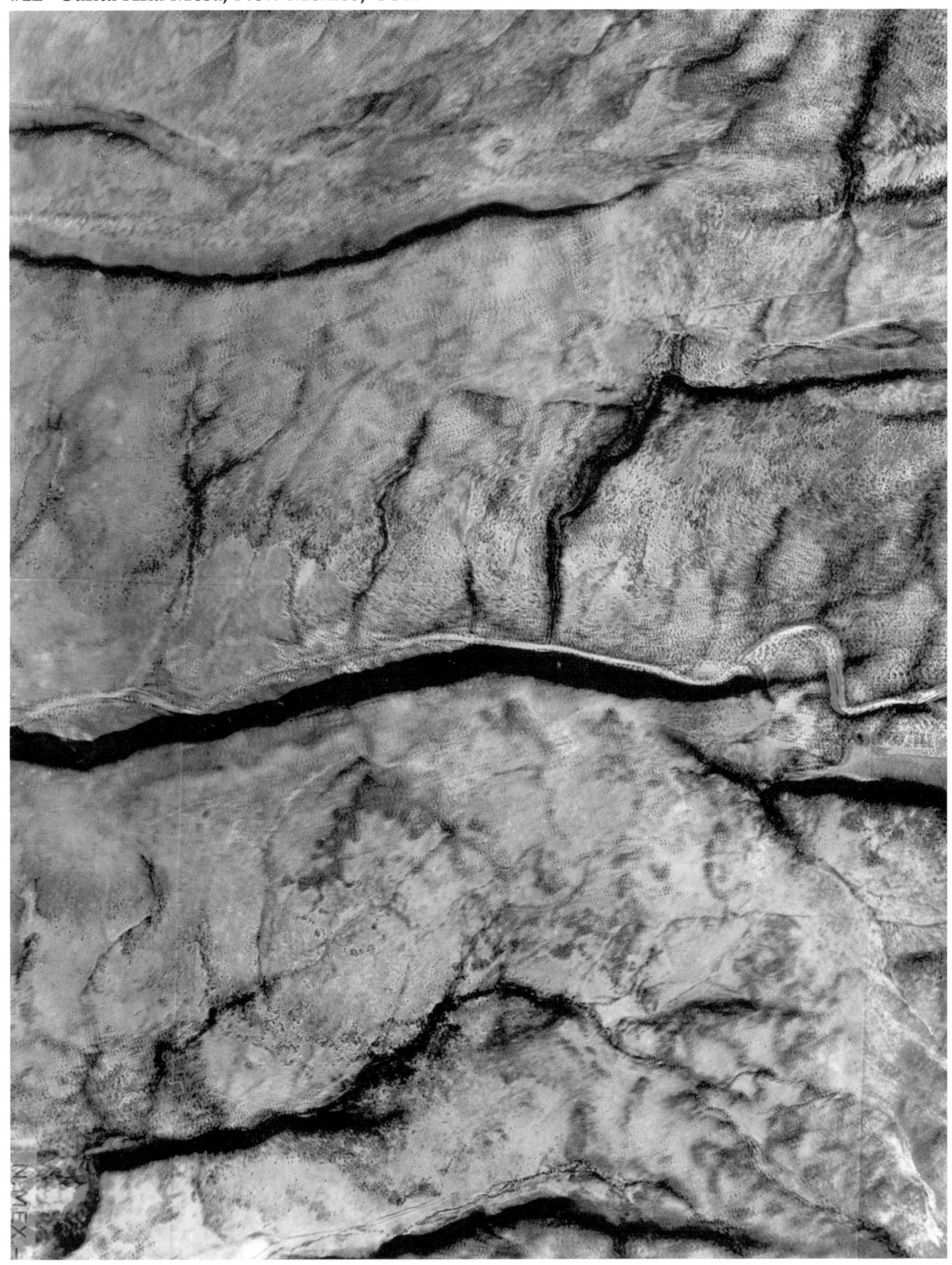

#13 King Hill, Idaho, USA

#14 Slumgullion, Colorado, USA

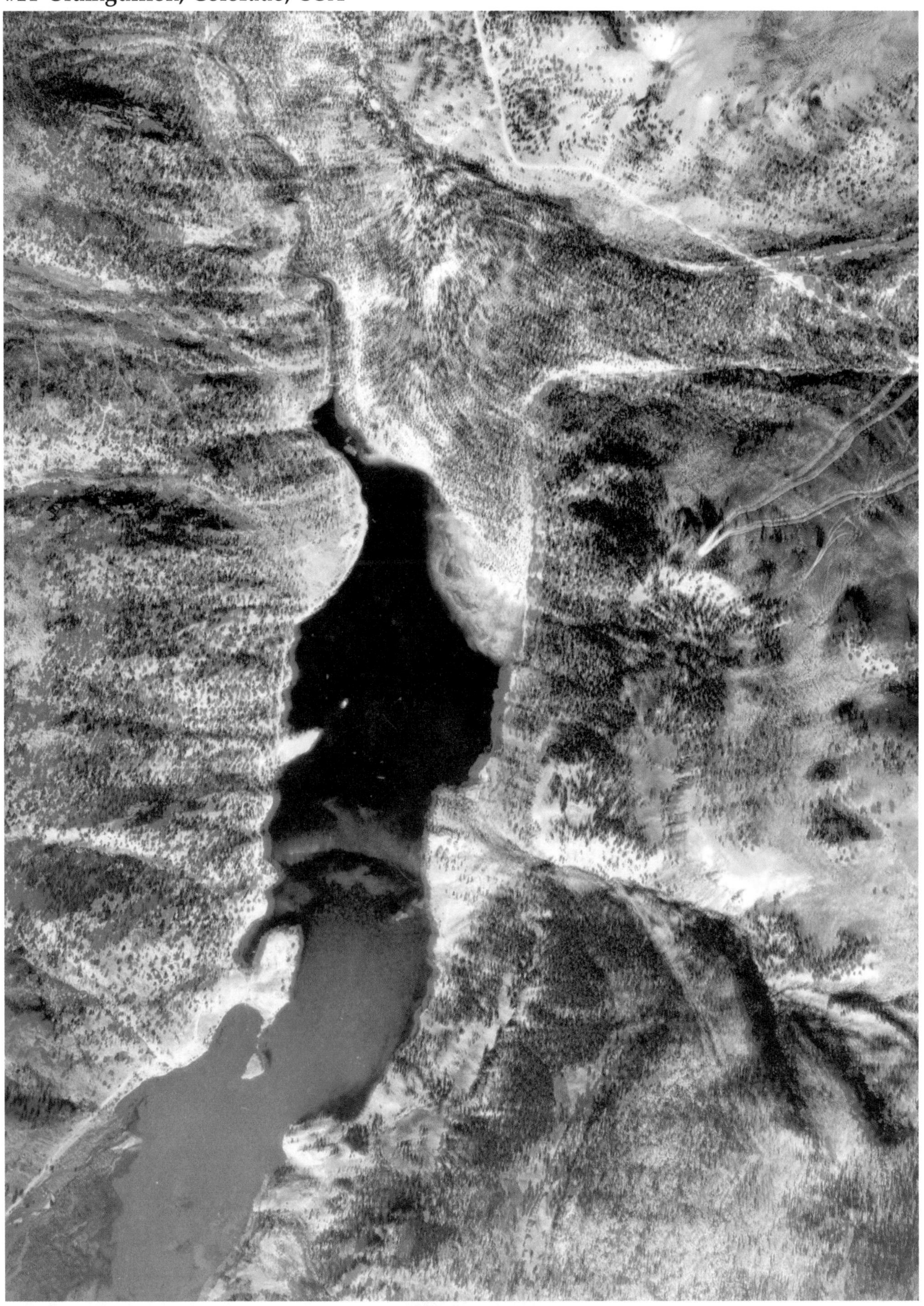

#15 Park City, Kentucky, USA

#16 Manati, Puerto Rico

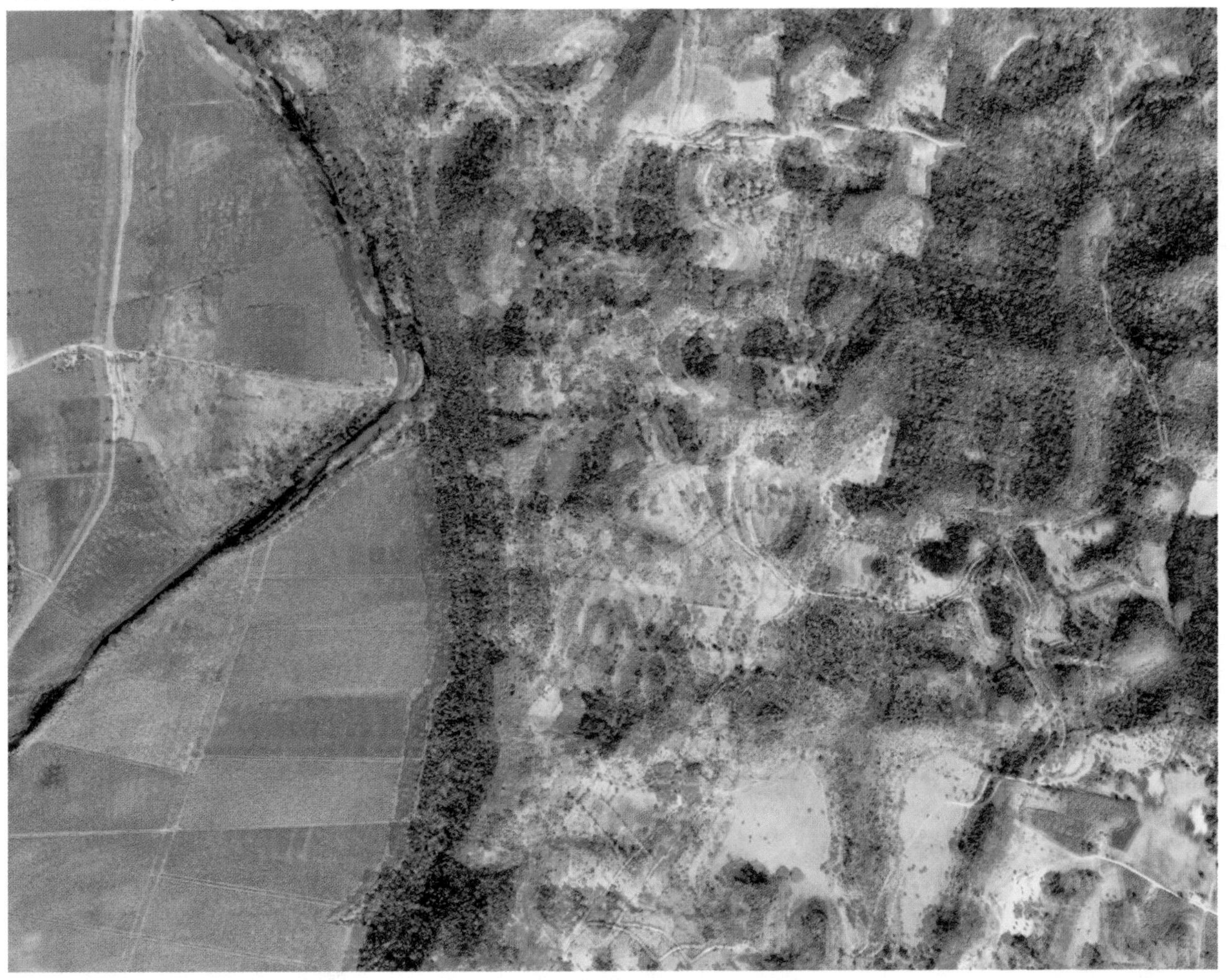

#17 Crillon Glacier, Alaska, USA

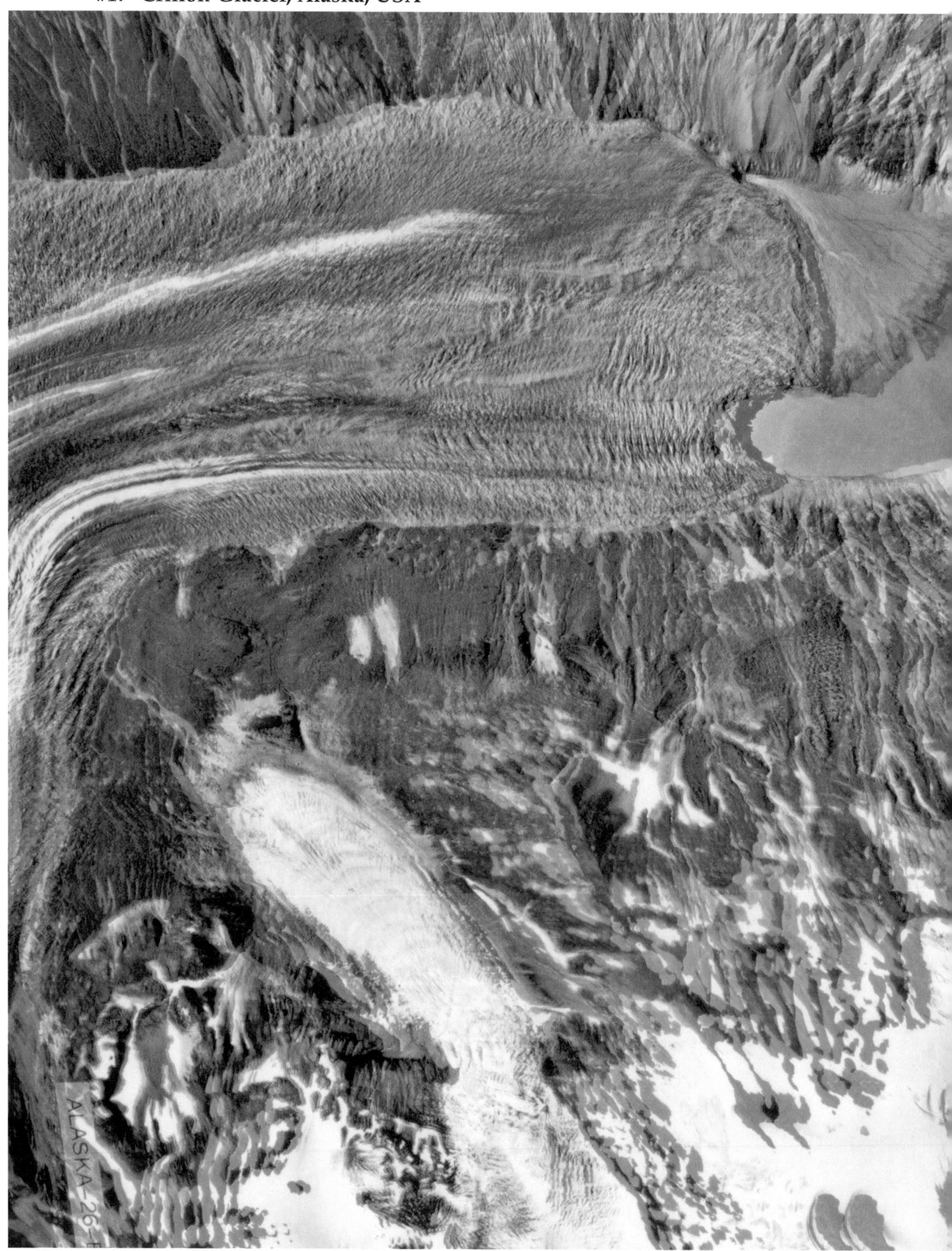

#18 Crillon Glacier, Alaska, USA

#19 Sunkhaze Stream, Maine, USA

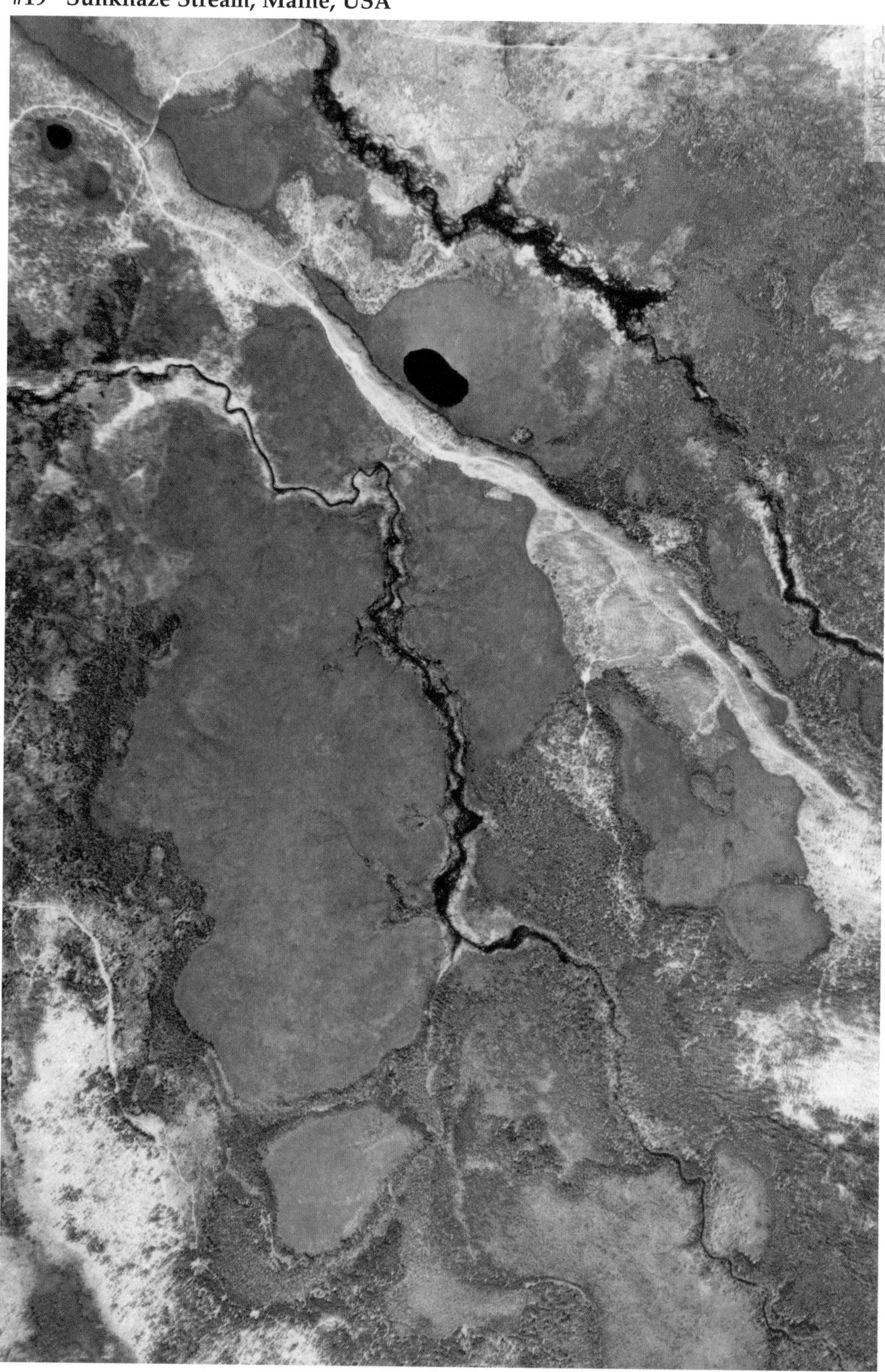

#20 Kidder County, North Dakota, USA

#21 Fond du Lac, Wisconsin, USA

#22 Fond du Lac, Wisconsin, USA

#23 Point Barrow, Alaska, USA

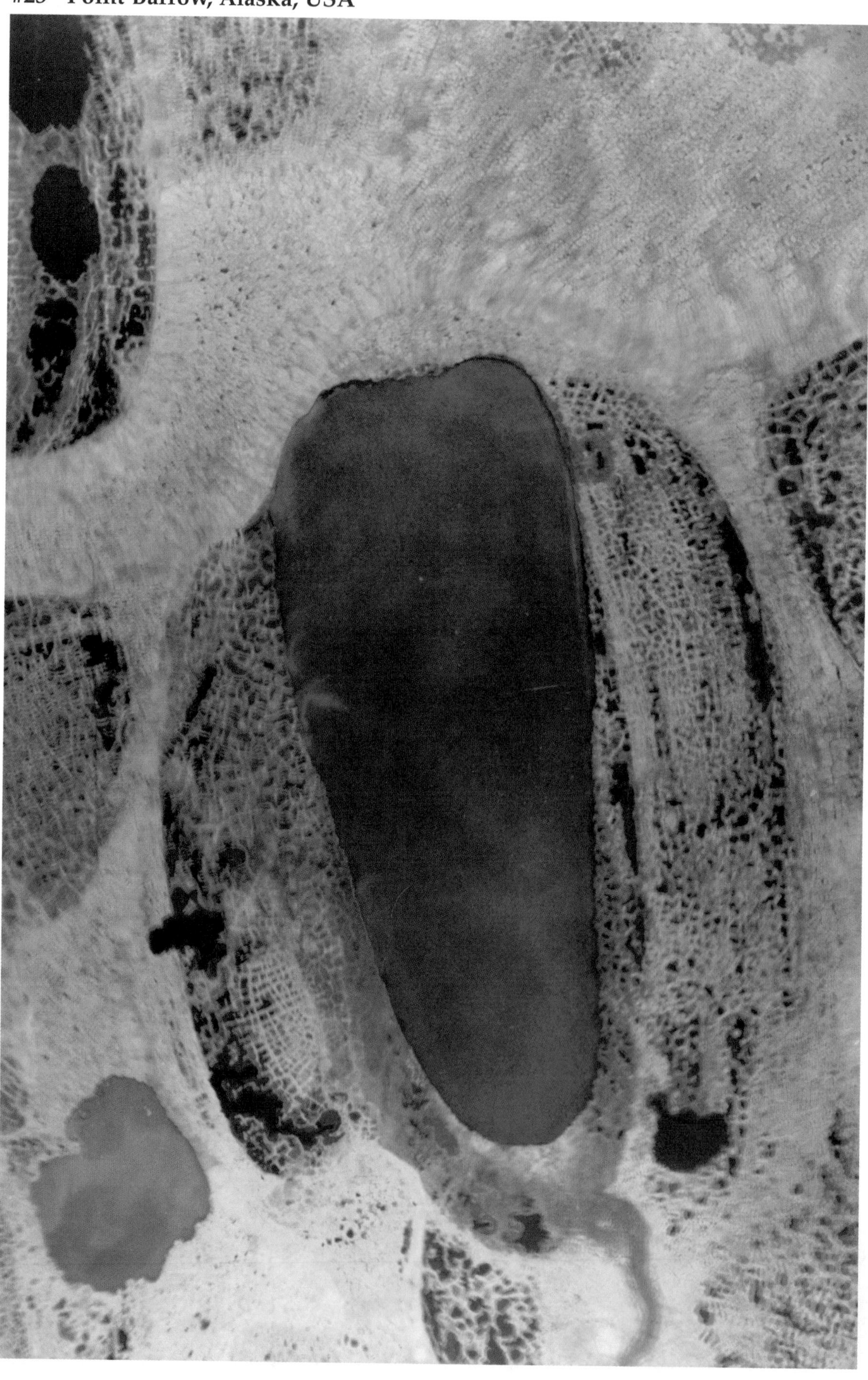

#24 Provincetown, Massachusetts, USA

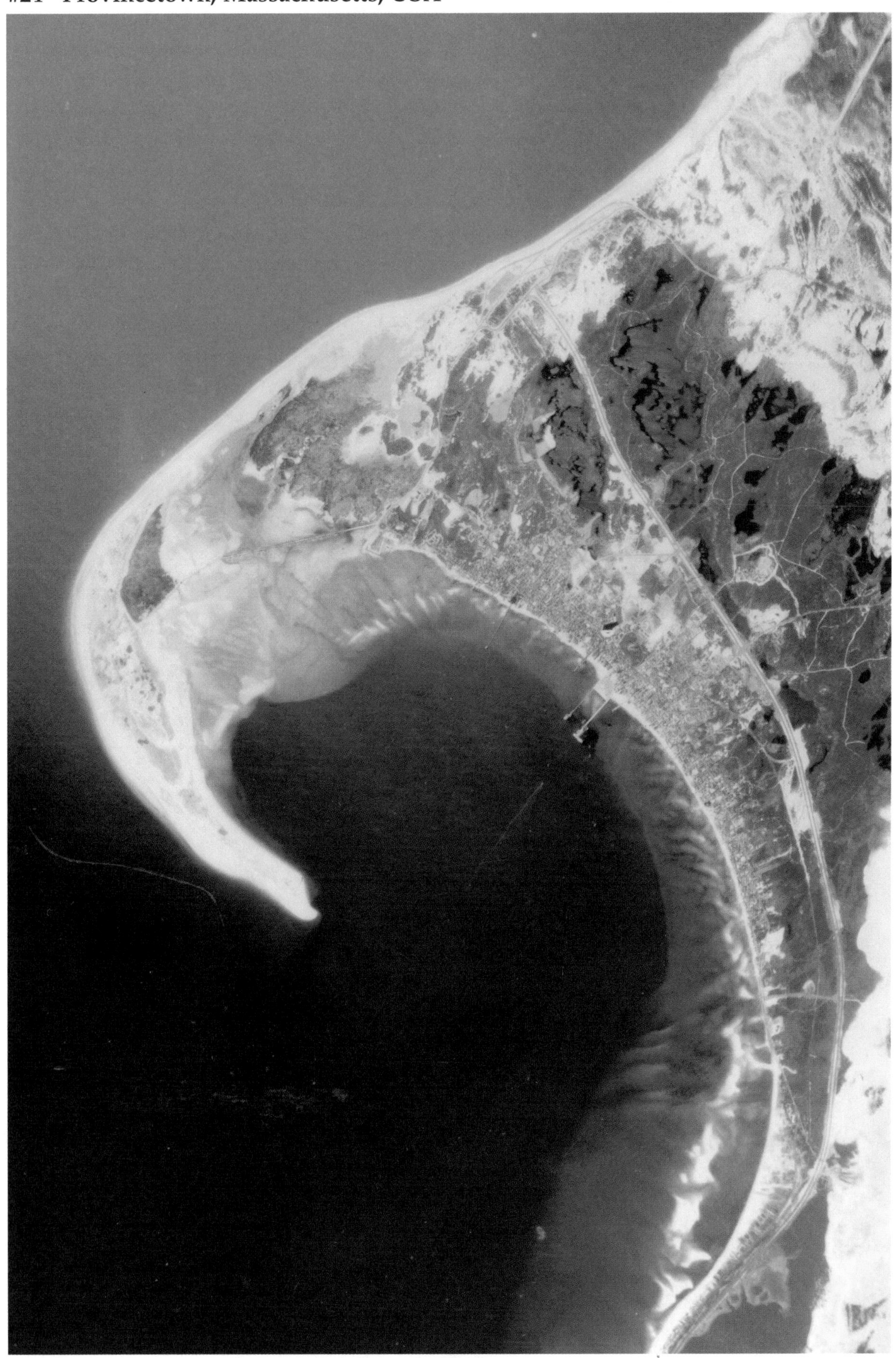

#25 Eel Point, San Clemente Island, California, USA

#26 Sacaton Mountains, Arizona, USA

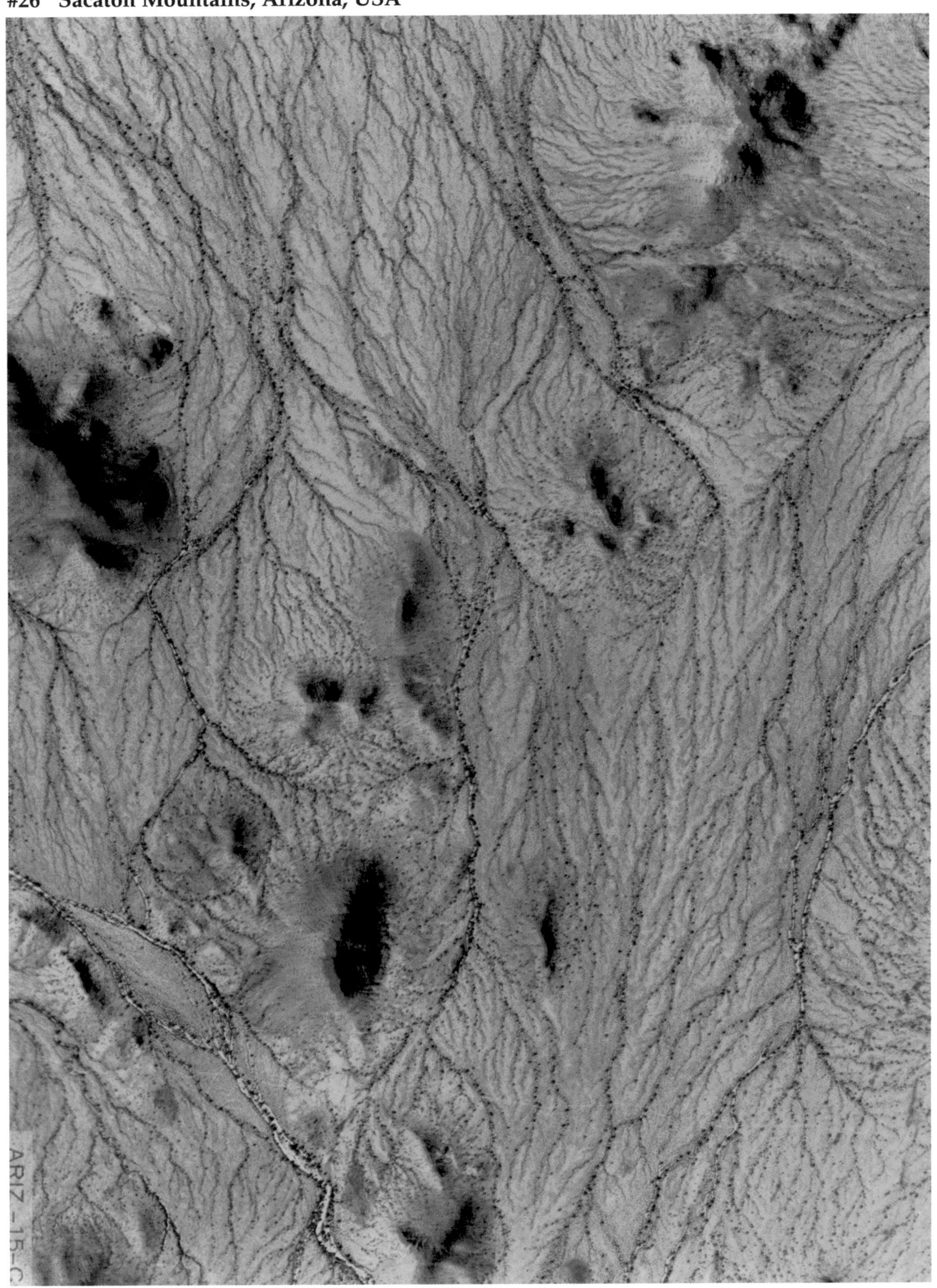

#27 Comb Ridge, Arizona, USA

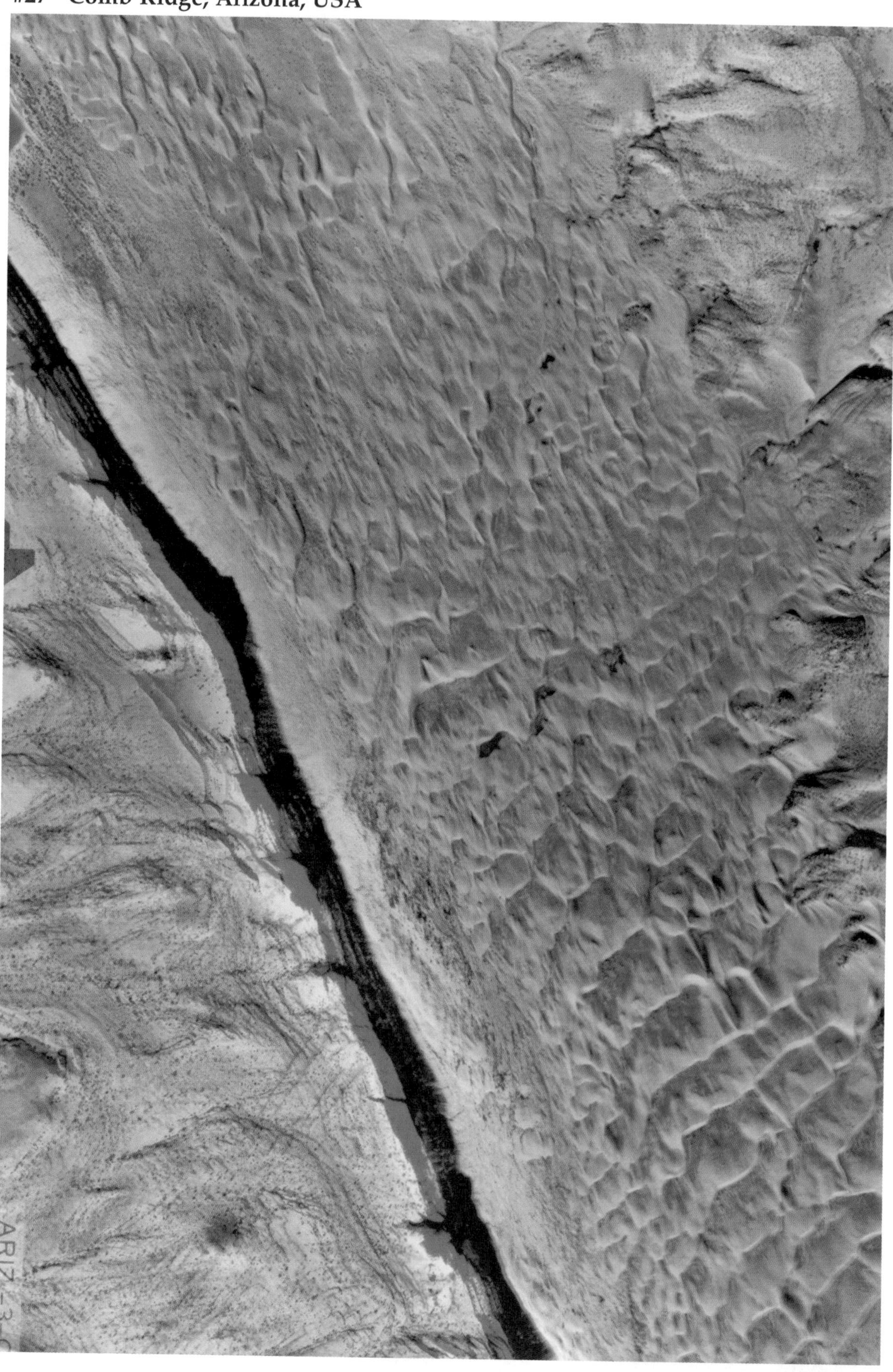

#28 Kharan Kalat, Pakistan

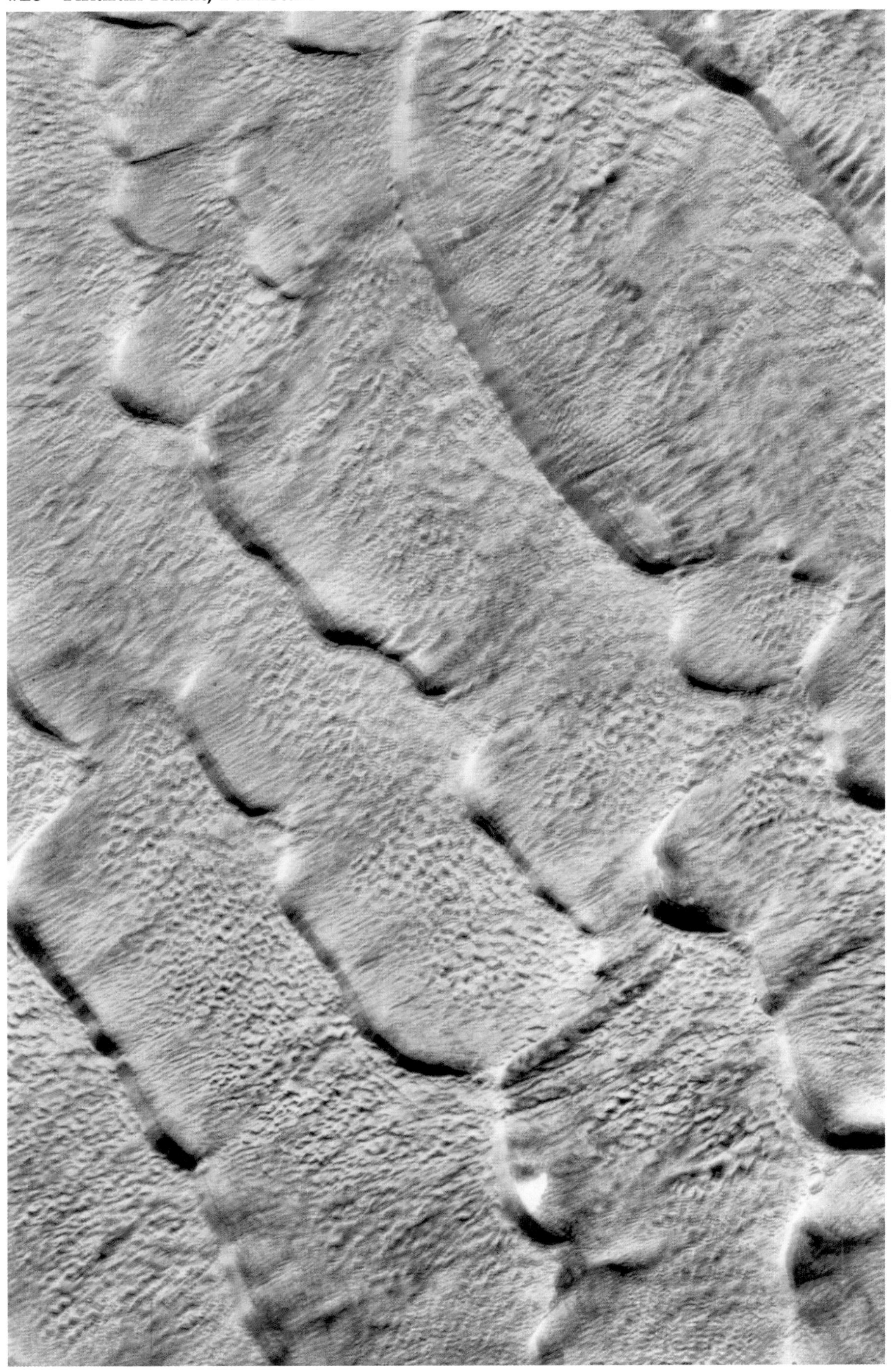

#29 Little Cottonwood Canyon, Utah, USA

#30 Little Cottonwood Canyon, Utah, USA

#31 Beartooth Mountains, Wyoming, USA

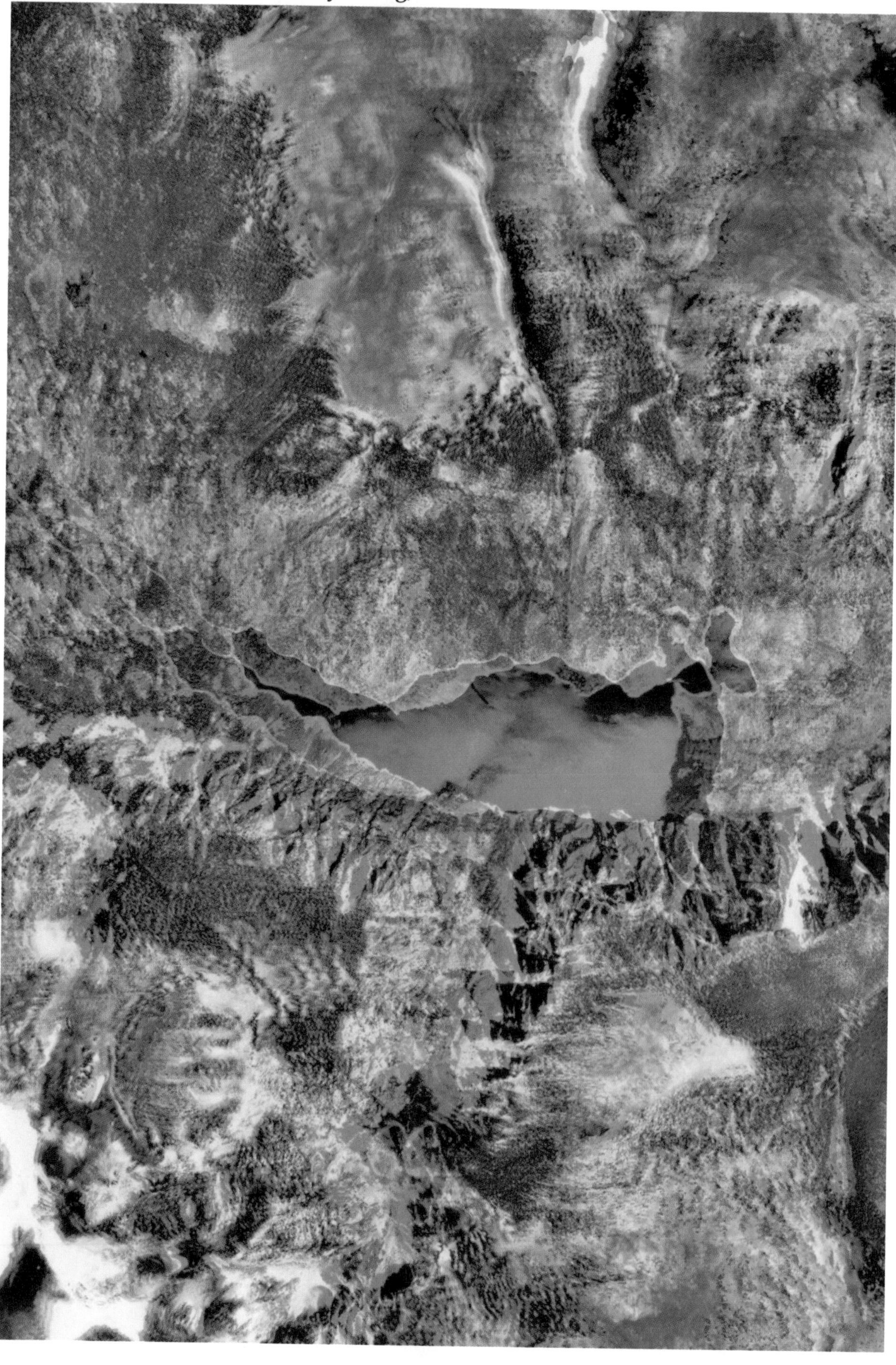

#32 Beartooth Mountains, Wyoming, USA

#33 Kapoho, Hawai'i, USA (1954)

#34 Kapoho, Hawai'i, USA (1961)

APPENDIX E

GEOLOGIC TIME SCALE

EONOTHEM / EON	ERATHEM / ERA	SYSTEM,SUBSYSTEM / PERIOD,SUBPERIOD		SERIES / EPOCH	Age estimates of boundaries in mega-annum (Ma) unless otherwise noted
Phanerozoic	Cenozoic (Cz)	Quaternary (Q)		Holocene	11,477 ±85 yr
				Pleistocene	1.806 ±0.005
		Tertiary (T)	Neogene (N)	Pliocene	5.332 ±0.005
				Miocene	23.03 ±0.05
			Paleogene (Pg)	Oligocene	33.9 ±0.1
				Eocene	55.8 ±0.2
				Paleocene	65.5 ±0.3
	Mesozoic (Mz)	Cretaceous (K)		Upper / Late	99.6 ±0.9
				Lower / Early	145.5 ±4.0
		Jurassic (J)		Upper / Late	161.2 ±4.0
				Middle	175.6 ±2.0
				Lower / Early	199.6 ±0.6
		Triassic (TR)		Upper / Late	228.0 ±2.0
				Middle	245.0 ±1.5
				Lower / Early	251.0 ±0.4
	Paleozoic (Pz)	Permian (P)		Lopingian	260.4 ±0.7
				Guadalupian	270.6 ±0.7
				Cisuralian	299.0 ±0.8
		Carboniferous (C)	Pennsylvanian (ℙ)	Upper / Late	306.5 ±1.0
				Middle	311.7 ±1.1
				Lower / Early	318.1 ±1.3
			Mississippian (M)	Upper / Late	326.4 ±1.6
				Middle	345.3 ±2.1
				Lower / Early	359.2 ±2.5
		Devonian (D)		Upper / Late	385.3 ±2.6
				Middle	397.5 ±2.7
				Lower / Early	416.0 ±2.8
		Silurian (S)		Pridoli	418.7 ±2.7
				Ludlow	422.9 ±2.5
				Wenlock	428.2 ±2.3
				Llandovery	443.7 ±1.5
		Ordovician (O)		Upper / Late	460.9 ±1.6
				Middle	471.8 ±1.6
				Lower / Early	488.3 ±1.7
		Cambrian (Є)		Upper / Late	501.0 ±2.0
				Middle	513.0 ±2.0
				Lower / Early	542.0 ±1.0

EONOTHEM / EON	ERATHEM / ERA	SYSTEM / PERIOD	Age estimates of boundaries in mega-annum (Ma) unless otherwise noted
Proterozoic (Ᵽ)	Neoproterozoic (Z)	Ediacaran	630
		Cryogenian	850
		Tonian	1000
	Mesoproterozoic (Y)	Stenian	1200
		Ectasian	1400
		Calymmian	1600
	Paleoproterozoic (X)	Statherian	1800
		Orosirian	2050
		Rhyacian	2300
		Siderian	2500
Archean (A)	Neoarchean		2800
	Mesoarchean		3200
	Paleoarchean		3600
	Eoarchean		~4000
Hadean (pA)			

Selected References

Billings, M. P. (1954). *Structural Geology*, Prentice-Hall, Inc., 514 pp.

Bolt, B. A.; Horn, W. L.; Macdonald, G. A.; and Scott, R. F. (1975). *Geological Hazards*, Springer-Verlag, 328 pp.

Butzer, K. W. (1976). *Geomorphology from the Earth.* Harper and Row, 463 pp.

Embleton, C and King, C. A. M. (1968). *Glacial and Periglacial Geomorphology*, St. Martin's Press, 608 pp.

French, H. M. (1976). *The Periglacial Environment*, Longman, 309 pp.

Jennings, J. N. (1971). *Karst*, The M.I.T. Press, 252 pp.

Leopold, L. B.; Wolman, M. G.; and Miller, J. P. (1964). *Fluvial Processes in Geomorphology*, W. H. Freeman and Co., 522 pp.

Monkhouse, F. J. and Wilkinson, H. R. (1964). *Maps and Diagrams.* Methuen, 432 pp.

Rona, P. A. (1973). Plate Tectonics and Mineral Resources. *Scientific American*, 229, p. 89.

Scovel, J. L.; McCormack, J. C.; Obrien, E. J.; and Chapman, R. B. (1965). *Atlas of Landforms*, John Wiley and Sons, Inc., 164 pp.

Sharpe, C. F. S. (1938). *Landslides and Related Phenomena*, Columbia University Press, 137 pp.

Strahler, A. N. (1975). *Physical Geography*, John Wiley and Sons, Inc., 643 pp.

Topographic Map Symbols

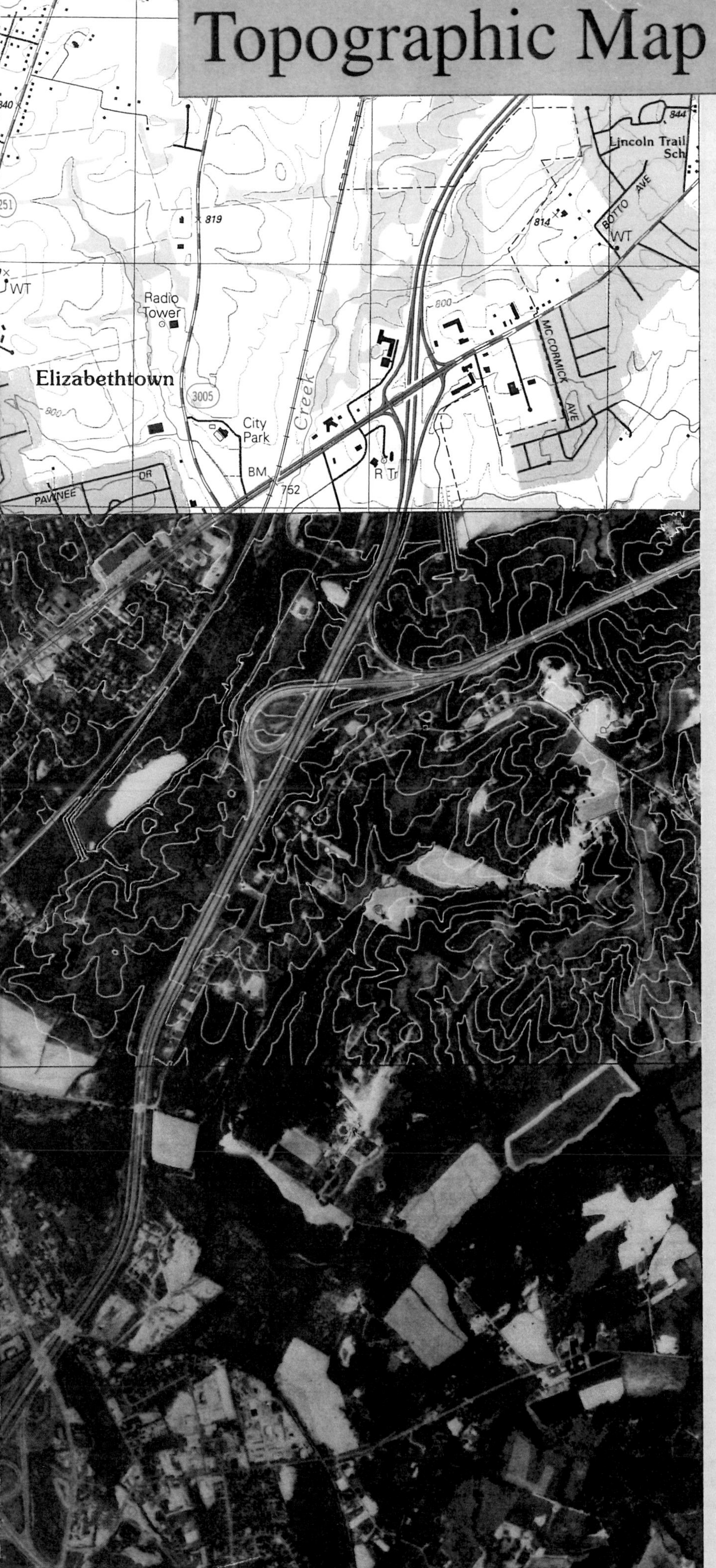

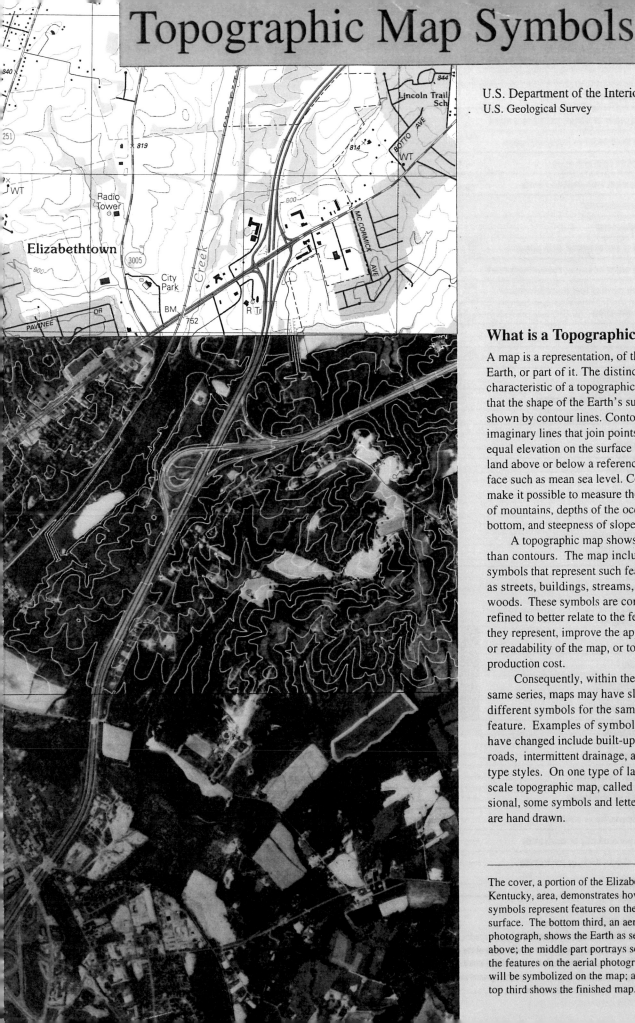

U.S. Department of the Interior
U.S. Geological Survey

What is a Topographic Map?

A map is a representation, of the Earth, or part of it. The distinctive characteristic of a topographic map is that the shape of the Earth's surface is shown by contour lines. Contours are imaginary lines that join points of equal elevation on the surface of the land above or below a reference surface such as mean sea level. Contours make it possible to measure the height of mountains, depths of the ocean bottom, and steepness of slopes.

A topographic map shows more than contours. The map includes symbols that represent such features as streets, buildings, streams, and woods. These symbols are constantly refined to better relate to the features they represent, improve the appearance or readability of the map, or to reduce production cost.

Consequently, within the same series, maps may have slightly different symbols for the same feature. Examples of symbols that have changed include built-up areas, roads, intermittent drainage, and some type styles. On one type of large-scale topographic map, called provisional, some symbols and lettering are hand drawn.

The cover, a portion of the Elizabethtown, Kentucky, area, demonstrates how map symbols represent features on the Earth's surface. The bottom third, an aerial photograph, shows the Earth as seen from above; the middle part portrays some of the features on the aerial photograph that will be symbolized on the map; and the top third shows the finished map.

CONTROL DATA AND MONUMENTS

Aerial photograph roll and frame number*	3-20
Horizontal control	
Third order or better, permanent mark	Neace Neace
With third order or better elevation	BM 45.1 Pike BM 45.1
Checked spot elevation	19.5
Coincident with section corner	Cactus Cactus
Unmonumented*	
Vertical control	
Third order or better, with tablet	BM 16.3
Third order or better, recoverable mark	120.0
Bench mark at found section corner	BM 18.6
Spot elevation	5.3
Boundary monument	
With tablet	BM 21.6 BM 71
Without tablet	171.3
With number and elevation	67 301.1
U.S. mineral or location monument	

CONTOURS

Topographic	
Intermediate	
Index	
Supplementary	
Depression	
Cut; fill	
Bathymetric	
Intermediate	
Index	
Primary	
Index Primary	
Supplementary	

BOUNDARIES

National	
State or territorial	
County or equivalent	
Civil township or equivalent	
Incorporated city or equivalent	
Park, reservation, or monument	
Small park	

*Provisional Edition maps only

Provisional Edition maps were established to expedite completion of the remaining large scale topographic quadrangles of the conterminous United States. They contain essentially the same level of information as the standard series maps. This series can be easily recongnized by the title "Provisional Edition" in the lower right hand corner.

LAND SURVEY SYSTEMS

U.S. Public Land Survey System	
Township or range line	
Location doubtful	
Section line	
Location doubtful	
Found section corner; found closing corner	
Witness corner; meander corner	WC MC
Other land surveys	
Township or range line	
Section line	
Land grant or mining claim; monument	
Fence line	

SURFACE FEATURES

Levee	Levee
Sand or mud area, dunes, or shifting sand	Sand
Intricate surface area	Strip mine
Gravel beach or glacial moraine	Gravel
Tailings pond	Tailings Pond

MINES AND CAVES

Quarry or open pit mine	
Gravel, sand, clay, or borrow pit	
Mine tunnel or cave entrance	
Prospect; mine shaft	X
Mine dump	Mine dump
Tailings	Tailings

VEGETATION

Woods	
Scrub	
Orchard	
Vineyard	
Mangrove	Mangrove

GLACIERS AND PERMANENT SNOWFIELDS

Contours and limits	
Form lines	

MARINE SHORELINE

Topographic maps	
Approximate mean high water	
Indefinite or unsurveyed	
Topographic-bathymetric maps	
Mean high water	
Apparent (edge of vegetation)	

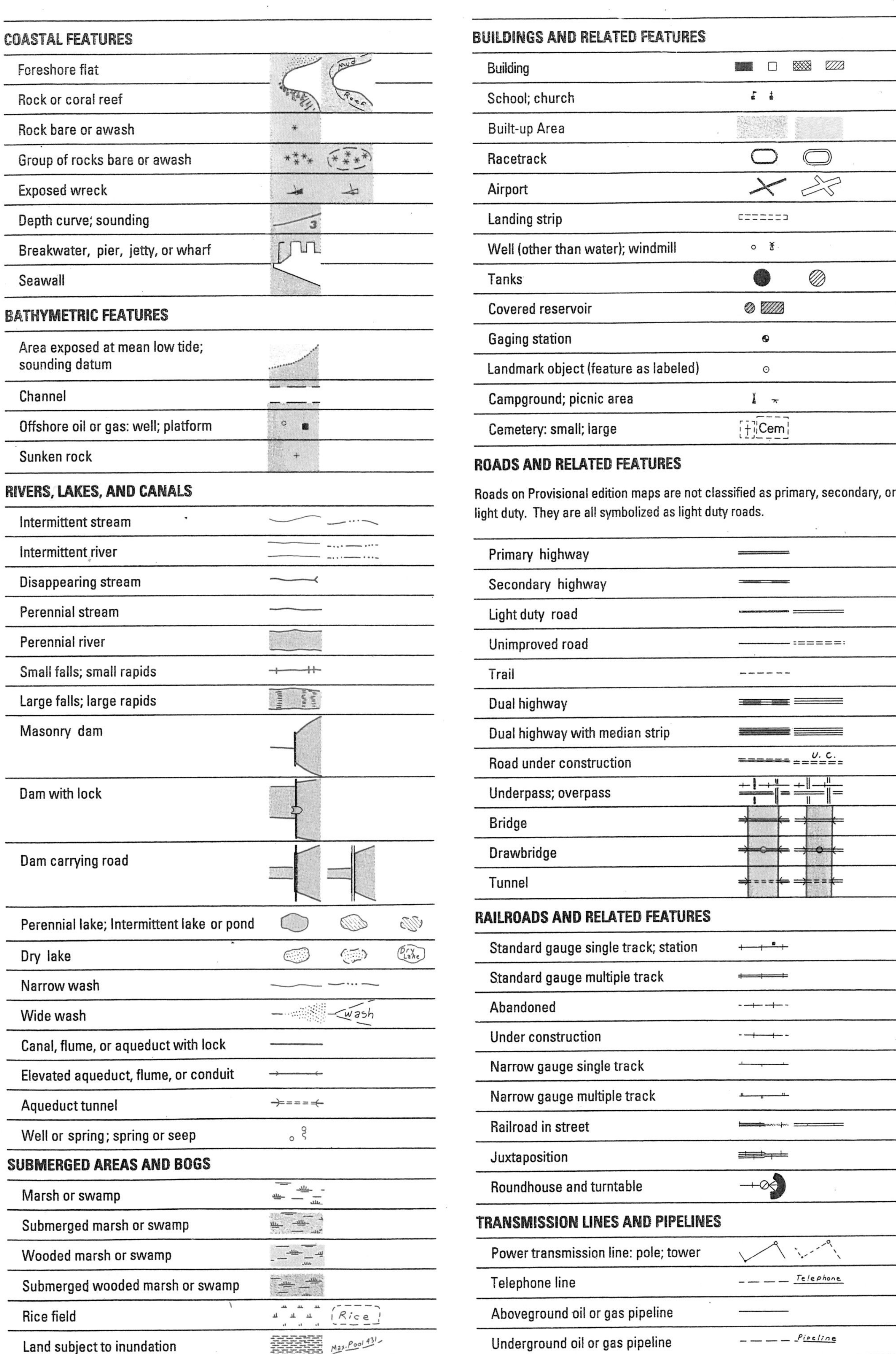

COASTAL FEATURES
Foreshore flat
Rock or coral reef
Mud
Reef
Rock bare or awash
Group of rocks bare or awash
Exposed wreck
Depth curve; sounding
3
Breakwater, pier, jetty, or wharf
Seawall
BATHYMETRIC FEATURES
Area exposed at mean low tide; sounding datum
Channel
Offshore oil or gas: well; platform
Sunken rock
RIVERS, LAKES, AND CANALS
Intermittent stream
Intermittent river
Disappearing stream
Perennial stream
Perennial river
Small falls; small rapids
Large falls; large rapids
Masonry dam
Dam with lock
Dam carrying road
Perennial lake; Intermittent lake or pond
Dry lake
Dry Lake
Narrow wash
Wide wash
Wash
Canal, flume, or aqueduct with lock
Elevated aqueduct, flume, or conduit
Aqueduct tunnel
Well or spring; spring or seep
SUBMERGED AREAS AND BOGS
Marsh or swamp
Submerged marsh or swamp
Wooded marsh or swamp
Submerged wooded marsh or swamp
Rice field
Rice
Land subject to inundation
Max. Pool 431
BUILDINGS AND RELATED FEATURES
Building
School; church
Built-up Area
Racetrack
Airport
Landing strip
Well (other than water); windmill
Tanks
Covered reservoir
Gaging station
Landmark object (feature as labeled)
Campground; picnic area
Cemetery: small; large
Cem
ROADS AND RELATED FEATURES
Roads on Provisional edition maps are not classified as primary, secondary, or light duty. They are all symbolized as light duty roads.
Primary highway
Secondary highway
Light duty road
Unimproved road
Trail
Dual highway
Dual highway with median strip
Road under construction
U. C.
Underpass; overpass
Bridge
Drawbridge
Tunnel
RAILROADS AND RELATED FEATURES
Standard gauge single track; station
Standard gauge multiple track
Abandoned
Under construction
Narrow gauge single track
Narrow gauge multiple track
Railroad in street
Juxtaposition
Roundhouse and turntable
TRANSMISSION LINES AND PIPELINES
Power transmission line: pole; tower
Telephone line
Telephone
Aboveground oil or gas pipeline
Underground oil or gas pipeline
Pipeline

Reading Topographic Maps

Interpreting the colored lines, areas, and other symbols is the first step in using topographic maps. Features are shown as points, lines, or areas, depending on their size and extent. For example, individual houses may be shown as small black squares. For larger buildings, the actual shapes are mapped. In densely built-up areas, most individual buildings are omitted and an area tint is shown. On some maps post offices, churches, city halls and other landmark buildings are shown within the tinted area.

The first features usually noticed on a topographic map are the area features such as vegetation (green), water (blue), some information added during update (purple), and densely built-up areas (gray or red).

Many features are shown by lines that may be straight, curved, solid, dashed, dotted, or in any combination. The colors of the lines usually indicate similar kinds or classes of information: topographic contours (brown); lakes, streams, irrigation ditches, etc. (blue); land grids and important roads (red); other roads and trails, railroads, boundaries, etc. (black); and some features that have been updated using aerial photography, but not field verified (purple).

Various point symbols are used to depict features such as buildings, campgrounds, springs, water tanks, mines, survey control points, and wells.

Names of places and features also are shown in a color corresponding to the type of feature. Many features are identified by labels, such as "Substation" or "Golf Course."

Topographic contours are shown in brown by lines of different widths. Each contour is a line of equal elevation; therefore, contours never cross. They show the general shape of the terrain. To help the user determine elevations, index contours are wider. Elevation values are printed in several places along these lines. The narrower intermediate and supplementary contours found between the index contours help to show more details of the land surface shape. Contours that are very close together represent steep slopes. Widely spaced contours, or an absence of contours, means that the ground slope is relatively level. The elevation difference between adjacent contour lines, called the contour interval, is selected to best show the general shape of the terrain. A map of a relatively flat area may have a contour interval of 10 feet or less. Maps in mountainous areas may have contour intervals of 100 feet or more. The contour interval is printed in the margin of each U.S. Geological Survey (USGS) map.

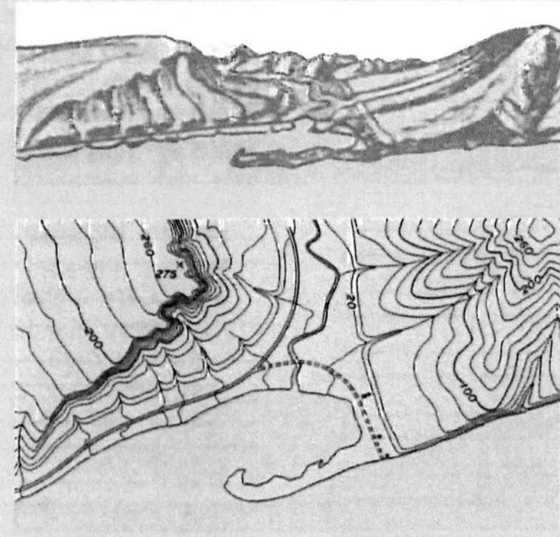

Ground configuration shown by contours

Bathymetric contours are shown in blue or black depending on their location. They show the shape and slope of the ocean bottom surface. The bathymetric contour interval may vary on each map and is explained in the map margin.

Topographic Map Information

For more information about topographic maps produced by the USGS, please call 1-800-USA-MAPS.